MOST®
Work Measurement
Systems

INDUSTRIAL ENGINEERING

A Series of Reference Books and Textbooks

Editor

WILBUR MEIER, JR.
Chancellor
University of Houston System
Houston, Texas

Additional Volumes in Preparation

MOST® Work Measurement Systems

Second Edition, Revised and Expanded

KJELL B. ZANDIN

H. B. Maynard and Company, Inc.
Pittsburgh, Pennsylvania

MARCEL DEKKER, INC.   **New York and Basel**

Library of Congress Cataloging-in-Publication Data

Zandin, Kjell B:
    MOST work measurement systems : Basic Most, Mini Most, Maxi Most / Kjell
B. Zandin.—2nd ed.
        p.   cm.—(Industrial engineering : v. 17)
    Includes index.
    On t.p. the registered trademark is superscript following "MOST" in the title.
    ISBN 0-8247-7604-6
    1. Work measurement. I. Title. II. Series.
T60.2.Z36 1989
658.5'42—dc19   88-25727
                                                                         CIP

MARCEL DEKKER, INC.
270 Madison Avenue, New York, New York 10016

Current printing (last digit):
10 9 8 7 6 5 4 3 2 1

PRINTED IN THE UNITED STATES OF AMERICA

To my son Mikael and daughter Christin

Measure of work brings knowledge. Through this knowledge, factual decisions and improvements can be made and control exercised.

When you can measure what you are speaking of and express it in numbers you know that on which you are discoursing. But if you cannot measure it and express it in numbers, your knowledge is of a very meagre and unsatisfactory kind.

Lord Kelvin

This text is unquestionably intended to give the reader a complete description of MOST Work Measurement Systems. It is not, however, the sole training device through which MOST Systems is learned. Any attempt to utilize the material in this text without proper classroom training and certification will be done at the discretion of the reader.

Through Chapters 3 (The Basic MOST System), 4 (The Mini MOST System), and 5 (The Maxi MOST System), this text is intended to give the reader a complete understanding of the MOST Work Measurement technique for industrial application. The Equipment Handling Sequences in Chapters 3 and 5 are described in detail; however, certain parameters must be validated prior to their application. The scope of MOST Clerical Systems, MOST Application Systems, and MOST Computer Systems is such that adequate coverage of these subjects could well be addressed in separate texts. With that in mind, Chapters 6, 7, and 8 are included in this volume for information purposes only.

Foreword

Work measurement has had an important place in productivity improvement since the early part of the twentieth century. The philosophy has been the same through the decades. Productivity can be maximized only when there exists a standard method of accomplishing a task and the time to perform a task according to a standard method can be measured.

The Maynard Operation Sequence Technique (MOST) is a clever mapping of surrogate measures to achieve results that sacrifice minimal accuracy while greatly reducing the observer time necessary to establish standards. The use of surrogates to measure time was introduced in the late 1950s to estimate the time required to care for patients in the hospital environment. The effectiveness of utilizing surrogate measures was verified in that setting. In the development of MOST, similar measures have been introduced that have the potential to significantly enhance the value of work measurement data.

In the development of work measurement systems, the objective has always been measurement, not design. Traditional determination of standard times requires so many labor-hours that the use of such information to design and evaluate manufacturing processes is not feasible. Even the conveniences of modern time study, such as digital readouts, data storage, and computer interfaces, do not readily permit design but rather continue to focus on measurement.

Measurement has and always will be an important component of productivity improvement, but the ability to utilize the vast information base gathered in the creation of standards to design optimal production systems has far more potential impact. Myriad predetermined time systems introduced the design notion over the past several decades but were too cumbersome to be of real utility. MOST, especially in its computer format, opens the door to combining work measurement and design to improve productivity.

From an academic point of view MOST has considerably more relevance to students who have been brought up with computers and such visual stimuli as television. These students find the conceptualization of MOST models challenging and are especially intrigued by the potential of the MOST data base to simulate alternative configurations of a process and, therefore, to aid in the design of improved processes.

This new edition introduces two extensions of Basic MOST—Mini MOST and Maxi MOST, and emphasizes the computerized version of these techniques. These extensions permit the use of MOST for short-cycle tasks for which more detail than is available in Basic MOST is desired and long-cycle tasks for which the accuracy of Basic MOST represents overkill. As the various versions of MOST have become available for PCs as well as VAX systems and IBM mainframes, this updated material is a welcome addition to the literature.

Harvey Wolfe
Professor and Chairman
Department of Industrial Engineering
University of Pittsburgh
Pittsburgh, Pennsylvania

Introduction to the Second Edition

Since the first edition of this book was published in 1980 a number of developments have made MOST Systems much more universally applicable. This second edition provides the reader with information on the application of MOST Systems ranging from very short, repetitive cycles to extremely long and complex operations. This edition also provides the reader with the keywords that are used in MOST Computer Systems, thereby making the move from using Manual MOST to using Computer MOST an easy transition.

MOST Computer Systems is now being used by hundred of companies. The program is available on a broad range of computers—mainframe, mini, micro, and personal—and is available throughout North America and Europe. Another milestone in the history of MOST occurred in 1986 when MOST Systems were licensed by a major Japanese consulting organization for application in Japanese industry. As of this writing, more than 15,000 people have been certified as MOST applicators worldwide.

MOST and MOST Computer Systems are now included in the curricula of more than one hundred colleges and universities. Training for industrial users is now accomplished with the most modern combination of video and computer equipment. Mini MOST has been developed for the analysis of highly repetitive, short-cycle operations, such as those found in electronic assembly work. Maxi MOST has been developed to analyze low-volume, long-cycle operations, such as those found in shipbuilding, maintentance utilities, and other heavy industries. Both Mini MOST and Maxi MOST are available on all the hardware configurations on which MOST Computer Systems are offered.

The promise that MOST Systems seemed to offer when they were first introduced into the United States in 1975 has been fulfilled. MOST has established a reputation as a superior and economical tool for the industrial engineer's kit. For the future, MOST Systems offer an effective and cost-effective means of incorporating good workplace methods and standards into advanced automated systems of process planning, design, and manufacturing.

Michael D. Ferrell, Chairman
H. B. Maynard and Company, Inc.
Pittsburgh, Pennsylvania

Introduction to the First Edition

One of the great rewards of any profession is the pleasure of being involved in an innovative development that has great potential benefits for the profession and for the industrial world. Countless instances of such developments have occurred in all professions over the years. In the history of the industrial engineering profession, H. B. Maynard and Company has been particularly fortunate in this respect. Our founder H. B. (Mike) Maynard and his close friend and collaborator G. J. (Gus) Stegemerten were two of the great innovators in the history of the industrial engineering profession. Together, they developed many widely used industrial engineering techniques, such as methods time measurement, skill and effort leveling factors, operations analysis, and universal maintenance standards.

When methods time measurement was first introduced publicly, its acceptance was eagerly anticipated throughout H. B. Maynard and Company. The professional staff was well aware of the potential importance of this development and the tremendous impact it could have on improving productivity throughout industry, business, and government. As MTM gained more and more acceptance there was a deep feeling of accomplishment not only by Mike Maynard and Gus Stegemerten, but by everyone in the firm who participated in its development and introduction.

For the last few years the professional group at H. B. Maynard and Company has been experiencing anew that same sort of feeling with the introduction of MOST Systems. Starting in the United States in 1975, MOST Systems has gained wide recognition as a major contribution to the body of industrial engineering technology. In the twelve years since MOST Systems has been available in the United States, literally thousands of organizations and over ten thousand individuals have been trained to use MOST. A number of leading industrial engineers throughout the world have acclaimed MOST Systems as the wave of the future in industrial engineering.

The development of MOST Systems from a base of methods time measurement is the result of a continuing evolution in industrial engineering technology. In 1940, the Methods Engineering Council (the former name of H. B. Maynard and Company) conducted a supervisory training program at a large plant of one of the major U.S. corporations. The training revolved around the role of the supervisor in improving shop productivity and included practical application of work simplification techniques to shop operations. Many substantial cost reduction ideas were generated during the training program, and the program was considered quite successful from a monetary standpoint.

In reviewing the results of the program, however, Maynard and Stegemerten questioned whether the program was completely successful because of the upsetting effect that the many changes caused in the plant. The training resulted in a very strong "methods correction" drive on the part of the foreman that was very fruitful but also very controversial because of the resistance to change that had to be overcome in the plant. They reasoned that if the industrial engineers had access to a better "methods-engineering" tool to set up operations correctly in the first place, then subsequent methods correction could be minimized, thus also minimizing the negative effects of changes within an organization.

This basic philosophy sent Maynard and Stegemerten on a research course to find a better way to engineer methods. With the assistance of J. L. Schwab and others, they did, indeed, find a better way. They created methods time measurement (MTM), which rapidly became one of the best known and most widely used work study systems. Its use has saved many billions of dollars in improved productivity and reduced costs.

One of the philosophies that Maynard advanced was that "with sufficient study any method can be improved." Following this philosophy, industrial engineers have been seeking improvements over methods time measurement and other predetermined motion time systems for several decades. These efforts have resulted in a considerable array of predetermined data systems such as MTM-2, MTM-3, MSD, USD, GPD, MTMV, and others. The objective, of course, was to retain the good features of MTM for analyzing methods and measuring work but to eliminate the handicap of lengthy application times inherent in the MTM system. Each of these evolving systems has been successful, to a degree, in meeting the objective of reducing the industrial engineering application time, and each system has had its advocates as the best such second-level MTM system to be used.

In the late 1960s, Kjell Zandin, then working for the Swedish Division of H. B. Maynard and Company, made an important discovery. While reviewing the rather extensive MTM data in the Maynard library in Gothenburg he detected striking similarities in the sequence of MTM defined motions whenever any object was handled. Invariably, the same set of basic motions would be used in the same general sequence. This discovery led Zandin and the Maynard management to question whether this phenomenon could be used to develop a new way to analyze methods and to measure operations. If successful, this approach could drastically reduce the time required to study operations.

For the next several years Zandin spent the bulk of his time conducting intensive research in the development of this new concept of work study. He isolated and developed models for three motion sequences that would analyze and measure practically all manual work. Later, he identified three other sequences that would measure practically all heavy material handling that required mechanical assistance. Again, relying on Maynard MTM library data and statistical methods, he developed a set of several index numbers to be used with the sequence models. After the application procedures were spelled out, Zandin and other Maynard personnel made elaborate tests of the system and data in a variety of industries in Sweden and Western Europe.

To the great satisfaction of all concerned, the new system worked remarkably well. Without question, it represented a very significant advance in the state of the art in industrial engineering. It was fast (forty to fifty times faster than MTM-1), accurate, methods conscious, and easy to learn and apply. The new system was called the Maynard Operation Sequence Technique (MOST) and was ready for wide distribution in 1975.

There is a solid future for MOST Systems throughout the world. Still in its infancy, MOST has been applied successfully in practically all industries, ranging in diversity from shipbuilding to electronics; truck assembly to textiles; freight car assembly to drugs; and furniture to food products. Applications have been made in offices, assembly shops, fabrication and welding shops, production lines, job shops, material handling, maintenance, warehouses, and finishing operations. In fact, the experience to date has shown that MOST Systems are truly universal in their application throughout industry, business, and government.

Continuing to evolve, MOST Systems have been developed into MOST Computer Systems, as explained in Chapter 8 of this book. MOST Computer Systems have incorporated all the benefits of the MOST Manual System, plus the great advantage of mass data updating, speed of application, data development capabilities, and rapid access to file information. With the constant improvement in computer technology, we anticipate that MOST Systems will continue to evolve to meet the unceasing demand for finding better ways to do things.

William M. Aiken
H. B. Maynard and Company, Inc.
Pittsburgh, Pennsylvania

Acknowledgments

It is not a one-person job to create a new work measurement system that will benefit and stimulate thousands of industrial engineers and will help them do their work better and more efficiently and with greater satisfaction. After several years of "creative thinking" and the development of a conventional type of work measurement system for machine shop activities, I was fortunate to come up with a new concept for predetermined time measurement.

Based on fundamental statistical principles and basic work measurement data compiled over many years, the idea of MOST evolved as the natural and logical way to measure work. At all stages of the development of MOST, the practical aspects of this new approach were consistently emphasized. The goal was to build an industrial engineering tool that would be easy to learn and simple to apply.

The first general move sequence model emerged late one afternoon in August 1967. The creation hit the desk in a crowded layout room as a ripe apple hits the ground. At that moment it was, however, inconceivable that the "sequence technique" as it was first called, would "conquer the world" a few years later. It was not until 1975 that the sequence technique got its current name: MOST (Maynard Operation Sequence Technique).

Many people have been very helpful and supportive in shaping and perfecting MOST. Their contribution and encouragement have been immensely appreciated and invaluable in making MOST the contemporary "star" in the work measurement world.

My lovely wife, Sonja, has always been my greatest supporter. I am most grateful for her comments and interest.

MOST would never have gotten off the ground without the vision, backing, and total faith in the new method by Lennart Gustavsson, Managing Director of Maynard MEC in Gothenburg, Sweden. I owe my warmest thanks to my good friend Lennart, for his extraordinary support and encouragement.

Without the foresight, experience, and business mind of the late William M. Aiken, former Chairman and CEO of H. B. Maynard and Company in Pittsburgh, MOST would probably not have been successfully launched in the United States. This book might not have been written without Bill's initiative to make MOST available to U.S. industry and government. For giving me and my family the challenging opportunity to move across the Atlantic Ocean in 1975, I owe my sincerest thanks to Bill. It has been a very exciting adventure and an extremely educational and rewarding experience. Bill's passing in April 1988 was a great loss not only to us at Maynard, but to the industrial engineering society as well. In addition, I lost a good friend.

It took many years to prepare, refine, and finalize the backup data for MOST. Numerous MTM analyses had to be made, tested, and validated. My former colleague and good friend, Thomas Vago, from Lund, Sweden, persistently and very ably assisted me with the nitty-gritty to make the foundation for MOST totally solid and unassailable. Thomas' profound competence and interest have been of great value, and I deeply appreciate his contribution. In May 1985 the sad news reached us that Thomas Vago had passed away. My memory of his great cultural mind, professional dedication, and true friendship will always live.

By utilizing just a small portion of his extensive knowledge, Dr. William D. Brinckloe, former Professor at the University of Pittsburgh, intelligently and explicitly clarified and confirmed the statistical theories behind MOST. Dr. Brinckloe was first to emphasize the unique consistency of MOST. My sincerest thanks to Bill for his professional and sincere help to settle the issue of the accuracy and precision of MOST.

One of the most demanding and time-consuming tasks in completing this book was to ensure that the text is logical and complete, the examples illustrative, well defined, and representative of common and typical industrial activities. William M. Yates, Jr., at the time Technical Coordinator of MOST Systems with H. B. Maynard and Company, did his utmost to streamline the text and make it understandable for the reader. Thanks to Bill's positive critique and dedicated work, the quality of the book improved immensely. A great supporter of MOST, particularly the Tool Use Sequence Model, Bill deserves my sincerest thanks. Besides his skillful handling of golf tools, Bill now promotes MOST on the U.S. West Coast with equal skill.

Mary Coughlin, Ph.D., was instrumental in devising the happy marriage between MOST and the computer. During the past several years, MOST Computer Systems has been superbly maintained, expanded, and enhanced by Ken Marino, Raghu Kalathur, Bela Molnar, and their competent programming staff. Ron Soncini devotedly and enthusiastically converted MOST for the measurement of clerical work. Many others—Stig Magnusson, Lennart Simren, Fred Berglund, and Bob Hooks, just to mention a few—have contributed with their knowledge and effort to make MOST a practical tool for the industrial engineer. Jack Cornelius not only has been counseling thousands of MOST students but also prepared the first training manuals for Mini MOST and Maxi MOST. Their work to advance and expand MOST is greatly appreciated.

My good friend from Finland, Berndt (Bebbe) Nyberg, has made a significant contribution through his extensive experience in the heavy engineering industry toward the development and application of Maxi MOST. Based on his long experience in the work measurement field, Winston T. Taylor, Senior Vice President of H. B. Maynard and Company, provided many valuable ideas and suggestions that made the Mini MOST development project get off the ground.

All sketches, diagrams, and tables were first skillfully drawn by the artistic hand of Bette J. McDonald and for the second edition by Lynette Webb. The text was untiringly typed by my secretary, Nancy Kuchar, and meticulously proofread by Robert I. Dietrich, who learned so much about MOST in the process that he became a MOST instructor and a training center counselor. Subsequently, Bob has provided excellent assistance and many ideas on how to improve the functionality of the MOST principles.

Finally, I owe a great deal to all the industrial engineers who practice MOST every day and who have expressed their satisfaction and encouragement and shared their experiences and ideas. Based on their appreciation, I am fully convinced that MOST will become a "way of life" for the modern industrial engineer. It already is for over ten thousand of us.

Kjell B. Zandin

Contents

Contents

1

The Concept of MOST—An Introduction

Work Measurement

The desire to know how long it should take to perform work must surely have been present in those individuals responsible for erecting ancient monuments or shaping tools. Why did the ancients and why do we need to be able to predict with accuracy the length of a working cycle? How was such a prediction made? How is it made now?

There are many reasons for wanting to know the amount of time a particular task should take to accomplish. It may simply be for reasons of curiosity. But, realistically, it is for any of three reasons: to *accomplish planning, determine performance*, and *establish costs*. Suppose an organization wishes to manufacture a new product. Using an economical, predetermined motion time system, the planning and budgeting process could be accomplished. Knowing the time to manufacture and assemble various parts and/or components, a manager could:

- Determine the total labor cost of the product.
- Determine the number of production workers needed.
- Determine the number of machines needed.
- Determine the amount of and delivery times for material.
- Determine the overall production schedule.
- Determine the feasibility of entering into production of the product.
- Set production goals.
- Follow up on production: Have goals been achieved?
- Check individual or departmental efficiency.
- Know the actual costs of production.
- Pay by results.

As a consequence, a manager can achieve an even and sufficiently high utilization of personnel, material, and equipment to result in an overall efficiency that will allow an organization to survive and grow.

It must be assumed that the original form of work measurement was guessing. It is interesting to note that the primitive guessing technique employed thousands of years ago is still in use today in many modern manufacturing organizations. Today's version is a much advanced form of the original technique, however, and is known as an *educated guess*. The educated guess is unscientifically supported by intuition, individual personal experience, the importance of the estimation to be made, and the inherent ability or inability of the applicator to make a confident-sounding response. Obviously, this technique is not scientific (well documented or statistically supported) and not accurate (with any degree of confidence or consistency), but it is fast.

Once products began to be manufactured or work tasks completed, another source of information was available from which future times could be estimated. The historical data concept of work measurement evolved. From records of what had been accomplished came the information for predicting times for future situations. Using historical data does one thing very well. It accurately tells you what has already happened. To use it to predict what will happen assumes two major points:

1. The conditions and actions under which the process was performed originally are what you wish to repeat (the best way of performing a task).
2. The actions to be performed will be performed exactly as those on which the historical data are based.

If these conditions are met, historical data should work well.

A true innovator, Frederick Taylor, looked at work as something that could be controlled or engineered. It did not have to be a haphazard repetition of what had gone on before; in fact, workers could be instructed as to the best way to perform certain tasks. The result was that tasks were broken down into elements or short tasks that could be arranged and managed to produce more efficient and productive and less fatiguing work. Each element was studied to determine which was productive and which was useless. Keeping only productive elements, a stopwatch was used to determine the time for each. The time recorded was the actual time taken by a particular individual to perform a certain task under specific conditions. To make such times transferable to other workers and other situations, time for the average worker working under average conditions had to be determined. This was and is now accomplished by performance rating. The performance rating is a determination by the analyst of the pace of the individual observed as compared to the ideal, imaginary average worker working at a level of 100% effort and skill. If the worker observed is not putting forth the effort imagined to be 100%, a rating of less than 100% would be applied to the time recorded by the stopwatch and the time would be leveled to 100%

performance. Likewise, if the worker observed was working with more skill and effort than the imagined average worker, a rating of over 100% would be applied to the time on the stopwatch and the time leveled to 100% performance. The scientific process of engineering a task using the time study methods just described has two weak points:

1. The individual analyst must *subjectively* rate or compare the operator to an estimated 100% performance standard.
2. No matter how sophisticated, expensive, or precise the timepiece, a watch simply does not forecast, predict, or accurately determine times for future situations; it only determines what has already occurred.

It was discovered by Frank and Lillian Gilbreth that all manual operations were combinations of basic elements. The Gilbreths isolated and identified these elements primarily so that methods could be more accurately explained and improved. They reasoned that to reduce the motion content of a task was to reduce the effort and the time to perform the task. The result is higher production.

Understandably, followers of Taylor practiced *time study,* but followers of the Gilbreths practiced *motion study.* As frequently occurs, a third party entered and joined together the best of both techniques. A marriage of the time study technique and the motion study philosophy was arranged. From this union of time and motion studies was born the predetermined motion time systems (PMTS). These systems utilized the time study and micromotion techniques of the earlier techniques to determine and assign times to specified basic motions. The motions and associated times were catalogued. Work measurement then became a matter of establishing the best basic motion pattern to perform a certain task and, from the catalog or data card, assigning the appropriate predetermined time for each basic motion in that pattern. Since the times for all motions are predetermined, one could now accurately predict future task times. The watch was needed only for timing machines. But what about performance rating? The authors of the best predetermined motion time systems built into their systems the leveled times for 100% performance. Therefore, with the catalogs of predetermined times already leveled to 100%, there no longer remained a need to rate an operator. The analyst began to focus on the actual work being accomplished, not on the operator.

Of all the predetermined motion time systems, the most well known is Methods-Time Measurement (MTM), as developed by Harold B. Maynard, G. J. Stegemerten, and J. L. Schwab and published in 1948. Because it is a very detailed system and in the public domain, MTM has been recognized as the most accurate and widely accepted predetermined motion time system in use today.

The MTM system has a detailed data card of basic motions (reach; move; grasp; position; release; body, leg, and foot motions; and so on), each concerned with particular variables. Basic motions are identified, and with the variables considered the appropriate times are chosen from the data card. Because of its detail, MTM can be a very exact system and also very slow to apply. Also, basic motion distances must be accurately measured and correctly classified. Because of the detail, applicator errors can be a problem. The times that result from performing an MTM analysis reflect a 100% performance level, and times can be established for operations prior to production.

Synthesized versions of MTM were developed to reduce applicator errors and the time of analysis. Two such versions are MTM-2 and MTM-3. These systems grouped or averaged together certain basic motions and/or variables to reduce the applicator effort required to apply the technique. A corresponding reduction in system accuracy also resulted (see Appendix A: Theory).

The analysis of work, as practiced by industrial engineers using a predetermined motion time system today, is performed by systematically breaking work down into very small and distinct units called *basic motions*. For highly repetitive, short-cycle operations, this attention to detail is usually necessary and, indeed, has been found to be quite effective in generating valuable methods improvements. For less repetitive operations or job shop production, however, this detailed approach is very tedious and requires a great deal of time and effort on the part of highly trained engineers and technicians. The benefits are often questionable when considering the amount of analysis effort required. It can be a very costly process.

Definition of Terms

In order to facilitate the understanding of the following text for the reader, the definition of several terms commonly used in connection with MOST Systems and throughout this book, as well as their relationship (see Figure 1.1), will be presented here. The terms defined below are:

- Operation
- Suboperation
- Time standard
- Activity
- Method step
- Sequence model
- Subactivity
- MOST Analysis

Since the logical result of a work measurement task is to establish a time standard for an operation, let us first define the term *operation*.

Operation

An *operation* is (1) a job or task, consisting of one or more work elements, usually done essentially in one location; (2) the performance of any planned

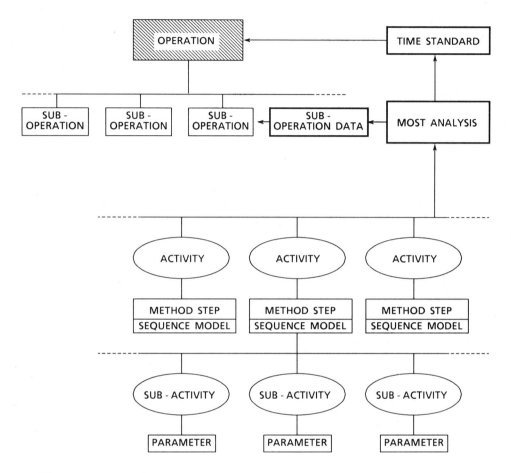

Figure 1.1 Terms and their relationship in connection with a MOST analysis.

work or method associated with an individual, machine, process, department or inspection or; (3) one or more elements that involve one of the following: the intentional changing of an object in any of its physical or chemical characteristics; the assembly or disassembly of parts or objects; the preparation of an object for another operation, transportation, inspection, or storage; planning, calculating, or the giving or receiving of information. (This definition of "operation" can be found in "Industrial Engineering Terminology" published by the Institute of Industrial Engineers, Industrial Engineering and Management Press, 25 Technology Park/Atlanta, Norcross, Georgia.)

Both the work measurement and standard setting procedure can be simplified and made more efficient through the use of fractions of operations called *suboperations*. The definition of a *suboperation* is as follows:

Suboperation

A suboperation is a discrete, logical and measurable part of an operation. The content of such a suboperation may vary depending on type of operation, accuracy requirements and application area. Two or more suboperations may be combined into a *combined suboperation.*

Time Standard

A *time standard* is the total allowed time including manual time, process time and allowances that it should take to perform a task or do a job. An *engineered time standard* is the time it should take to perform a task or do a job based on established and documented work conditions and specified work methods. (The pure operation time without allowances is called "normal time.")

Activity

An *activity* is here defined as a series of logical events that take place when an object is moved, observed or treated by hand, a tool or a transportation device. An *activity* starts when an operator leaves his or her normal location (work place) to perform these events and concludes when the operator has returned to the original location or releases the object. The word *activity* also may be used in a general sense designating a task or a series of events.

Method Step

A *method step* is a descriptive formulation of an activity. One or more (usually 5–20) method steps organized in sequence according to the applied method will constitute an operation or suboperation.

Sequence Model

A *sequence model* is a multi-character representation of a single activity. One sequence model is applied to each method step. Several predefined sequence models represent different types of activities.

Subactivity

A *subactivity* is a defined, discrete subdivision of an activity or sequence model.

Parameter

A *parameter* is a one-character representation of a subactivity.

MOST Analysis

A *MOST Analysis* is a complete study of an operation or a suboperation consisting of one or several method steps and corresponding sequence models, as well as appropriate parameter time values and total normal time for the operation or suboperation (excluding allowances).

The Concept of MOST Work Measurement Technique

Because industrial engineers are taught that with sufficient study any method can be improved, many efforts have been made to simplify the work measurement analyst's task. This has, for instance, led to a variety of higher level MTM data systems now in use. This attitude also led us to examine the whole concept of work measurement to find a better way for analysts to accomplish their mission. The result was the formation of the concept later to be known as MOST, Maynard Operation Sequence Technique.

Work to most of us means exerting energy to accomplish some task or to perform some useful activity. In the study of physics, we learn that work is defined as the product of force times distance ($W = f \times d$), or more simply, work is the displacement of a mass or object. This definition applies quite well to the largest portion of the work accomplished every day (e.g., pushing a pencil, lifting a heavy box, or moving the controls on a machine). Thought process or thinking time is an exception to this concept, as no objects are being displaced: For the overwhelming majority of work, however, there is a common denominator from which work can be studied, the *displacement of objects.* All basic units of work are organized (or should be) for the purpose of accomplishing some useful result by simply moving objects. That is *what* work is. MOST is a system to measure work; therefore, *MOST concentrates on the movement of objects.*

Work, then, is the movement of objects (maybe we should add: following a tactical production outline). Efficient, smooth, productive work is performed when the basic motion patterns are tactically arranged and smoothly choreographed (methods engineering). It was noticed that the movement of objects follows certain consistently repeating patterns, such as reach, grasp, move, and position the object. These patterns were identified and arranged as a *sequence of events* (or subactivities) followed in moving an object. A model of this sequence is made and acts as a standard guide in analyzing the movement of an object. It was also noted that the subactivities in that sequence vary independently of one another in their actual motion content.

This concept provides the basis for the MOST sequence models. The primary work units are no longer basic motions as in MTM, but fundamental activities (collections of basic motions) dealing with moving objects. These activities are described in terms of subactivities fixed in sequence. In other words, to move an object, a standard sequence of events occurs. Consequently, the basic pattern of an object's movement is described by a universal sequence model instead of random, detailed basic motions.

Objects can be moved in only one of two ways: either they are picked up and moved freely through space, or they are moved and maintain contact with another surface. For example, a box can be picked up and carried from one end of a workbench to the other or it can be pushed across the top of the workbench. For each type of move, a different sequence of events occurs; therefore, a separate MOST activity sequence model applies. The use of tools is analyzed through a separate activity sequence model that allows the analyst the opportunity to follow the movement of a hand tool through a standard sequence of events, which, in fact, is a *combination* of the two basic sequence models.

Consequently, only three Basic MOST activity sequences are needed for describing manual work, plus a fourth for measuring the movements of objects with manual cranes:

- The *General Move Sequence* (for the spatial movement of an object freely through the air)
- The *Controlled Move Sequence* (for the movement of an object when it remains in contact with a surface or is attached to another object during the movement)
- The *Tool Use Sequence* (for the use of common hand tools)

The Basic MOST Sequence Models

General Move is defined as moving objects manually from one location to another freely through the air. To account for the various ways in which a General Move can occur, the activity sequence is made up of four subactivities:

A   Action distance (mainly horizontal)
B   Body motion (mainly vertical)
G   Gain control
P   Placement

These subactivities are arranged in a *sequence model* (Fig. 1.2), consisting of a series of parameters organized in a logical sequence. The sequence model defines the events or actions that always take place in a prescribed order when an object is being moved from one location to another. The *General Move Sequence Model,* which is the most commonly used sequence model, is defined as follows:

A	B	G	A	B	P	A
Action distance	Body motion	Gain control	Action distance	Body motion	Place	Action distance

Basic MOST® WORK MEASUREMENT TECHNIQUE		
ACTIVITY	SEQUENCE MODEL	SUB - ACTIVITIES
GENERAL MOVE	A B G A B P A	A - ACTION DISTANCE B - BODY MOTION G - GAIN CONTROL P - PLACEMENT
CONTROLLED MOVE	A B G M X I A	M - MOVE CONTROLLED X - PROCESS TIME I - ALIGNMENT
TOOL USE	A B G A B P A B P A	F - FASTEN L - LOOSEN C - CUT S - SURFACE TREAT M - MEASURE R - RECORD T - THINK

Figure 1.2 Sequence models comprising the Basic MOST technique.

These subactivities, or sequence model *parameters,* are then assigned time-related index numbers based on the motion content of the subactivity. This approach provides complete analysis flexibility within the overall control of the sequence model. For each object moved, any combination of motions might occur, and using MOST, any combination may be analyzed. For the General Move Sequence, these index values are easily memorized from a brief data card (introduced in Chap. 3: Fig. 3.1). A fully indexed *General Move Sequence,* for example, might appear as follows:

$$A_6 \quad B_6 \quad G_1 \quad A_1 \quad B_0 \quad P_3 \quad A_0$$

where: A_6 = Walk three to four steps to object location
B_6 = Bend and arise
G_1 = Gain control of one light object
A_1 = Move object a distance within reach
B_0 = No body motion
P_3 = Place and adjust object
A_0 = No return

This example could, for instance, represent the following activity: walk three steps to pick up a bolt from floor level, arise, and place the bolt in a hole.

General Move is by far the most frequently used of the three sequence models. Roughly 50% of all manual work occurs as a General Move, with the percentage running higher for assembly and material handling and lower for machine shop operations.

The second type of move is described by the *Controlled Move Sequence* (Fig. 1.1). This sequence is used to cover such activities as operating a lever or crank, activating a button or switch, or simply sliding an object over a surface. In addition to the A, B, and G parameters from the General Move Sequence, the sequence model for a controlled move contains the following subactivities:

$$\textbf{M} \qquad \textbf{X} \qquad \textbf{I}$$

Move   Process   Align
controlled   time

As many as one-third of the activities occurring in machine shop operations may involve controlled moves. In assembly work, however, the fraction is usually much smaller. A typical activity covered by the Controlled Move Sequence is the engaging of the feed lever on a milling machine. The sequence model for this activity might be indexed as follows:

$$\textbf{A}_1 \quad \textbf{B}_0 \quad \textbf{G}_1 \quad \textbf{M}_1 \quad \textbf{X}_{10} \quad \textbf{I}_0 \quad \textbf{A}_0$$

where: A_1 = Reach to the lever a distance within reach
           B_0 = No body motion
           G_1 = Get hold of lever
          M_1 = Move lever up to 12 inches (30 cm) to engage feed
         X_{10} = Process time of approximately 3.5 seconds
           I_0 = No alignment
          A_0 = No return

The third sequence model included in the Basic MOST Work Measurement Technique is the *Tool Use Sequence Model.* This sequence model covers the use of hand tools for such activities as fastening or loosening, cutting, cleaning, gauging, and recording. Also, certain activities requiring the use of the brain for mental processes can be classified as Tool Use, e.g., reading and thinking. As indicated above, the Tool Use Sequence Model is a combination of General Move and Controlled Move activities. It was developed as a part of the Basic MOST Systems, merely to simplify the analysis of activities related to the use of hand tools. It will later become obvious to the reader that any hand tool activity is made up of General and Controlled Moves.

The use of a wrench, for example, might be described by the following sequence:

$$\textbf{A}_1 \quad \textbf{B}_0 \quad \textbf{G}_1 \quad \textbf{A}_1 \quad \textbf{B}_0 \quad \textbf{P}_3 \quad \textbf{F}_{10} \quad \textbf{A}_1 \quad \textbf{B}_0 \quad \textbf{P}_1 \quad \textbf{A}_0$$

where: A_1 = Reach to wrench
        B_0 = No body motion
        G_1 = Get hold of wrench
        A_1 = Move wrench to fastener a distance within reach

B_0 = No body motion
P_3 = Place wrench on fastener
F_{10} = Tighten fastener with wrench
A_1 = Move wrench a distance within reach
B_0 = No body motion
P_1 = Lay wrench aside
A_0 = No return

These three sequence models just described with their subactivities are presented in Figure 1.2.

Time Units

The time units used in MOST are identical to those used in the basic MTM (Methods-Time Measurement) system and are based on hours and parts of hours called *Time Measurement Units* (TMU). One TMU is equivalent to 0.00001 hour. The following conversion table is provided for calculating standard times:

1 TMU = 0.00001 hour
1 TMU = 0.0006 minute
1 TMU = 0.036 second

1 hour   = 100,000 TMU
1 minute = 1,667 TMU
1 second = 27.8 TMU

The time value in TMU for each sequence model is calculated by adding the index numbers and multiplying the sum by 10. In our previous General Move Sequence example, the time would be $(6 + 6 + 1 + 1 + 0 + 3 + 0) \times 10 = 170$ TMU, approximately 0.1 minute. The time values for the other two examples are computed in the same way. The Controlled Move example totals $(1 + 0 + 1 + 1 + 10 + 0 + 0) \times 10 = 130$ TMU, and the Tool Use example $(1 + 0 + 1 + 1 + 0 + 3 + 10 + 1 + 0 + 1 + 0) \times 10 = 180$ TMU.

All time values established by MOST reflect the activity of an *average skilled operator* working at an *average performance level* or *normal pace*. This is often referred to as the 100% performance level that in time study is achieved by using "leveling factors" to adjust times to defined levels of skill and effort. Therefore, when using MOST, it is *not necessary* to adjust times unless they must conform with particular high or low task plans used by some companies. This also means that a properly established time standard, using MOST, MTM, or stopwatch time study, will give nearly identical results in TMU.

The analysis of an operation will consist of a series of sequence models describing the movement of objects to perform the operation. Total time for the complete MOST analysis is arrived at by adding the computed sequence times.

The operation time may be left in TMU or converted to minutes or hours. Again, this time would reflect pure work content (no allowances) at the 100% performance level.

Parameter Indexing

The objective of an effective work measurement system is to provide for the documentation of a specific work method with the corresponding time. As we have seen, this is accomplished in MOST by applying time-related index numbers to each sequence model parameter, based on the motion content of the subactivity. Parameter indexing, as it is called, is the process of selecting the appropriate parameter variant from a data card or table (Figure 3.1, for example) and applying the corresponding index number. With training and practice, parameter variants and index numbers are committed to memory by the MOST analyst. Practically all analysis work can therefore be performed without any direct assistance from data cards or index tables. On the other hand, with a MOST Computer System in place, index numbers will be assigned automatically by the computer program based on the input of a limited number of *keywords* representing the parameter variants.

Time values for each parameter variant located on the data cards are based on detailed MTM-1 or MTM-2 backup analyses. These MTM analyses are arranged or "slotted" into fixed time ranges represented by an index number corresponding to the median time of each range. The time ranges were calculated using statistical accuracy principles (see Appendix A: Theory).

Application Speed

MOST was designed to be much faster than other work measurement techniques because of its simpler structure. Predetermined motion time systems are traditionally based on assigning selected time values to minute human motions. For example, to arrive at a time standard for putting a part into a machine, each basic motion involved must be identified, recorded, and assigned time values selected from tables. The values are then added together to arrive at the time for performing the complete operation.

MOST does not require that operations be broken down into such detail. Instead, MOST *groups together* the basic motions that frequently occur into a predefined sequence. Arriving at a standard time with MTM for putting a part into a drill press might require the identification of as many as 15 separate basic motions followed by the assignment of time values to each from the MTM card. Using MOST, the same analysis requires the identification directly from memory of only seven subactivities. The predefined sequence models are preprinted on the analysis form, leaving the analyst with the task of filling in only the variable index numbers.

Work Measurement Technique	Total TMU's Produced Per Analyst Hour
MTM - 1	300
MTM - 2	1,000
MTM - 3	3,000
Mini MOST®	4,000
Basic MOST®	12,000
Maxi MOST®	25,000

Figure 1.3 Comparison of application speeds.

A comparison between the speed of MOST and other work measurement techniques is shown in Figure 1.3. In this study, 1 hour of analyst time yielded 300 TMU of measured work with MTM-1. MTM-2 and MTM-3 yielded 1000 and 3000 TMU, respectively. Using MOST, the same amount of analyst time yielded 12,000 TMU. As a general rule, 1 hour of work can be measured using basic MOST with an average of 10 hours of analyst time. *Note:* The above analyses were performed under laboratory conditions; actual in-plant application may yield total TMU output other than the indicated numbers.

Accuracy

The accuracy principles that apply to MOST are the same as those used in statistical tolerance control. That is, the accuracy to which a part is manufactured depends on its role in the final assembly. Likewise, with MOST, time values are based on calculations that guarantee the overall accuracy of the final time standard. Based on these principles, MOST provides the means for covering a high volume of manual work with accuracy comparable to existing predetermined motion time systems. A more detailed discussion of the accuracy concept is presented in Appendix A: Theory.

Documentation

One of the most burdensome problems in the standards development process is the volume of paperwork required by the most widely used predetermined work measurement systems. The more detailed systems, for example, require between 40 and 100 pages of documentation. MOST, however, requires as few as 5. The substantially reduced amount of paperwork enables the analysts to complete studies faster and to update standards more easily. An example comparing the documentation required for work measurement techniques is shown in Figure

Work Measurement Technique	Number of Documentation Pages Used (3 - minute operation)
MTM - 1	16
MTM - 2	10
MTM - 3	8
Mini MOST®	2
Basic MOST®	1
Maxi MOST®	$\frac{1}{2}$

Figure 1.4 Comparison of documentation required. Mini MOST requires 2 to 3 times as many sequence models as Basic MOST, while Maxi MOST generates $2^1/_2$ times fewer sequence models than Basic MOST.

1.4 for an operation approximately 3 minutes long. It is interesting to note that the reduction of paper generated by MOST does not lead to a lack of definition of the method used to perform the task. On the contrary, the method description within MOST Systems is a clear, concise plain-language sentence describing the activity in a practical way. Because they are easy to read and understand, MOST method description can and have been used for operator training and instructions.

Method Sensitivity

Too often, work study analysts perceive their jobs as simply estimating the time required for an operation. The result is that one of the analyst's most important functions, that of *methods improvement,* is often given little or no consideration. Especially vulnerable to this misconception is the time study analyst whose attention is necessarily focused on a watch. Also, when using time study, a quantitative comparison of methods cannot be produced unless another time study is taken of the new method. MOST, like any predetermined motion time system, is concerned primarily with the motions that make up an operation. The times or index values for these motions have already been predetermined and are immediately available to the analyst from data cards or, after experience, from memory, or (even better) in the computer memory. It is the analyst's responsibility to recognize the specific motion patterns and to assign the appropriate index values to each sequence model parameter. Since MOST index values are time related, they provide a quick means for evaluating the relative length of time required for performing a specific method. The analyst's attention is automatically focused on motions requiring longer times, such as subactivities with index values of 6 or greater. This is especially true since a complete MOST analysis will quite often require no more than one page. It is therefore easy for the analyst to see the effect of rearranging the workplace layout or introducing a new tool or a fixture. By doing so, high index numbers may be reduced or even eliminated. The analyst can, on a copy of the analysis, change appropriate index numbers and thereby compute the savings resulting from the improved method. The edit function in the MOST Computer Systems makes this task very simple and fast.

MOST, then, is a *method-sensitive* technique; i.e., it is sensitive to the variations in time required by different methods. This feature is very effective in evaluating alternative methods of performing operations with regard to time and cost. The MOST analysis will clearly indicate the more economical and less fatiguing method. By reviewing a completed MOST analysis, the analyst can quickly detect activities that may be considered inefficient or unproductive (e.g., those having high index numbers).

That MOST systems is method sensitive greatly increases its worth as a work measurement tool. Not only does it indicate the time needed to perform various activities, it also provides the analyst with an instant cue that a method should be reviewed. The results are clear, concise easily understood time calculations that indicate the opportunities for saving time, money, and energy.

The Keyword Concept

In the process of sketching the computer version of MOST, the use of *keywords* seemed to be the logical approach to solve the data input problem. Properly defined keywords combined with a pre-established and coherent sentence structure brought clarity and consistency into the description of methods. Consequently, the keywords served a dual purpose: (1) to make the computer select proper index values and (2) to bring quality and uniformity into the method descriptions. This "common language" based on a limited number of keywords became very easy to understand and use by everyone involved with the development and application of work measurement data.

Not only is the keyword concept an appealing and efficient practice for the MOST Computer user, but for the manual MOST user as well. Although the computer *requires* the discipline of inputting prescribed keywords into a structured method step as a necessary entry for the correct index values to appear, the same discipline should be learned and practiced diligently by the manual MOST user. It should, however, be emphasized that the same benefits—uniformity and consistency and clarity—can be achieved in manual applications provided that the "keyword principles" are followed. It is therefore highly recommended that the *keyword concept* be applied by the manual MOST user. In addition to the indicated advantages, it will obviously be a much easier task to complete a transition from a manual to a computer system if the proper keyword language is used.

Because of the extensive use of keywords with MOST Computer Systems, it can be considered a *language-based* system. This made it possible to apply today's software technology during the latter part of the 1970s. It will also be possible to further utilize AI (artificial intelligence) principles to enhance the performance of MOST Computer Systems.

The use of the keyword concept is described in more detail throughout several of the chapters in this book.

2

The MOST Systems Family

The MOST Systems family (see Fig. 2.1) has grown significantly since the birth of the General Move Sequence. It now provides a comprehensive set of practical work measurement tools that have been put to use in many situations. Because of its excellent reputation, MOST has many friends among industrial engineers, who have made these tools their top choice for tasks related to work measurement. So that the reader may become better acquainted with this "family" of work measurement tools, its members will be introduced here with brief descriptions and the types of applications for which they are best suited. More detailed descriptions are provided in the following chapters.

Levels of Work Measurement

MOST is used to economically measure work ranging from the building of ships and railroad cars to minute electronic assembly and rapid-pace yarn-handling operations. Basic MOST is routinely used to analyze the very wide range of manual operations most common to industry. Mini MOST provides detailed analysis of highly repetitive operations, such as small assembly and the packaging of small items. Even though the precision of Mini MOST is comparable to that of more detailed systems, the application speed is substantially higher. Clerical MOST, an extension of Basic MOST, is used for analyzing office activities. Maxi MOST is used for longer cycle operations, such as setups, maintenance, material handling, heavy assembly, and job shop work. The sections following "Work Measurement System Selection" provide a more precise indication of the applicability of each system.

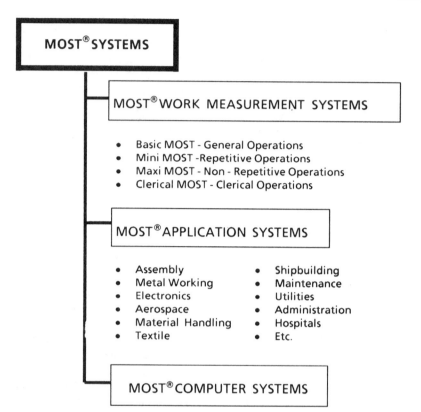

MOST® SYSTEMS

MOST® WORK MEASUREMENT SYSTEMS

- Basic MOST - General Operations
- Mini MOST - Repetitive Operations
- Maxi MOST - Non - Repetitive Operations
- Clerical MOST - Clerical Operations

MOST® APPLICATION SYSTEMS

- Assembly
- Metal Working
- Electronics
- Aerospace
- Material Handling
- Textile
- Shipbuilding
- Maintenance
- Utilities
- Administration
- Hospitals
- Etc.

MOST® COMPUTER SYSTEMS

BASIC PROGRAM

- Work Measurement (Basic, Mini, Maxi MOST)
- Database Management
- Time Standards Calculation
- Mass Update
- DataTransfer
- Where Used/Data History
- Work Management Manual Documentation

SUPPLEMENTARY MODULES

- Maching Data
- Welding Data
- Line Balancing
- Multi - Man - Machine Analysis
- Mega MOST
- Auto MOST

APPLICATION PROGRAMS

- Systems Integration Module
- Manpower Planning
- Process Planning
- Tool / Fixture Tracking
- Cost Estimating
- Performance Reporting

Figure 2.1   Overview of MOST Systems.

Compatibility of MOST Systems

MOST Systems are designed to provide the optimal combination of speed, detail, and accuracy of analysis at all levels of application. Because of the consistent structure within and between the work measurement systems, as soon as a user is familiar with one activity sequence, that user is already acquainted with all other sequences. Defined subactivities, such as Action Distance, analyzed on the A parameter, are used in similar sequence models at all levels. Every parameter is always indexed with a number from the set of MOST indexes: 0, 1, 3, 6, 10, 16, and so on. The only difference is that index value 3, for example, stands for 3 TMU in Mini MOST, 30 TMU in Basic MOST, and 300 TMU in Maxi MOST, since the index ranges differ by a factor of 10 from level to level.

Another feature that provides consistency and improves communication is the use of "keyword" language to describe the methods being analyzed. This technique is described in Chapter 3.

MOST Application Systems

MOST Applications Systems have been devised by experienced data development experts to assure that MOST work measurement data are obtained and used in the most efficient and effective manner. This expertise has been applied to a large variety of work measurement projects, substantially reducing the resources needed and increasing the immediate usefulness and long-term integrity of the data. MOST Application Systems training is usually provided at the beginning of a data development project. (See Chap. 7 for a brief description of MOST Application Systems.)

MOST Computer Systems

MOST Computer Systems can be considered a remarkable development in the field of industrial engineering. Long before natural-language interfaces began to emerge as a desirable feature in application software, MOST Computer Systems was being used to convert common-language method descriptions into completed MOST analyses. Although this capability is at the heart of MOST Computer Systems, it does considerably more to utilize the power of computers in the development, application, and maintenance of both small and extremely large collections of work measurement data. The list in Figure 2.1 hints at the comprehensive functions being performed by this fully integrated system. Chapter 8 provides an overview of MOST Computer Systems.

Work Measurement System Selection

The consistent multilevel design of MOST Systems made it possible to establish simple guidelines for deciding which version is the most appropriate for measuring work. Appendix A provides a detailed explanation of the theory that supports these guidelines. Your awareness of the kinds of situations best analyzed with each version will increase even further as you study them in detail in the following chapters. For example, although there are some overlaps in the ranges of application, distances are typically analyzed to the nearest inch (centimeter) with Mini MOST, within reach or a few steps with Basic MOST, and more than two steps with Maxi MOST. Just as you would avoid measuring a football field with a micrometer rule, these guidelines will help you avoid being too meticulous with MOST.

Maxi MOST

At the highest level, Maxi MOST is used to analyze operations that are likely to be performed fewer than 150 times per week. An operation in this category may be less than 2 minutes to more than several hours in length. Maxi MOST index ranges accommodate the wide cycle-to-cycle variations that are typical in such work as setups or heavy assembly. Even at this level, the method descriptions resulting from Maxi MOST are very practical for instructional purposes.

Basic MOST

At the intermediate level, operations that are likely to be performed more than 150 but fewer than 1500 times per week should be analyzed with Basic MOST. An operation in this category may range from a few seconds to 10 minutes in length. (Operations longer than 10 minutes may be analyzed with Basic MOST, with 0.5–3 minutes being typical cycle time for Basic MOST). The majority of operations in most industries fall into this category. Basic MOST index ranges readily accommodate the cycle-to-cycle variations typical at this level. The method descriptions that result from Basic MOST analyses are sufficiently detailed for use as operator instructions.

Mini MOST

At the lowest level, Mini MOST provides the most detailed and precise methods analysis. In general, this level of detail and precision is required to analyze any operation likely to be repeated more than 1500 times per week. Operations having an occurrence frequency this high have cycle times of less than 1.6 minutes (10 seconds or less is typical). Such operations usually have little variation from cycle to cycle owing to the operator's high level of practice and to management efforts to improve the design, layout, and method. Opportunities for small but significant improvements in these areas are often highlighted by a Mini MOST analysis.

Regardless of the cycle length, Mini MOST should also be used to analyze any operation in which nearly all reach and move distances for an operation are less than 10 inches (25 cm). However, since its focus is on highly repetitive work within reach of the operator, Mini MOST was not designed for analyzing operations in which the operator action distances exceed two steps, body motions other than Bend and Arise occur, or the weight or resistance per hand exceeds 10 pounds (5 kg). Basic MOST would normally be used to analyze these situations. (In the rare instances when these guidelines contradict, you may divide the operation into suboperations and apply the appropriate system to each. The separate analyses will be recombined when the time standard is calculated.)

Decision Diagram

The decision diagram in Figure 2.2 provides a simple procedure for selecting the appropriate MOST Work Measurement System. Although the operation occurrence frequency is the most important factor, the questions are arranged so those easiest to answer are asked earlier. Note that the occurrence frequency numbers 150 and 1500 are based on an overall accuracy requirement of $\pm 5\%$ with a 95% confidence level. If the required accuracy is only $\pm 10\%$ with 90% confidence, these numbers should be increased to 770 and 7700, respectively. (More on this subject can be found in Appendix A. See especially "Establishing Overall Accuracy" and "Occurrence Frequency Grouping for MOST.")

The two questions in the second column of the decision diagram (Fig. 2.2) reflect the fact that MOST is method sensitive. Either version allows the analyst to focus attention on work methods, but a lower-level version requires a closer examination of the method than a higher-level system. So if the emphasis is on improving methods, design, or layouts, the analyst may choose Basic MOST instead of Maxi MOST (or Mini MOST instead of Basic MOST) to increase the ability to create improvements.

System Selection Charts

Figures 2.3 and 2.4 provide another approach to applying these selection guidelines. These charts are based on two principles: (1) the longer the analyzed time, the more accurate the analysis (due to the balancing effect); (2) the overall accuracy of a group of analyses improves as short-cycle analyses are properly combined. These charts are designed to ensure that any set of standards that includes short-cycle analyses will have the expected level of accuracy.

Each chart covers one of the two levels of accuracy most often required by government and industry. With either chart, if you know or can *estimate* the approximate length of the operation in minutes and the percentage of the standard calculation period occupied by repetitions of the operation, you can quickly

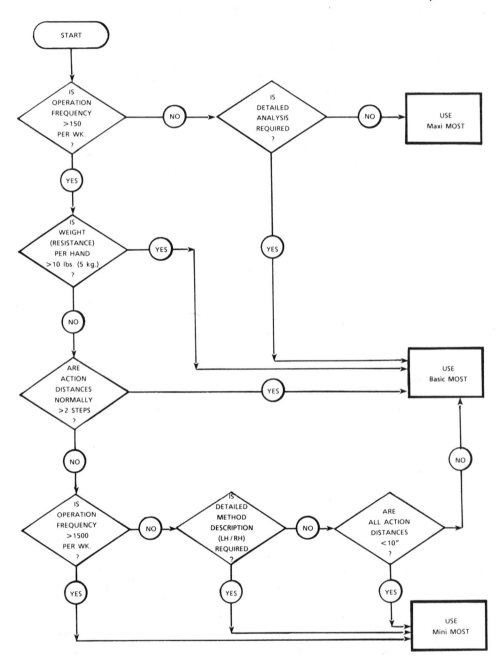

Figure 2.2 Procedure for selecting the appropriate MOST Work Measurement System.

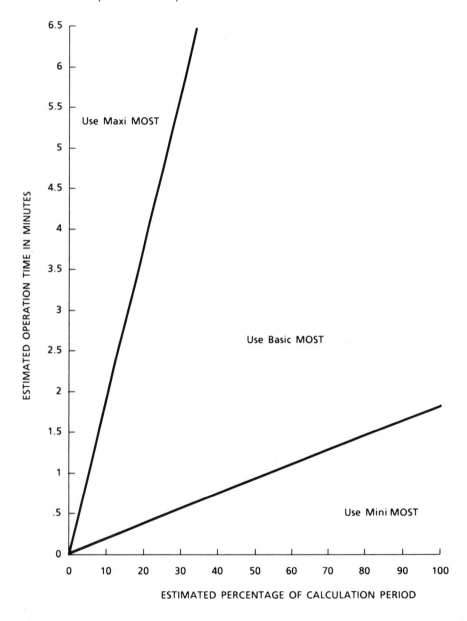

Figure 2.3 MOST systems selection guidelines for ±5% accuracy at a 95% confidence level.

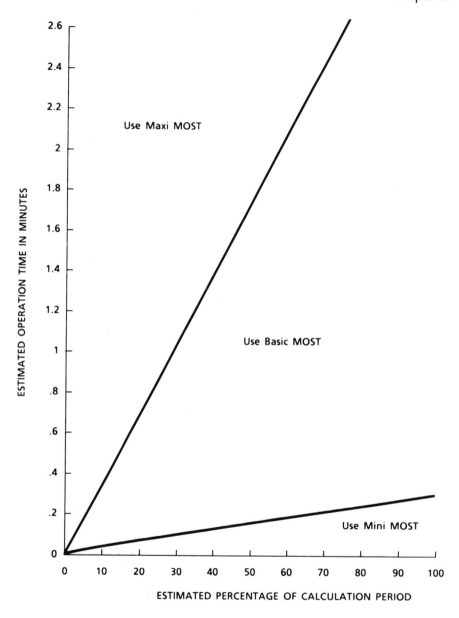

Figure 2.4 MOST systems selection guidelines for ±10% accuracy at a 90% confidence level.

determine which MOST version will be sufficiently accurate for the analysis. This provides a useful guideline for avoiding the extra work that would be required to analyze operations with a version of MOST more detailed than necessary.

For example, using Figure 2.3, if the operation is about one minute long and will be repeated enough times to occupy about 30% of the pay period, a Basic MOST analysis will be sufficiently accurate. If repetitions of this same operation occupy 70% of the period, however, then Mini MOST must be used for the analysis. A similar determination is made for each analysis. When all analyses of the operations that fill the calculation period fall within the charted limits, overall accuracy within ±5% is assured. To maintain overall accuracy, when estimating the cycle time for the operation, do not include the time for any step or sequence of steps that is repeated identically *within* the operation cycle. For further details see "Effect of Variations Within an Operation Cycle" in Appendix A.

3

The Basic MOST System

The Basic MOST System as introduced in Chapter 1 satisfies the most common work measurement situations in the manufacturing arena. Every company very likely has some operations for which Basic MOST is the logical and most practical work measurement tool. Mini MOST and Maxi MOST can be considered supplements to Basic MOST.

The sequence models of Basic MOST represent the only two basic activities necessary to measure manual work: *General Move* and *Controlled Move*. The two remaining sequence models included in Basic MOST were added to simplify the measurement of *hand tool use* and the movement of objects by *manual crane*. The Manual Crane Sequence Model has application only where heavy objects are being moved within a work-station.

The Basic MOST System is the core of MOST Work Measurement Systems and should therefore be studied by all practitioners of MOST, independent of the version that is selected for later use.

A. The General Move Sequence

The *General Move Sequence* deals with the spatial displacement of an object. Under manual control, the object follows an unrestricted path through the air. If the object is in contact with or restrained in any way by another object during the move, the General Move Sequence is not applicable.

Characteristically, General Move follows a fixed sequence of subactivities identified by the following steps:

1. Reach with one or two hands a distance to the object(s), either directly or in conjunction with body motions or steps.
2. Gain manual control of the object.
3. Move the object a distance to the point of placement, either directly or in conjunction with body motion or steps.
4. Place the object in a temporary or final position.
5. Return to workplace.

These five subactivities form the basis for the activity sequence describing the manual displacement of an object freely through space. This sequence describes the manual events that can occur when moving an object freely through the air and is therefore known as a *sequence model*. The major function of the sequence model is to guide the attention of the analyst through an operation, thereby adding the dimension of having a preprinted and standardized analysis format. The existence of the sequence model provides increased analyst consistency and reduces subactivity omission.

The Sequence Model

The sequence model takes the form of a fixed series of letters (called *parameters*) representing each of the various subactivities of the General Move Activity Sequence. The parameters of the General Move Sequence describe the five-step pattern already indicated:

A   B   G   A   B   P   A

where: A = Action distance
         B = Body motion
         G = Gain control
         P = Placement

Parameter Definitions

A   Action Distance

This parameter is used to analyze all spatial movement or actions of the fingers, hands, and/or feet, either loaded or unloaded. Any control of these actions by the surroundings requires the use of other parameters.

B   Body Motion

This parameter is used to analyze either vertical (up and down) motions of the body or the actions necessary to overcome an obstruction or impairment to body movement.

G Gain Control

This parameter is used to analyze all manual motions (mainly finger, hand, and foot) employed to obtain complete manual control of an object(s) and to subsequently relinquish that control. The G parameter can include one or several short-move motions whose objective is to gain full control of the object(s) before it is to be moved to another location.

P Placement

This parameter is used to analyze actions at the final stage of an object's displacement to align, orient, and/or engage the object with another object(s) before control of the object is relinquished.

Phases of the General Move Sequence

The displacement of an object through space occurs in three distinct phases, as shown by the following General Move Sequence breakdown:

Get	Put	Return
A B G	A B P	A

The first phase, referred to as *Get,* describes the actions to reach the object, with body motions (if necessary), and gain control of the object. The A parameter indicates the distance the hand or body must travel to reach the object, and the B indicates the need for any body motions during this action. The degree of difficulty encountered in gaining control of the object is described by the G parameter.

The *Put* phase of the sequence model describes the action to move the object to another location. As before, the A and B parameters indicate the distance the hand or body travels with the object and the need for any body motions during the move before the object is placed. The manner in which the object is placed is described by the P parameter.

The third phase simply indicates the distance traveled by the operator to *Return* to the workplace following the placement of the object.

The MOST analyst should strictly adhere to the three-phase breakdown of the General Move Sequence Model. Such adherence provides consistency in application and ease in communication.

Method Description in Keyword Language

Another valuable technique, which assures efficient communication and enables correct analysis, entails the consistent description of methods in *keyword language.* Keyword language consists of simple phrases in sentence formats that are compatible with MOST sequence models. The phrases are constructed with keywords like GET, PUT and RETURN, which represent subactivities; the prepositions FROM, TO, ONTO, INTO, and AT; and the names of items located in the work area. For example, a method step MOVE PART FROM BIN INTO BOX AND RETURN TO WORKBENCH obviously represents the three phases of a General Move Sequence Model. This example illustrates how keyword language, as a natural byproduct of the MOST technique, serves as an ideal way to document methods for analysis.

Keyword language was originally developed for inputting method descriptions with MOST Computer Systems. (See Chap. 8.) This system is designed to recognize and act on the keywords and phrases of a method step entry to automatically produce an appropriate MOST analysis. With recent enhancements in the MOST Computer Systems language capability, keyword language has become the best way to express methods—even for manual applications of MOST:

- Only a small, easily remembered vocabulary of keywords is needed to describe methods.
- Keywords are compatible with the subactivity variants and phases of the MOST sequence models.
- Each keyword represents a tabulated parameter and index number, which the user (or the computer system) is able to transcribe from memory.
- Correct analysis actually results from the appropriate use of keyword language.
- The prescribed sentence formats assure concise, uniform, and easy-to-read method descriptions that correspond with the analysis.
- The use of keyword language in manual MOST applications facilitates conversion to computerized MOST.

For these reasons, from the inception of any MOST work measurement project, describing methods in keyword language is highly recommended. Equally important is a definition of the work area data, including workplaces and action distances between these workplaces.

To further understand this concept, examine Figure 3.1 for the General Move Sequence Model. Notice that only 19 activity keywords are needed to express all possible variants of Gain Control and Placement. A method step to gain control of a "heavy object" (GET) and place it "with care" (POSITION) could be written simply GET AND POSITION PART in keyword language.

This level of simplicity is possible because the keyword concept incorporates some practical built-in assumptions and conventions. First, since initial item locations and normal walking distances between workplaces are documented separately with the workplace layout, origin locations, destination locations, and number of steps need not be stated if these are obvious from the context. Furthermore, certain variants, such as "light object" and "within reach," are usu-

Basic MOST® System

INDEX X 10	A — ACTION DISTANCE		B — BODY MOTION	
	PARAMETER VARIANT	KEYWORD	PARAMETER VARIANT	KEYWORD
0	≤2 in. ≤5 cm.	CLOSE		
1	Within reach			
3	1 - 2 steps	1 STEP 2 STEPS	Bend and arise 50 % occ.	PBEND
6	3 - 4 steps	3 STEPS 4 STEPS	Bend and arise	BEND
10	5 - 7 steps	5 STEPS 6 STEPS 7 STEPS	Sit or stand	SIT STAND
16	8 - 10 steps	8 STEPS 9 STEPS 10 STEPS	Through Door Climb on or off Stand and bend Bend and sit	DOOR CLIMB / DESCEND STAND AND BEND BEND AND SIT

Figure 3.1 General Move data card.

ally assumed if not stated explicitly. In addition, each method step begins with an activity keyword to emphasize that indexed parameters result from keywords (and these assumptions), not the reverse.

To further illustrate, consider a method step to pick up a light object within reach, move it to a location within reach, place it with adjustments, then relinquish control (no body motions, no return). In the context of a MOST analysis, the single keyword PLACE will completely and correctly represent all seven parameters and indexes for this General Move Sequence:

$$A_1 \quad B_0 \quad G_1 \quad A_1 \quad B_0 \quad P_3 \quad A_0$$

A B G A B P A					GENERAL MOVE
G GAIN CONTROL		**P** PLACEMENT			INDEX X 10
PARAMETER VARIANT	KEYWORD	PARAMETER VARIANT	KEYWORD		
		Hold Toss	THROW TOSS CARRY PICKUP		**0**
Light object Light objects simo	GRASP (optional)	Lay aside Loose fit	MOVE PUT		**1**
Non Simo Obstructed Heavy / Bulky Interlocked Blind Collect Disengage	GET DISENGAGE FREE COLLECT	Adjustments Light pressure Double placement	PLACE REPLACE		**3**
		Care Precision Blind Obstructed Heavy pressure Intermediate moves	POSITION REPOSITION		**6**
					10
					16

Therefore, the method description for this entire sequence of motions may be written: PLACE PART. As long as the keywords and phrases essential for the analysis are included in the method description syntax, the analyst is then free to add any locations, adjectives, or remarks needed to clarify the method. But keyword and object specifications are usually sufficient.

As examples elsewhere in this text demonstrate, all MOST analyses can be expressed effectively in keyword language. Additional keywords are available, including those reserved for each sequence model in each MOST version—Basic, Mini, and Maxi MOST. Keywords and sentence formats are explained in more detail in the MOST Computer Systems Language Manual.

Parameter Indexing

The MOST analyst should always ask these questions prior to indexing a sequence model:

1. What item is being moved?
2. How is the item moved (determine the appropriate sequence model)?

Then, assuming a General Move Sequence:

3. What does the operator do to *get* the item (determine index values for A, B, and G—first phase)?
4. What does the operator do to *put* the item (determine index values for A, B, and P—second phase)?
5. Does the operator *return* or "clear" hands (determine index value for the final A—third phase)?

An additional question should be asked if the analyst is also seeking method improvements:

6. Is this activity necessary to do the job (eliminate any unnecessary subactivities from the analysis)?

(Similar questions must be asked for a Controlled Move or Tool Use Sequence Model. See the MOST Analysis Decision Diagram in Figure 3.34.)

Asking these questions is vital to the effective application of MOST. The answers help the analyst:

- Avoid overlooking any operator activity or analyzing any unnecessary activity
- Correctly divide an operation into method steps and phases
- Describe each step in appropriate keyword language
- If necessary (manual application), determine the index for each parameter (subactivity)
- Apply MOST consistently

Indexing each parameter of the General Move Sequence Model is accomplished by observing or visualizing the operator's actions during each phase of the activity and selecting the appropriate parameter variants from the data card (Fig. 3.1) that describes those actions. For manual applications of MOST, the value for each parameter is taken from the extreme left or right column of the data card and is written just below and to the right of the sequence model parameter, for example, A_3. With MOST Computer Systems, the correctly indexed parameters are generated automatically from the *work area data* and the *method description,* provided each method step includes the appropriate activity keyword(s) from the data card.

Consider the example of a machine operator getting a finished part from a workplace table, putting it on a pallet and returning. Assume that the operator is standing directly in front of the part, which is light in weight and the pallet is located 10 steps away on the floor. The sequence model for this activity is filled out as follows.

$$A_1 \quad B_0 \quad G_1 \quad A_{16} \quad B_6 \quad P_1 \quad A_{16}$$

Since the operator is standing directly in front of the part, the first A parameter in the sequence is indexed A_1 because the part is located within reach. (Look under the action distance column of the data card [Figure 3.1] for Within Reach, and note the corresponding index value to the left.) No Body Motion is needed to reach the part; therefore, a 0 is assigned to the Body Motion parameter (B_0), and control of the object is gained with no difficulty—G_1 (light object under Gain Control column). The part is then moved 10 steps away (A_{16}) and placed on the floor, B_6 (Bend and Arise). No difficulty is encountered in placing the part on a pallet; it is simply laid aside, P_1. The operator then walks back (returns) to the workplace, which is 10 steps away (A_{16}).

The time to perform this activity is computed simply by adding all index numbers in the sequence and multiplying by 10 to convert to TMU: $(1 + 0 + 1 + 16 + 6 + 1 + 16) \times 10 = 410$ TMU. In keyword language this method step would be written MOVE FINISHED PART TO PALLET AND RETURN. Using MOST Computer Systems, this entry would cause the indexed sequence model and calculations to be generated automatically.

In the remainder of this chapter, the parameter variants for each of the General Move Sequence parameters are examined in detail. The parameter values up to and including index value 16 (i.e., all values on the General Move data card) should be familiar enough to the MOST analyst to be applied from memory. Therefore, the majority of work performed within the confines of a well-designed workplace can be analyzed without the aid of the data card.

Note: The capitalized words to the right of parameter variants are the corresponding keywords used in MOST Computer Systems in describing methods.

Action Distance (A)

Action Distance covers all spatial movement or actions of the fingers, hands, and/or feet, either loaded or unloaded. Any control of these actions by the surroundings requires the use of other parameters.

A_0 ≤2 inches (5 cm)   CLOSE

Any displacement of the fingers, hands, and/or feet a distance less than or equal to 2 inches (5 cm) will carry a zero index value. Time for traversing these short distances are included within the Gain Control and Placement parameters.

Example: Used when reaching between the number keys on a pocket calculator or placing nuts or washers on bolts located less than 2 inches (5 cm) apart.

A₁ Within Reach

Actions are confined to an area described by the arc of the outstretched arm pivoted about the shoulder: *no keyword needed*. With body assistance—a short bending or turning of the body from the waist—this "within reach" area is extended somewhat. However, taking a step for further extension of the area exceeds the limits of an A_1 and must be analyzed with an A_3 (one to two steps).

Example: In a well defined workstation such as that shown in Figure 3.2, all parts and tools can be reached without displacing the body by taking a step.

The parameter value A_1 also applies to the actions of the leg or foot reaching to an object, lever, or pedal. If the trunk of the body is shifted, however, the action must be considered a step (A_3).

A₃ One to Two Steps   1 STEP, 2 STEPS

The trunk of the body is shifted or displaced by walking, stepping to the side, or turning the body around using one or two steps. Steps refer to the total number of times each foot hits the floor.

A₆ Three or More Steps   3 STEPS, 4 STEPS, . . .

Index values for longer action distances involving walking are found in Figure 3.3. Although these values generally refer to the horizontal movement of the

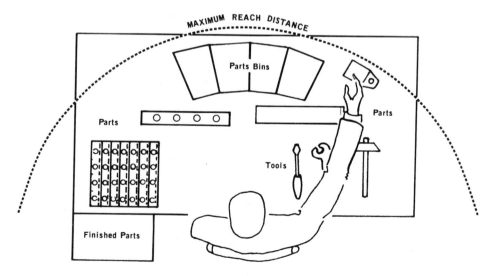

Figure 3.2 All parts and tools located within reach.

ACTION DISTANCE			
INDEX VALUE (A)	STEPS	DISTANCE (FEET)	DISTANCE (M)
24	11-15	38	12
32	16-20	50	15
42	21-26	65	20
54	27-33	83	25
67	34-40	100	30
81	41-49	123	38
96	50-57	143	44
113	58-67	168	51
131	68-78	195	59
152	79-90	225	69
173	91-102	255	78
196	103-115	288	88
220	116-128	320	98
245	129-142	355	108
270	143-158	395	120
300	159-174	435	133
330	175-191	478	146

Figure 3.3 Extended Action Distance table. The values in the distance columns are read "up to and including."

body, they also apply to walking up or down normally inclined stair steps. Index values are given in terms of both Steps and Feet. When using Figure 3.3, however, the preferred method is to count the number of steps taken. This is because research has shown that the time required to take a step is relatively constant regardless of the size of the load carried. In other words, a worker uses the same amount of time to take five steps while carrying a heavy load as to take five steps with no load. However, the influence of the load shortens the step length, thereby increasing the number of steps required to cover a specific distance. In this way, the effect of any load is reflected in the action distance parameter. Therefore, whenever possible, action distance values should be based on the number of steps taken by the operator rather than the distance walked.

Occasionally, however, it is not possible to observe the operator at work. If this is the case, action distance values must be determined from distances measured at the workplace or obtained from drawings. The distances in Figure 3.3 are based on an average step length of $2^1/_2$ feet (0.75 m). *Note:* The action distance values were generated to include walking in a normal manufacturing environment, and as a result they include an average pace of $2^1/_2$ feet (0.75 m), obstructed and unobstructed walking, walking up or down normally inclined stairs, and walking with or without weight. Should a particular job contain several long, unobstructed, and unencumbered walking distances, the action distances provided may not be appropriate and the values should then be validated.

Return Phase

The last A parameter in the General Move Sequence Model is normally used to allocate time for an operator to *return by walking* to his or her ordinary workplace (starting position). This allows for a logical break point between sequence models or suboperations. If all suboperations begin and end at the same location (regular workplace), gaps or overlaps between suboperations can be avoided.

Time for *returning hand(s)* without steps is normally not allowed on the last A parameter, since moving the hand(s) to another object or objects is part of the initial A parameter of the subsequent sequence model. An exception to this rule is a final A for the hand(s) from inside a machine or moving the hand(s) aside to permit the performance of the next activity (keyword CLEAR).

Body Motion (B)

Body Motion refers to either vertical (up and down) motions of the body or the actions necessary to overcome an obstruction or impairment to body movement.

B₆   Bend and Arise   BEND

From an erect standing position, the trunk of the body is lowered by bending from the waist and/or knees to allow the hands to reach below the knees and subsequently return to an upright position. It is not necessary, however, for the hands to actually reach below the knees, only that the body be lowered sufficiently to allow the reach. B_6 may be simply bending from the waist with the knees stiff, stooping down by bending at the knees, or kneeling down on one knee. See Figure 3.4.

B₃   Bend and Arise, 50% Occurrence   PBEND

Bend and Arise is required only 50% of the time during a repetitive activity, such as stacking or unstacking several objects. In stacking (Fig. 3.5), the first few objects may require a full Bend and Arise to place the objects at floor level.

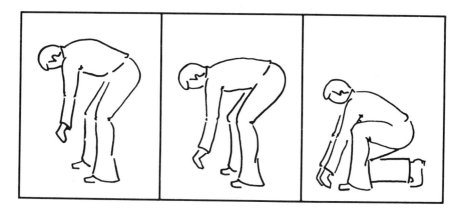

Figure 3.4 Examples of Bend and Arise. Notice that in each case the hands are able to reach below the knees.

Figure 3.5 Bend and arise, 50% occurrence.

As the stack becomes taller, the last objects for stacking require no body motions at all. (The keyword PBEND stands for Partial Bend.)

B_{10} Sit or Stand   SIT, STAND

When the act of sitting down or standing up requires a series of several hand, foot, and body motions to move a chair or stool into a position that allows the body to either Sit or Stand, a B_{10} is appropriate. All the motions to manipulate the chair and body are included in the B_{10} body motion. If the chair or stool is stationary and several foot and body motions are necessary either to situate the body comfortably in the seat or to climb on or off the stool, a B_{10} would also apply. Note that B_{10} covers either Sit or Stand, not both.

A special situation may be encountered in industry when an operator sits or stands without moving the chair, such as sitting on a bench. A special index value B_3, *Sit or Stand without moving chair*, may be used in this situation.

B_{16} Stand and Bend   STAND + BEND

Occasionally a person sitting at a desk must stand up and walk to a location to gain control of an object placed below the knee level, where a Bend and Arise is required. The index value appears on the first B parameter of the sequence model.

B_{16} Bend and Sit   BEND + SIT

As with Stand and Bend, the combined body motion of Bend and Sit applies when the Gain Control of an object requires a Bend and Arise followed by a Sit prior to placing the object. The index value appears on the B parameter in the Put phase.

B_{16} Climb On or Off   CLIMB, DESCEND

This parameter variant covers *climbing on or off* a work platform on any raised surface (approximately 3 feet or 1 m high) using a series of hand and body motions to lift or lower the body. Climbing onto a platform is accomplished by first placing one hand on the edge and then lifting the knee to the platform. By placing the other hand on the platform and bending forward, the weight of the body is shifted, allowing the other knee to be lifted onto the platform. The activity is completed by arising from both knees. Climbing off the platform consists of the same actions, but performed in the reverse order.

Example: Climb onto a truck frame on an assembly line to attach a bracket for the exhaust system.

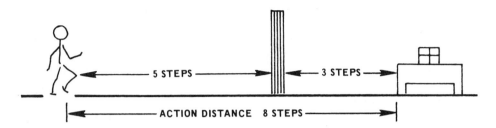

Figure 3.6 Application of a B_{16} in conjunction with an action distance.

B_{16} Passing Through Door   DOOR

Passing through a door normally consists of reaching for and turning the handle, opening the door, walking through the door, and subsequently closing the door. This value will apply to virtually all hinged, double, or swinging doors.

The three or four steps required to pass through the doorway are included in the B_{16} value. These steps should not be added to the action distance or subtracted from it.

The proper application of a B_{16} in conjunction with an action distance is graphically shown in Figure 3.6. *Example:* An operator walks five steps to a door, passes through the door, and walks three steps to a desk where a light object is picked up and placed on the floor beside the desk.

Note that the five steps to the door and the three steps beyond the door are all part of getting the object. The proper application of B_{16} requires adding the steps prior to and after the doorway to allow a single action distance value for eight steps (A_{16}). The steps to actually pass through the doorway are included in the B_{16} value. The appropriate analysis for this example is:

GET			PUT			RETURN	
A_{16}	B_{16}	G_1	A_1	B_6	P_1	A_0	410 TMU

Gain Control (G)

Gain Control covers all manual motions (mainly finger, hand, and foot) employed to obtain complete manual control of an object and subsequently to relinquish that control. The G parameter can include one or several short-move motions whose objective is to gain full control of the object(s) before it is to be moved to another location.

G₁ Light Object   GRASP (OPTIONAL)

Any type of grasp can be used as long as no difficulty is encountered as described by the G₃ parameter variants. The object may be jumbled with other objects, lying close against a flat surface, or simply lying by itself. Control may be gained simply by touching the object with the fingers, hand, or foot (contact grasp), or a more difficult grasping action, such as that needed to pick one object out of a jumbled pile of objects, may be required. Either one or two hands may be used as long as only one object is obtained and that object is accessible for the simultaneous grasps of both hands. If several objects are grouped together or arranged in such a way that they may be picked up as one object, G₁ will still apply.

Note: The keyword GRASP for gain control of "light object" or "light objects simo" is optional. The default option for gain control in MOST Computer Systems will produce a G₁ in the General Move Sequence Model without the input of GRASP. The same principle can be applied to a manual MOST analysis.

Examples: Pick up a hammer from a work bench. Obtain one washer from a parts bin full of washers. Using both hands, pick up a manual lying by itself. Obtain one sheet of paper from the top of a desk. Pick up pencils grouped together in a holder (several objects grouped as one). Obtain one bolt from a jumbled pile of bolts. Grasp a lever, crank, knob, toggle switch, pushbutton, foot pedal, or other activating device (to be applied in the Controlled Move Sequence Model). With a hand already touching an object, grasp the object with the same hand in order to lay it aside.

G₁ Light Objects Simo   GRASP (OPTIONAL)

Simo refers to manual actions performed simultaneously by different body members. That is, one hand gains control of a light object (G₁), while the other hand obtains another light object (G₁). The total time, then, is no more than that required to gain control of one light object. For application of a keyword, see preceding note.

Example: Using both hands, pick up a hammer and nail lying side by side. Using both hands, pick up two small suitcases. Pick up a pencil and a straightedge using both hands.

G₃ Light Object(s) Non Simo   GET

Because of the nature of the job or the conditions under which the job is performed, the operator is unable to gain control of two objects or of two suitable grasping points of one object simultaneously. While one hand is grasping an object, the other hand must wait before it can grasp the other object. Therefore, gain control time must be allowed for both hands; hence the larger index value G₃ applies.

The ability of the operator to perform simultaneous motions is largely dependent on the amount of practice opportunity available. For example, an assembly operator who continuously gets parts from the same two locations will have no trouble performing the activity "simo." After repeating a number of cycles, the operator develops an automatic reaction to the exact location of each part.

On the other hand, simultaneous motions will sometimes be difficult for workers in a job shop. Because of the infrequent occurrence of many operations, the operator will have little practice opportunity to gain the automatic skills necessary to perform simultaneous motions.

Regarding selection of the Simo versus Non Simo parameter, the analyst should observe the operator's actions wherever possible. Normally, *simo actions* can easily be recognized by their automatic appearance. (For further discussion, see Sec. E of this chapter).

G₃ Heavy or Bulky   GET

Control of heavy or bulky objects is achieved only after the muscles are tensed to a point at which the effects of the difficulty created by the weight, shape, or size are overcome. We can identify this variant by the *hesitation* or *pause* needed for the attainment of sufficient muscular force required to move the object.

This effect is influenced not only by the actual weight of the object but also by the location of the object with respect to the body, the existence of handles or grips for easy grasping, or even the strength of the individual. Poorly located objects, even smaller or lighter ones, for example, may require some hesitation or the movement of the body for balance or additional muscular control for leverage. With the existence of handles or other easy grasping devices located appropriately on the object, the effect of the weight can be significantly reduced.

Therefore, when considering this parameter variant for gain control, the major criterion is not the actual weight of the object, but the hesitation or pause needed for the muscles to tense or the body to stiffen prior to moving the object. See Figure 3.7.

Examples: Get hold of an automobile battery located on the floor. Take hold of a loaded hand cart before pulling. Get hold of a briefcase by reaching over other baggage. Brace your body before pushing a heavy carton across a bench. Pick up a large, empty television packing box.

The weight or bulk of an object can also affect the method of gaining control. Before a heavy or bulky object can be completely controlled, it may be necessary to move or reorient the object. This may require obtaining a temporary grip and sliding the object closer to the body before complete control of the object is obtained (see Fig. 3.8). In extreme cases calling for several "intermediate moves" of the object, analysis is accomplished through the use of additional parameters or sequence models if necessary. For example, use a Controlled

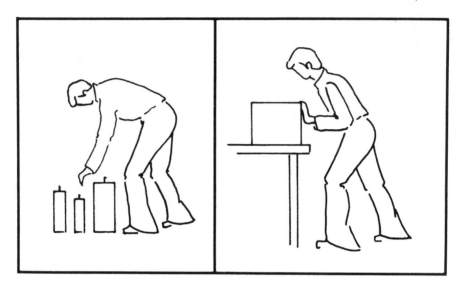

Figure 3.7   Examples of G_3, gain control of heavy or bulky objects.

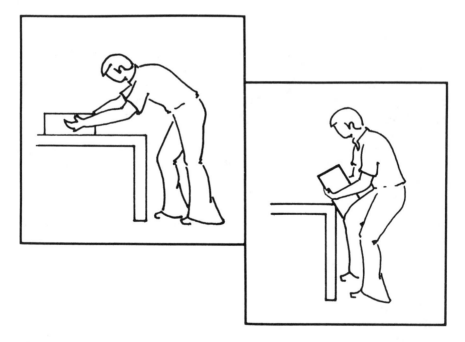

Figure 3.8   Gain control of heavy object requiring intermediate moves.

Move Sequence Model to analyze sliding the object closer. However, we suggest that the method in such a case be reviewed and improved if possible.

G_3 Blind or Obstructed   GET, FREE

The accessibility to the object is restricted because an obstacle either prevents the operator from seeing the object or creates an obstruction to the hand or fingers when attempting to gain control of the object. If the location is blind, the operator must *feel around* for the object before it can be grasped. When an obstruction presents itself, the fingers or hand must be *worked around* the obstacle before reaching the object.

Examples: Obtain a washer from a stud located on the other side of a panel (blind). Work the fingers around the wiring in an electrical assembly to get a part (obstructed). Get a pocket knife from your pocket.

G_3 Disengage   DISENGAGE

The application of muscular force is needed to free the object from its surroundings. *Disengage* is characterized by the application of pressure (to overcome resistance), followed by the sudden movement and recoil of the object. The recoil of the object, however, must follow an unrestricted path through the air (not to be confused with unseating a lever, crank, or other controlled devices).

Examples: Disengage a tightly fitting socket from a ratchet tool. Remove a knife stuck in wood. Disengage the cork from a wine bottle.

G_3 Interlocked   FREE

The object is intermingled or tangled with other objects and must be separated or worked free before complete control is achieved.

Examples: Remove a hammer from a crowded toolbox (the hammerhead is buried beneath other tools). From a box of springs, gain control of one spring that is tangled with another.

G_3 Collect   COLLECT

Gaining control of several objects is accomplished. The objects may be jumbled together in a pile or spread out over a surface. If jumbled, control of several objects is achieved by digging down into the pile with the hand(s) and bringing up a handful. When spread out, the objects may be swept together with the hand(s) and fingers and picked up as one object. If the items are in very close proximity to one another and picked up individually, G_3 will cover gaining control of up to two objects (two grasps) per hand (i.e., a total of four if two hands are used simultaneously). If even more items are grasped individually, a series of G_1 or additional G_3 grasping actions may be applied. Repeated or additional reaches (A_1) may be included if required. *Note:* Ascertain that the best method is being performed and that these additional grasps are in fact necessary.

Examples: Grasp a handful of nails from a bin. Collect several sheets of paper lying on a desk. Get a handful of change from your pocket. Gather up a pen, pencil, and eraser spread out on a desk with one sweeping motion of the hand. Collect two bolts lying on the top of a workbench (with one "sweeping" motion).

Placement (P)

Placement refers to actions occurring at the final stage of an object's displacement to align, orient, or engage the object with another before control of the object is relinquished. Basically, the index value for the placement parameter is chosen by the difficulty encountered during the placement. Placement includes a limited amount of insertion (up to 2 inches, 5 cm) as part of the placement. For insertions greater than this, a combination of General Move and Controlled Move sequences must be used. This will be explained in more detail in the next section.

P_0 Pickup Object(s)   PICKUP, CARRY

Placement does not occur. The object is picked up and held. Placement occurs in a later sequence model.

Note: The keyword HOLD is optional and should be used when operator holds the object(s) in hand(s). PICKUP should be used "within reach" and CARRY for a "pickup" followed by steps.

P_0 Toss Object(s)   TOSS, THROW

Placement does not occur. The object is released during the preceding move (action distance parameter) without placing motions or pause to point the object toward the target.

Examples: Toss a finished part into a tote bin. Toss a completed assembly down a drop chute. Throw balled-up paper into a trash can.

P_1 Lay Aside   MOVE

The object is simply placed in an approximate location with no apparent aligning or adjusting motions. This placement requires low control by the mental, visual, or muscular senses.

Examples: Lay a hand tool aside after using. Place a pencil on a desk. Lay a manual on a table.

P₁ Loose Fit   PUT

The object is placed in a more specific location than that described by the Lay Aside parameter, but tolerances are such that only a very modest amount of mental, visual, or muscular control is necessary to place it. The clearance between the engaging parts is loose enough so that a single adjusting motion, without the application of pressure, is required to seat or position the object.

Examples: Place a washer on a bolt. Replace a telephone receiver on the hook. Put a coat hanger on a rack. Place a dull pencil into a sharpener.

The use of stops at a workplace can make it possible for an operator to place an object to a precise location with little or no hesitation. For this reason, laying an object against stops can be considered a "loose fit" placement (P_1).

Example: PUT part in drill jig. (If adjustments are made, the placement will be a P_3 in most situations.)

P₃ Adjustments   PLACE, REPLACE

Adjustments are defined as the corrective actions occurring at the point of placement caused by difficulty in handling the object, closeness of fit, lack of symmetry of the engaging parts, or uncomfortable working conditions. These adjustments are recognized as obvious efforts, hesitations, or correcting motions at the point of placement to align, orient, and/or engage the object.

Examples: Place a key in a lock. Align a center punch to scribe a mark. Place a screw on a threaded junction and pick up the threads.* Place the looped end of a small piece of wire around a terminal.

P₃ Light Pressure   PLACE, REPLACE

Because of close tolerances or the nature of the placement, the application of muscular force is needed to seat the object even if the initial positioning action could be classified as loose (P_1). This could occur, for example, as the snapping action required to seat a socket on a ratchet tool.

Examples: Place a moist stamp on an envelope. Press a thumbtack into a corkboard. Insert an electric plug into a socket (light muscular force is required to seat the object after orienting with a single adjustment).

P₃ Double   PLACE, REPLACE

Two distinct placements occur during the total placing activity. For example, to assemble two parts held by a fixture, a bolt is first placed through a hole in both parts before the nut is placed on the bolt with the other hand (Fig. 3.9). The first

---

*Threaded positions are nearly always a P_3, unless they are either blind or obstructed (P_6) or placed in a hole up to 2 inches (5 cm) deep, where the threaded pickup action is not required (P_1).

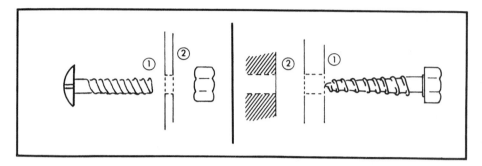

Figure 3.9 Left: Place bolt through hole before placing nut. Right: Fasten one object to another.

placement occurs with the bolt through the holes followed by a second placement of the nut on the bolt.

This parameter can also be applied to an object being lined up to two different marks following a general move. For P_3 to apply, however, these marks must be within 4 inches (10 cm) of each other. If there is more than 4 inches (10 cm) between each mark, special eye times are needed, which require additional care in the placement (P_6). (For more detailed information, see Alignment in Sec. B.)

Example: Place an original on a photocopy machine.

P_6 Care or Precision POSITION, REPOSITION

Extreme care is needed to place an object within a closely defined relationship with another object. The occurrence of this variant is characterized by the obvious slow motion of the placement owing to the high degree of concentration required for mental, visual, and muscular coordination.

Examples: Thread a needle. Position a soldering iron to a crowded circuit connection.

P_6 Heavy Pressure POSITION, REPOSITION

As a result of very tight tolerances, not the weight of an object alone, a high degree of muscular force is needed to engage the object. Occurring only rarely in practice, heavy pressure can be easily recognized as the regrasping of an object, tensing of the muscles, and the preparation of the body prior to the application of pressure.

Example: Position a book in a very tight slot on a bookshelf.

Note: An index value for P is never chosen by the weight of the object alone. Although weight may influence the difficulty in placement, it is the difficulty that determines the value chosen for P, not the weight. For example, a heavy suitcase may simply be laid to rest on the floor, in which case a P_1 (lay aside) would be chosen, while a light package may have to be squeezed into a tight space between two other boxes on a shelf and a P_6 (heavy pressure) is appropriate.

P_6 Blind or Obstructed   POSITION, REPOSITION

Conditions are similar to those encountered by the Gain Control parameter with the same title. Accessibility to the point of placement is restricted because an obstacle either prevents the operator from seeing the point of placement or creates an obstruction to the hand or fingers when attempting to place the object. If the location is blind, the operator must *feel around* for the placement location before the object can actually be placed (normally with adjustments). When an obstruction presents itself, the fingers and/or hands must be *worked around* the obstacle before placing the object with adjustments.

Examples: Place a nut on a hidden bolt. Position a spark plug in an engine block after working the hands between the distributor wiring.

P_6 Intermediate Moves   POSITION, REPOSITION

Several intermediate moves of the object are required before placing it in a final location. These intermediate moves are necessary because the nature of the object or the conditions surrounding the object prevent direct placement. With heavy, bulky, or difficult-to-handle objects, this parameter is recognized as a series of placing, shifting of grasps, and moving actions occurring before final placement. This additional handling is needed to overcome the awkward nature of the object.

Examples: Place chairs in a neat row by first setting a chair down and then aligning it with several sliding moves. Place a large box down on its corner, and "walk it" into position. Place a heavy or bulky box on a pallet and stack neatly. Place a splined shaft into a gearbox.

A special case of this variant is encountered when placing one object from a handful of different objects in the palm. Before actually placing the object, several finger and hand movements are required to select and shift one of the objects from the palm to the fingertips. This unpalming action is more than a simple regrasp. The hand must first be turned over, allowing visual selection of the appropriate object. Several complex finger motions (intermediate moves) are then needed to shift the object up to the fingertips before placement can occur.

Note: This case (P_6) applies only to a handful of different objects. If the objects held in the palm are all similar, visual selection is not necessary. Therefore, a simple regrasp will be sufficient for unpalming any of the objects. As this regrasp normally occurs during the action distance to place the object, no additional regrasp time is needed. However, if the action distance in the Put phase is 2 inches (5 cm) or less (A_0), then a regrasp (G_1), should be allowed.

The value for P is then chosen from the data card by the amount of difficulty required to place the object.

Examples: From a handful of change, use the thumb to push a dime to the fingertips and place it in a vending machine. Using the thumb, select a $1/2$-inch washer from a handful of assorted washers and nuts and place it on a bolt.

Special Parameter Variants

The parameter variants found on the data card and defined earlier cover most activities observed in normal production situations. However, special situations are always a possibility and must also be analyzed. Two such cases that may appear in work observed by the MOST analyst are defined below. Their infrequent occurrence does not merit their placement on the General Move data card; however, the need for a consistent analysis approach and consistent definitions is considered necessary.

B_3 Sit or Stand without Moving Chair   STAND-SIMPLE, SIT-SIMPLE

When the body is simply lowered into a chair from an erect position, without hand or foot motions required to manipulate the chair, or it is raised from a seated position without the aid of hand or foot motions, then sit or stand without moving chair (B_3) is appropriate. Note that this value covers either sit or stand, not both.

Examples: Lower the body to a sitting position on a bench. Stand up from a theater seat.

P_3 Loose Fit Blind   PLACE

Conditions are similar to those encountered by the Gain Control parameter with the same title. In such a situation, the operator must feel around for the placement location before a loose placement can occur.

Examples: Place a washer on a hidden stud. Place a pen into an inside coat pocket.

Placement with Insertion

In the introduction to placement, it was stated that the placement parameter value includes up to 2 inches (5 cm) of insertion.

For additional insertion, the Controlled Move sequence must be used. While the application will be clearer once you have reviewed the section on Controlled Move, the following examples indicate the proper application of the data.

Example: A mechanic obtains an oil dipstick within reach and places it into the engine block with adjustments while bending. The dipstick is inserted 10 inches (25 cm). The analysis for this example is:

A_1	B_0	G_1	A_1	B_6	P_3	A_0	**110 TMU**
A_0	B_0	G_0	M_1	X_0	I_0	A_0	**10 TMU**
							120 TMU

The M_1 value in the Controlled Move sequence covers an insertion of up to 12 inches (30 cm).

Example: A mechanic obtains an oil dipstick within reach and places it into the engine block with adjustments while bending. The dipstick is inserted 18 inches (45 cm). The analysis for this example is:

A_1	B_0	G_1	A_1	B_6	P_3	A_0	**110 TMU**
A_0	B_0	G_0	M_3	X_0	I_0	A_0	**30 TMU**
							140 TMU

The M_3 value in the Controlled Move sequence covers an insertion of more than 12 inches (30 cm).

Parameter Frequencies

Often, one or more parameters within the General Move Sequence occur more than once—for example, when placing several objects from a handful. This activity is shown on the sequence model by placing parentheses around the parameters that are repeated and writing the number of occurrences in the frequency column of the calculation sheet (see Sec. E), also within parentheses. The time calculation is performed as follows:

1. Add all index values for the parameters within parentheses.
2. Multiply this value by the number of occurrences (the number in parentheses in the frequency column).
3. Add this product to the remaining parameter index values.
4. Convert the total to TMU by multiplying by 10.

If an entire sequence occurs more than once, the number of occurrences is placed in the frequently column without parentheses. The time calculation is performed by taking the total TMU for the sequence model times the frequency.

Example: Get a handful of washers and place on six bolts located 5 inches (12 cm) apart.

$$A_1 \quad B_0 \quad G_3 \quad (A_1 \quad B_0 \quad P_1) \quad A_0 \quad (6)$$

GET	$\lceil A_1$	Reach to washers
	B_0	No body motion
	$\lfloor G_3$	Collect a handful of washers
PUT	$\lceil A_1$	Reach to place washer
	B_0	No body motion
	$\lfloor P_1$	Place washer, loose fit
RETURN	A_0	No return

As indicated, only the parameters in the Put phase of this sequence model are repeated six times. The operator reaches A_1 with no body motions B_0 and places a washer P_1.

The time calculation steps are as follows:

1. $(A_1 \quad B_0 \quad P_1) = (1 + 0 + 1) = 2$
2. $2 \times 6 = 12$
3. $1 + 0 + 3 + 12 + 0 = 16$
4. $16 \times 10 = 160$ TMU

These four steps could also be written as

$$[(1 + 1) \times (6) + 1 + 3] \times 10 = 160 \text{ TMU}$$

Additionally, if the entire sequence (the placement of six washers) occurs twice, the following analysis would apply:

$$A_1 \quad B_0 \quad G_3 \quad (A_1 \quad B_0 \quad P_1) \quad A_0 \quad (6) \quad 2$$

$$[(1 + 0 + 1) \times (6) + 1 + 0 + 3 + 0] \times 10 \times 2 = 320 \text{ TMU}$$

This situation, in which the Put phase of the sequence model is repeated, illustrates a situation involving frequencies. Actually, a frequency could be applied to any one or any combination of parameters. The frequency can be a whole number, decimal, or fraction. In MOST Computer Systems, the frequency within parenthesis is designated PF (Partial Frequency). For instance, if the Put phase (parameters 4, 5, and 6 of the General Move Sequence Model) is repeated six times as in the preceding example, this is entered into the computer as PF 6 (4 5 6). The output is identical to the sequence model. *Note:* More than one set of parentheses may be used in a sequence model, provided the same frequency applies to all parameters within parentheses.

General Move Examples

1. A man walks four steps to pick up a small suitcase from a low conveyor belt and, without moving farther, places it on a table within reach.

$$A_6 \quad B_6 \quad G_1 \quad A_1 \quad B_0 \quad P_1 \quad A_0$$

$$(6 + 6 + 1 + 1 + 1) \times 10 = 150 \text{ TMU}$$

2. An operator standing in front of a lathe walks six steps to a heavy part lying on a pallet picks up the part, walks six steps back to the machine, and places it in a three-jaw chuck with several adjusting actions. The part must be inserted 4 inches (10 cm) into the chuck jaws.

$$A_{10} \quad B_6 \quad G_3 \quad A_{10} \quad B_0 \quad P_3 \quad A_0$$

$$A_0 \quad B_0 \quad G_0 \quad M_1 \quad X_0 \quad I_0 \quad A_0$$

$$(10 + 6 + 3 + 10 + 0 + 3 + 0) \times 10 = 320 \text{ TMU}$$
$$(0 + 0 + 0 + 1 + 0 + 0 + 0) \times 10 = \underline{\quad 10 \text{ TMU}}$$
$$330 \text{ TMU}$$

3. From a stack located 10 feet (3 m) away, a heavy object must be picked up and moved 5 feet (2 m) and placed on top of a workbench with some adjustments. The height of this stack will vary from waist to floor level. After placing the object on the workbench, the operator returns to the original location, which is 11 feet (3.5 m) away.

$$A_6 \quad B_3 \quad G_3 \quad A_3 \quad B_0 \quad P_3 \quad A_{10}$$
$$(6 + 3 + 3 + 3 + 3 + 10) \times 10 = 280 \text{ TMU}$$

4. An assembly worker gets a handful of washers (six) from a bin located within reach and puts one on each of six bolts located within reach, which are four inches (10 cm) apart.

$$A_1 \quad B_0 \quad G_3 \quad (A_1 \quad B_0 \quad P_1) \quad A_0 \quad (6)$$
$$[(1 + 0 + 1) \times (6) + 1 + 0 + 3 + 0] \times 10 = 160 \text{ TMU}$$

5. A worker gains control of two fittings that are within reach and located more than two inches (5 cm) apart, one at a time, and places them on separate trays that are within reach and located less than two inches (5 cm) apart.

$$(A_1 \quad B_0 \quad G_1) \quad A_1 \quad B_0 \quad (P_1) \quad A_0 \quad (2)$$
$$[(1 + 1 + 1) \times 2 + 1] \times 10 = 70 \text{ TMU}$$

Method Descriptions Using Keywords

Each of the previous examples represents a method step in a MOST analysis. By using the General Move keywords and sentence format, these method steps would be expressed as follows:

MOVE SUITCASE FROM CONVEYOR TO TABLE
GET + PLACE PART FROM PALLET TO 3-JAW CHUCK WITH INSERTION 4″
(10 CM)
GET + PLACE OBJECT FROM STACK TO WORKBENCH AND RETURN
COLLECT + PUT 6 WASHERS FROM BIN ON TO 6 BOLTS
PUT 2 FITTINGS IN TO 2 TRAYS 2″ (5 CM) APART

B. The Controlled Move Sequence

The *Controlled Move Sequence* describes the manual displacement of an object over a "controlled" path. That is, movement of the object is restricted in at least one direction by contact with or an attachment to another object, or the nature of the work demands that the object be deliberately moved along a specific or controlled path.

Similar to the General Move Sequence, Controlled Move follows a fixed sequence of subactivities identified by the following steps:

1. Reach with one or two hands a distance to the object, either directly or in conjunction with body motions or steps.
2. Gain manual control of the object.
3. Move the object over a controlled path (within reach or with steps).
4. Allow time for a process to occur.
5. Align the object following the controlled move or at the conclusion of the process time.
6. Return to workplace.

These six subactivities form the basis for the activity sequence describing the *manual displacement* of an object over a *controlled path*.

The Sequence Model

The sequence model takes the form of a series of letters (parameters) representing each of the various subactivities of the Controlled Move Sequence.

A   B   G   M   X   I   A

where: A = Action distance
        B = Body motion
        G = Gain control
        M = Move controlled
        X = Process time
        I = Alignment

Parameter Definitions

Only three new parameters are introduced; the A, B, and G parameters were discussed with the General Move Sequence and remain unchanged.

M Move Controlled

This parameter is used to analyze all manually guided movements or actions of an object over a controlled path.

X Process Time

This parameter is used to account for the time for work controlled by electronic or mechanical devices or machines, not by manual actions.

I Alignment

This parameter is used to analyze manual actions following the controlled move or at the conclusion of process time to achieve the alignment of objects.

Phases of the Controlled Move Sequence

A Controlled Move is performed under one of three conditions. (1) The object or device is restrained by its attachment to another object, such as a pushbutton, lever, door, or crank; (2) it is controlled during the move by the contact it makes with the surface of another object, such as pushing a box across a table; or (3) must be moved on a controlled path to accomplish the activity, such as folding a cloth, coiling a rope, winding a spool, or moving a balanced item, or to avoid a hazard, such as electricity, sharp edges, or running machinery. If the object can be moved freely through space and remain unaffected by any of these conditions, its movement must be analyzed as a General Move.

A breakdown of the Controlled Move Sequence Model reveals that, like the General Move, three phases occur during the Controlled Move activity:

		Move		
		or		
Get		Actuate		Return
A B G		M X I		A

The Get and Return phases of Controlled Move carry the same parameters found in the General Move Sequence Model and therefore describe the same subactivities. The fundamental difference lies in the activity immediately following the G parameter. This phase describes actions either to simply *move* an object over a controlled path or to *actuate* a control device—often to initiate a process. Normally, "move" implies that the M and I parameters of the sequence model are involved, but "actuate" usually applies to situations involving the M and X parameters. Of course, for either situation (move or actuate) any or all of the parameters in the sequence model could be used, and all should be considered. A move, for example, would occur when opening a tool cabinet door or sliding a box across a table. Engaging the clutch on a machine or flipping an electrical switch to start a process are examples of actuate.

Parameter Indexing Using Keywords

Documenting and analyzing a Controlled Move is best accomplished by describing the method in keyword language. The keywords unique to Controlled Moves are found on the Controlled Move Sequence data card (Fig. 3.10), which lists the variants for the M, X, and I parameters and their corresponding index values. Since the first and third phases of a Controlled Move are the same as for

Basic MOST® System   A B G M X I A   **CONTROLLED MOVE**

INDEX X 10	M — MOVE CONTROLLED			X — PROCESS TIME			I — ALIGNMENT		INDEX X 10
	PUSH / PULL / PIVOT	KEYWORD	CRANK (REVS.)	SECONDS	MINUTES	HOURS	OBJECT	KEYWORD	
1	≦12 Inches (30 cm) Button/Switch/Knob	PUSH PULL ROTATE		.5	.01	.0001	To 1 Point	ALIGN - POINT	**1**
3	>12 Inches (30 cm) Resistance Seat or Unseat High Control 2 Stages ≦12 Inches (30 cm)	SLIDE SEAT TURN UNSEAT OPEN SHIFT SHUT PRESS PUSH + PULL (INCHES,CM OR STAGES)	1	1.5	.02	.0004	To 2 Points ≦4 Inches (10 cm)	ALIGN - POINTS CLOSE	**3**
6	2 Stages >12 Inches (30cm) With 1 - 2 Steps	OPEN + SHUT OPERATE PUSH OR PULL WITH 1 or 2 PACES	3	2.5	.04	.0007	To 2 Points >4 Inches (10 cm)	ALIGN - POINTS	**6**
10	3 - 4 Stages With 3 - 5 steps	MANIPULATE MANEUVER PUSH OR PULL WITH 3, 4 or 5 PACES	6	4.5	.07	.0012			**10**
16	With 6 - 9 steps	PUSH OR PULL WITH 6, 7, 8 or 9 PACES	11	7.0	.11	.0019	Precision	ALIGN -PRECISION	**16**

Figure 3.10 The Controlled Move data card. Values are read "up to and including."

the General Move "Get" and "Return" phases, the keywords and index values for the A, B, and G parameters are identical to those found in Figure 3.1.

For manual application of MOST, parameter indexing is accomplished by selecting from the data card a keyword for each parameter variant that appropriately describes the observed or visualized Controlled Move and then applying the corresponding index value to the sequence model. For example, a Controlled Move in which the operator uses a sweeping motion to move several parts 15 inches (38 cm) to a drop chute may be written: COLLECT+SLIDE PARTS FROM TRAY INTO CHUTE. In MOST Computer Systems this entry would automatically result in the correct analysis:

A_1 B_0 G_3 M_3 X_0 I_0 A_0 **70 TMU**

PUSHBUTTON PTIME .06 MIN is an example of an "actuate" Controlled Move in keyword language. After the method description is written with appropriate keywords, producing the analysis is a simple matter.

Move Controlled (M)

Move Controlled covers all manually guided movements or actions of objects over a *controlled path*. Index values for the M parameter are tabulated under two separate categories on the Controlled Move data card. The most frequently occurring parameter variants of Move Controlled (M) fall under the general heading Push/Pull/Pivot. The "crank" category applies to a special type of Controlled Move dealing with cranks, handwheels, or other devices requiring a circular "cranking" motion.

The following parameter variants apply to moves of an object or device that is hinged or pivoted at some point (e.g., a door, lever, or knob), restricted because of its surroundings (e.g., by guides, slots, or friction from surface), or restricted by other special circumstances requiring movement over a controlled path.

Typical keywords are written in capital letters to the right of each variant. The default value of some of these keywords may be modified by attributes. For example, PUSH normally results in an M_1 index value but PUSH > 12" produces an M_3 and PUSH with 5 STEPS an M_{10}. OPEN defaults to an M_3 index value, but OPEN < 12" results in an M_1.

M_1 One Stage ≤12 inches (30 cm)   PUSH, PULL

Object displacement is achieved by a movement of the fingers, hands, or feet not exceeding 12 inches (30 cm).

Examples: Engage the feed on a cutting machine with a short hand lever. Press a light clutch pedal with the foot. Open a hinged lid on a small tool box. Push a box 10 inches (25 cm) across a workbench.

M₁ Button/Switch/Knob
PUSH, PULL, ROTATE

The device is actuated by a short pressing, moving, or rotating action of the fingers, hands, wrist, or feet.

Examples: Press a telephone hold button. Flip a wall light switch. Turn a door knob.

M₃ One Stage > 12 inches (30 cm)
SLIDE, TURN, OPEN, SHUT

Object displacement is achieved by a movement of the hands, arms, or feet exceeding 12 inches (30 cm). The maximum displacement covered by this parameter occurs with the extension of the arm plus body assistance.

Examples: Push a carton across conveyor rollers. Pull a chain hoist full length. Close a cabinet door by pulling it shut. Open a file drawer full length.

M₃ Resistance, Seat/Unseat
PRESS, SEAT, UNSEAT

Conditions surrounding the object or device require that resistance be overcome prior to, during, or following the Controlled Move. This parameter variant covers the muscular force applied to "seat" or "unseat" an object or, if necessary, the short manual actions employed to latch or unlatch the object. Also, the object is moved and resistance is present throughout the move.

Examples: Engage the emergency brake on an automobile. Twist on a radiator cap securely. Push a heavy box across a table.

M₃ High Control
SLIDE, TURN

Care is needed to maintain or establish a specific orientation or alignment of the object during the Controlled Move. Characterized by a higher degree of visual concentration, this parameter variant is sometimes recognized by noticeably slower movements to keep within tolerance requirements or to prevent injury or damage. The successful performance of this Controlled Move demands that eye contact be made with the object and its surroundings during the move.

Examples: Turn the dial on a combination lock to a specific number. Slide a fragile item carefully across a workbench. Carefully slide a plank toward a running table saw blade. Set a cup full of hot water on a table within reach.

M₃ Two Stages ≤ 12 inches (30 cm)
PUSH + PULL, SHIFT

An object is displaced in two directions or increments a distance not exceeding 12 inches (30 cm) per stage *without relinquishing control.*

Examples: Engage and subsequently disengage the feed on a cutting machine with a short hand lever. Open and subsequently close a small tool box. Shift from the first to the third gear with a manual gearshift.

M₆   Two Stages > 12 inches (30 cm) or with one–two steps   OPEN + SHUT, OPERATE, PUSH OR PULL WITH 1, 2 PACES

An object is displaced in two directions or increments a distance exceeding 12 inches (30 cm) per stage without relinquishing control.

Examples: Open and subsequently close a cabinet door. Shift a lever back and forth more than 12 inches (30 cm) in each direction. Raise and lower the cover of a copying machine.

One or several object(s) are moved (manually pushed) along a controlled path (i.e., conveyor rollers or a cart on the floor) outside the area of normal reach requiring one to two steps to complete the move. The time to start the move of the object(s) is included in the index value "with steps." If resistance occurs during the move, the number of steps taken will normally increase (shorter steps), which will automatically allow the extra time to overcome resistance. If more than two steps are required, an M_{10} (three–five steps) or an M_{16} (six–nine steps) will be the selected index value.

Note: For situations in which a two-stage move exists but the distance the object is moved over one stage is ≤ 12 inches (30 cm) and the other stage contains a move of > 12 inches (30 cm), the total distance moved for the two stages must be estimated. If the total distance exceeds 24 inches (60 cm) an M_6 will be assigned; for less than 24 inches (60 cm), an M_3 is the proper index value.

Example: Reach to a lever and, without relinquishing control, push it forward 6 inches (15 cm) and then to the side 20 inches (50 cm).

A_1 B_0 G_1 M_6 X_0 I_0 A_0 **80 TMU**

M₁₀   Three to Four Stages or with Three–Five Steps   MANIPULATE, MANEUVER, PUSH OR PULL WITH 3, 4, 5 PACES

An object is displaced in three or four directions or increments without relinquishing control or pushed/pulled on a conveyor belt.

Examples: From the reverse position, shift to the first gear on a four-speed automobile transmission. Set the feed/speed selector on an engine lathe. Push box on conveyor belt walking four paces.

M₁₆   Move Controlled with Six–Nine Steps   PUSH or PULL WITH 6, 7, 8, 9 PACES

Push or pull object(s) with six–nine steps is analyzed by applying an M_{16}. In certain situations pushing or pulling object(s) (i.e., on a conveyor belt) may require more than nine steps. Therefore, a table with extended index values has been included (Fig. 3.11).

PUSH OR PULL	
INDEX VALUE	PACES
M 24	10-13
M 32	14-18
M 42	19-24
M 54	25-31
M 67	32-39

Figure 3.11 Extended index values for Push or Pull.

Summary of Foot Motions

Movement of the foot could appear in a Controlled Move Sequence Model under the Action Distance (A), the Gain Control (G), or the Move Controlled (M) parameter. A summary follows:

Activity	Analysis
Foot to pedal (without dis- placing the trunk of the body	A_1
Take one step	A_3
Gain control of pedal	G_1
Push pedal $\leq$ 12 inches (30 cm)	M_1
Push pedal $>$ 12 inches (30 cm) or with resistance	M_3
Operate pedal with High Control (engage clutch)	M_3

Crank

CRANK (NO.) REVOLUTION(S)

This category of Move Controlled refers to the manual actions employed to rotate such objects as cranks, handwheels, and reels. These "cranking" actions are performed by moving the fingers, hand, wrist, and/or forearm in a circular path more than half a revolution using one of the patterns pictured in Figure 3.12. Any motion less than half a revolution is not considered a crank and must be treated as a "Push/Pull/Pivot." The overall distance the hand covers when making repetitive circular motions may be larger than any other motions described under the parameter Move Controlled. It is for this reason that a separate column is provided on the Controlled Move data card for Crank.

In addition to the actual "cranking time," index values for Crank also include a factor that covers the actions that sometimes occur before or after the cranking motion. These actions may involve the application of muscular force to seat or unseat the crank or the short manual actions employed to engage or disengage the device undergoing the cranking motion. Figure 3.13 lists index values for cranking based on the number of revolutions completed, rounded to the nearest whole number.

Examples: Move an engine lathe carriage by cranking a handwheel. Drill a hole in a wooden block by cranking the handle on a manual hand drill.

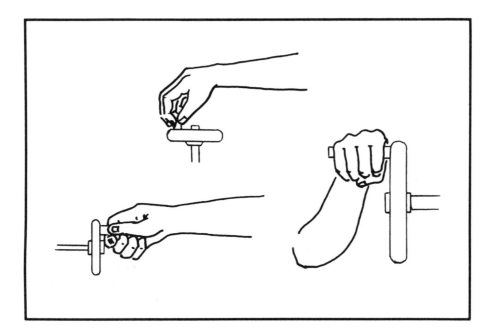

Figure 3.12 Examples of Crank.

CRANK	
INDEX VALUE	NO. OF REVOLUTIONS
M $_1$	-
M $_3$	1
M $_6$	3
M $_{10}$	6
M $_{16}$	11
M $_{24}$	16
M $_{32}$	21
M $_{42}$	28
M $_{54}$	36

Figure 3.13 Index values for cranking based on the number of revolutions completed (rounded to the nearest whole number).

Push–Pull Cranking   PUSH, PULL, PUSH+PULL

Occasionally a method of cranking (as illustrated at the right in Fig. 3.12) will result in back-and-forth movement of the elbow instead of pivoting at the wrist and/or elbow. This "push–pull" cranking is analyzed by using the number of pushes plus pulls as a frequency for the M_1 parameter. (The M_3 parameter is used if there is substantial resistance during the cranking.) Whenever possible, push–pull (reciprocal) cranking should be replaced by the more efficient pivotal cranking method.

Process Times (X)   PTIME OR PT (NO.) HOURS/MINUTES/SECONDS/TMUS

Process time occurs as that portion of work controlled by electronic or mechanical devices or machines, not by manual actions. The X parameter of the Controlled Move Sequence is intended to cover predominantly fixed process times of relatively short duration (up to the upper limit of the time range for index value 330). Longer and variable process times, such as machining times based on

PROCESS TIME (X)			
INDEX VALUE (X)	SECONDS	MINUTES	HOURS
1	.5	.01	.0001
3	1.5	.02	.0004
6	2.5	.04	.0007
10	4.5	.07	.0012
16	7.0	.11	.0019
24	9.5	.16	.0027
32	13.0	.21	.0036
42	17.0	.28	.0047
54	21.5	.36	.0060
67	26.0	.44	.0073
81	31.5	.52	.0088
96	37.0	.62	.0104
113	43.5	.72	.0121
131	50.5	.84	.0141
152	58.0	.97	.0162
173	66.0	1.10	.0184
196	74.5	1.24	.0207
220	83.5	1.39	.0232
245	92.5	1.54	.0257
270	102.0	1.70	.0284
300	113.0	1.88	.0314
330	124.0	2.06	.0344

Figure 3.14 Index values for process times (X). Values are read "up to and including."

feeds and speeds are normally calculated and entered separately as a process time. Figure 3.14 lists index values for process times based on the actual clock time (in seconds, minutes, or hours) during which the machine process takes place. The X parameter is indexed by selecting the appropriate index value that corresponds to the observed or calculated "actual time." The times listed in Figure 3.14 are inclusive. The upper index range limits for each index number (the times appearing on the data card) were calculated in TMU or 1/100,000 hour; therefore, some rounding was needed to determine the upper limit of each index range in terms of the larger, more convenient units (seconds, hours, etc.). For example, the calculated upper limit of index number 6 is 77 TMU, which equals 2.77 seconds; on the data card this time was rounded *downward* to 2.5 seconds. As a rule of thumb, the process time expressed as an index number should not exceed 2 minutes for cycle times over 10 minutes or 20% of the cycle time for cycle times less than 10 minutes in order to maintain a consistent level of accuracy. If the process time exceeds these limits, the discrete value should be allowed on a separate line as "Process Time" (PT).

Note: The actual clock time is never placed on the X parameter of the sequence model. Only the index value that statistically represents the actual time should be placed in the sequence model.

Note: With MOST Computer Systems, if the process time resulting from actuating a particular device or machine is included in the work area data, the keyword PROCESS is used to automatically access such data.

Examples: There is a process time of 6 seconds between the time a button is pushed and the time a photocopy machine produces a copy. After a switch is thrown, there is a warm-up period in a cathode ray tube. A punch press cycles in 1.5 seconds after the palm buttons are hit.

Alignment (I)

Alignment refers to manual actions following the Move Controlled or at the conclusion of process time (i.e., adjust instrument setting) to achieve an alignment or specific orientation of objects.

Normally, any adjusting motions required during a controlled move are covered in the M_3 parameter variant for High Control. That index value, however, is not sufficient to cover the activity to line up an object to one or more points following the Move Controlled. This type of alignment is influenced by the ability (or inability) of the eyes to focus on the point(s) in more than one area at a time.

The average area covered by a single eye focus is described by a circle 4 inches (10 cm) in diameter at a normal reading distance of about 16 inches (40 cm) from the eyes (Fig. 3.15). Within this "area of normal vision," the alignment of an object to those points can be performed without any additional

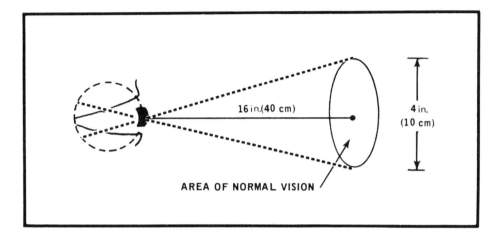

16 in.(40 cm)

4 in.
(10 cm)

AREA OF NORMAL VISION

Figure 3.15 Area of normal vision.

"eye times." If one of the two points lies outside this area, two separate alignments are required, owing to the inability of the eyes to focus on both points
simultaneously. In fact, an object would first be aligned to one point, the eyes
would next shift to allow the alignment to the second point, and then the object
would be finally adjusted to correct for the minor shifting from the first point.
The area of normal vision is therefore the basis for defining most of the Alignment parameter variants.

I_1 To One Point   LOCATE

Following a Controlled Move, an object is aligned to one point. Use when the
demand for a precise alignment is modest and can be satisfied with a single
correcting action. This variant is similar to the P_1 variant except that I_1 occurs
following an M in Controlled Move; the P_1 occurs following an A in General
Move.

Example: Locate a mark on a work block to a bandsaw blade prior to cutting.

I_3 To Two Points $\leq$ 4 inches (10 cm) Apart   GUIDE

The object is aligned to points not more than 4 inches (10 cm) apart following a
Controlled Move. For example, a straightedge is aligned with two marks located
3 inches (7.5 cm) apart, as shown in Figure 3.16 (left). Both points are within
the area of normal vision. An increasing demand for precision occurs in this
situation. This also includes the time to make more than one correcting motion
of the object within the area of normal vision.

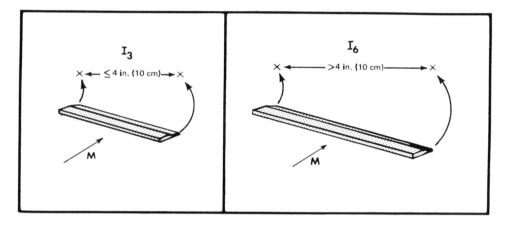

Figure 3.16 Align an object to points located $\leq$4 inches (10 cm) apart (left) and >4 inches (10 cm) apart (right).

I₆ To Two Points >4 inches (10 cm) Apart   GUIDE + ADJUST

The object is aligned to points more than 4 inches (10 cm) apart following a Controlled Move. For example, a straightedge is aligned with two marks located 8 inches (20 cm) apart, as shown in Figure 3.16 (right). One point is outside the area of normal vision; therefore, additional eye time must be allowed. Several correcting motions and eye focuses are included to allow the time for the hand-eye coordination to be accomplished.

I₁₆ Precision   ALIGN-ACCURATE

The object is aligned to several points with extreme care or precision following a Controlled Move. For example, the actions to align a french curve or a drawing template with several points require an I_{16}.

Whenever a Controlled Move involves the Alignment activity, the preceding M parameter is used to describe only the distance the object travels, either $\leq$ 12 inches (30 cm) (M_1) or >12 inches (30 cm) (M_3).

The Alignment (I) parameter applies only when an alignment follows a Controlled Move. Should an object be moved freely without restrictions and then be "aligned to two points," the General Move Placement (P) parameter is the appropriate selection. In fact, a direct relationship between the General Move and the Controlled Move activities should be pointed out at this time. That relationship is: I:M as P:A. The alignment (I) of an object occurs after the object is moved over a controlled path (M) and accounts for the time to orient and/or align the object, just as the placement (P) of an object occurs after the spatial displacement of an object (action distance A) and accounts for the time to orient and/or position the object.

Machining Operations

A special group of Alignment parameter variants is frequently encountered in machine shop operations. Dealing with the alignment of "machining tools," these parameter variants cover the activity following the cranking action (M) to locate the tool on a cutting machine to the correct cutting position. Since these index values are limited in their application to a specific area, they are omitted from the Controlled Move data card. But, because of their importance in this one area, these index values are presented as supplementary data in Figure 3.17 and defined below.

I_3 To Workpiece   GUIDE

The machining tool is aligned to the workpiece prior to making a cut. Following any cranking actions (M) to locate the tool near the cutting position, the crank or handwheel is manipulated so that the cutting edge of the tool just touches the workpiece.

I_6 To Scale Mark   GUIDE + ADJUST

The machining tool is aligned to a scale mark prior to making a cut. Following any cranking actions (M) to locate the tool near the cutting position, several taps on the fist of the hand (holding the handwheel) using the other hand are performed to line up the cutting edge of the tool with a scale mark.

ALIGNMENT		
INDEX VALUE	ALIGN TO	KEYWORD
I_3	WORKPIECE	ALIGN - WORKPIECE
I_3	SCALE MARK	ALIGN - SCALE MARK
I_3	INDICATOR DIAL	ALIGN - INDICATOR DIAL

Figure 3.17   Parameter variants for the alignment of machining tools.

I₁₀ To Indicator Dial   ALIGN

The machining tool is aligned to the correct indicator dial setting prior to making a cut. Following any cranking actions (M) to locate the tool near the cutting
position, the machine operator must visually locate the indicator dial, read the
indicator setting, and carefully adjust the tool to the correct setting by tapping
the hand that holds the handwheel several times with the other hand.

Alignment of Nontypical Objects

The final positioning (I-Alignment) of nontypical objects which are particularly
flat, large, flimsy, sharp, or require special handling usually occurs following
the Move Controlled (M) parameter. Such activities are normally seen with
press, shear, or cut-off operations. Alignment will be observed as a series of
short correcting motions (less than 2 inches or 5 cm of movement) following the
Move Controlled. The alignment is normally made to stops, guides, or marks.
(See Figure 3.18 for index values and keywords.)

Alignment values are chosen based on the number of adjustments required to
properly situate the object. The alignment value includes the short movement of
the object along with one or two visual checks for proper positioning. After
each adjustment, the movement will stop.

If an object is extremely heavy where the feet must be shifted prior to the
next movement, the value for alignment of nontypical objects will apply. If the

INDEX VALUE	POSITIONING METHOD	KEYWORD	NONTYPICAL OBJECT CHARACTERISTICS
I₀	AGAINST STOP(S)		
I₃	1 ADJUSTMENT TO STOP	GUIDE	
I₆	2 ADJUSTMENTS TO STOP (S) 1 ADJUSTMENT TO 2 STOP (S)	ADJUST	FLAT, LARGE, FLIMSY, SHARP, DIFFICULT TO HANDLE
I₁₀	3 ADJUSTMENTS TO STOP (S) 2-3 ADJUSTMENTS TO LINEMARK	SITUATE	

Figure 3.18 Index values and keywords for alignment of heavy objects.

object(s) can be realigned without shifting the feet, the original align values will apply. In addition, separate Controlled Moves should be used since the alignment values do not include time to move the body or gain control of the object.

Note: Stops or guides at the workplace may eliminate the need for adjustments. In this case, the Align value will be zero with the total time for the operation being covered by the Move Controlled parameter.

Example: A press operator moves a 4-foot (1.2 m) by 8-foot (2.4 m) sheet of thin gauge steel, which is flimsy, a distance of 14 inches (35 cm). The steel sheet must be aligned to two stops on opposite ends of the sheet. It is not necessary for the operator to reposition the hands during the activity. The operator must take one step back to gain control of the sheet. The correct analysis for this operation is as follows:

$$A_3 \quad B_0 \quad G_3 \quad M_3 \quad X_0 \quad I_6 \quad A_0 \qquad \textbf{150 TMU}$$

In the previous example, if the operator had to make separate grasps of the object, the correct analysis would be:

$$A_3 \quad B_0 \quad G_3 \quad M_3 \quad X_0 \quad I_3 \quad A_0 \quad 2 \qquad \textbf{240 TMU}$$

Note the frequency of 2 for the activity. This analysis is only correct if a step had to be taken for the second movement of the object.

Controlled Move Examples

1. From a position in front of a lathe, the operator takes two steps to the side, turns the handwheel two revolutions, and sets the machining tool against a scale mark.

CRANK HANDWHEEL AT LATHE 2 REVOLUTIONS WITH GUIDE + ADJUST

$$A_3 \quad B_0 \quad G_1 \quad M_6 \quad X_0 \quad I_6 \quad A_0$$

$$(3 + 1 + 6 + 6) \times 10 = 160 \text{ TMU}$$

2. A milling cutter operator walks four steps to the quick-feeding cross lever and engages the feed. The machine time following the 4 inch (10 cm) lever action is 2.5 seconds.

PULL LEVER AT MILL PTIME 2.5 SECONDS

$$A_6 \quad B_0 \quad G_1 \quad M_1 \quad X_6 \quad I_0 \quad A_0$$

$$(6 + 1 + 1 + 6) \times 10 = 140 \text{ TMU}$$

3. A material handler takes hold of a heavy carton with both hands and pushes it 18 inches (45 cm) across conveyor rollers.

GET+SLIDE CARTON ACROSS ROLLERS AT CONVEYOR

A_1 B_0 G_3 M_3 X_0 I_0 A_0

$(1 + 3 + 3) \times 10 = 70$ TMU

4. Using the foot pedal to activate the machine, a sewing machine operator makes a stitch requiring 3.5 seconds process time. (The operator must reach the pedal with the foot.)

PUSH PEDAL PTIME 3.5 SECONDS (FOR STITCH)

A_1 B_0 G_1 M_1 X_{10} I_0 A_0

$(1 + 1 + 1 + 10) \times 10 = 130$ TMU

C. The Tool Use Sequence

Manual work is not always performed with the hands alone. The use of tools extends the strength and capabilities of the hands through leverage. Even though much mechanization has occurred in industry, a large and very critical portion of work remains literally "in the hands of the worker." Because of the desirability of having the MOST Work Measurement Technique apply to all manual work, and since analysis of the frequent use of certain tools through a series of General and Controlled Moves could be time-consuming and could result in inconsistent applications, a third manual sequence model was developed—the *Tool Use Sequence Model.*

Occasionally, an activity will contain a pattern of several Controlled Moves or a combination of General and Controlled Moves in succession. For example, multiple moves or actions are frequently encountered when fastening or loosening threaded fasteners using either the hand or such hand tools as screwdrivers, wrenches, or ratchets. Special Fasten/Loosen parameter variants and a special Tool Use Sequence have been created to describe these multiple moves in terms of the body member performing the action (i.e., finger, wrist, or arm). For example, running a nut down with the fingers is considered a finger action, but tightening a wood screw with a screwdriver requires a wrist action. These actions are by literal definition a series of Controlled Moves.

Any activity involving a hand tool can be analyzed as a series of General and/ or Controlled Moves: for example, get and position screwdriver (General Move) or tighten screw (a series of Controlled Moves). However, as explained in the text that follows, special Tool Use parameters have been developed not only for fastening and loosening using common hand tools, but also for activities related to cutting, measuring, and writing—even thinking! Because of the ease of use, the consistency provided, and the analysis time saved, such sets of multiple moves are usually analyzed with the Tool Use Sequence.

The development of the Tool Use Sequence Model not only increased consistency and application speed, but it also provided analyses that were more accurate than those using a series of sequence models to analyze the use of tools. By repeating individual analyses, deviations existed between the allowed time (assigned index number) and the "actual time" could occur, whereas developing values using the statistically determined index ranges and assigning one index number, representing Tool Use, eliminated the compounding of any deviation. Accuracy was therefore maintained through the system design and was independent of the nature or complexity of the manual actions being performed. (This is substantiated by the system theory explained in Appendix A.) For these reasons, the Tool Use Sequence should be used in MOST analyses whenever appropriate. When the existing index tables will not cover a special tool or a tool with an identical or similar motion pattern, the procedure in Section E can be followed to develop new index values for such tools.

The Tool Use Sequence is composed of phases and subactivities from the General Move Sequence, along specially designed parameters describing the actions performed with hand tools or, in some cases, mental processes required when using the senses as a tool. In most cases, the use of all the following tools can be analyzed with the Tool Use Sequence:

Wrenches	Thread
Ratchet	Snap
Box end	Plug
Open end	Depth
T-wrench	Markers
Allen key	Pencil
Adjustable	Pen
Power	Marker
Pliers	Scribe
Cutting	Other tools
Slip-Joint	Screwdriver
Locking	Hammer
Measuring devices	Scissors
Fixed Scale	Knife
Steel Tape	Brush
Caliper	Wiping cloth
Micrometer	Air nozzle
Gauges	Hand or fingers (when
Feeler	used like a tool)
Profile	

Other hand tools for which the method of use is identical or similar to the tools listed above can be analyzed by comparing them to the tools in the tables. For instance, a winding key for a clock has a method of use similar to a small T-wrench, and therefore the index values for the T-wrench can be used to analyze the winding key operation.

Subactivities by Phase

Tool Use follows a fixed sequence of subactivities, which occur in five phases:

1. Get Tool (Object)
   a. Reach (with) hand(s) a distance to tool (or object), either directly or in conjunction with body motions or steps.
   b. Gain manual control of the tool (or object).
2. Put Tool (Object) in Place
   a. Move the tool (or object) a distance to where it will be used, either directly or in conjunction with body motions or steps.
   b. Place the tool (or object) in position for use.
3. Use Tool: Apply some number or extent of Tool Action(s).
4. Put Tool (Object) Aside: Retain the tool (or object) for further use (hands and fingers are *always* retained), toss or lay the tool aside, return the tool to its original location, or move it to a new location for disposition, either directly or in conjunction with body motions or steps.
5. Return: Step or walk to the original (or other) workplace.

The Sequence Model

The five subactivity phases just listed form the basis for the activity sequence describing the *handling and use of hand tools*. The sequence model takes the form of a series of letters representing each of the various subactivities of the *Tool Use Activity Sequence:*

Get Tool or object	Put tool or object in place	Use tool	Put tool or object aside	Return operator
A B G	A B P		A B P	A

where: A = Action distance
          B = Body motion
          G = Gain control
          P = Placement

The blank space in the sequence model ("Use Tool" phase) is provided for the insertion of one of the following Tool Use parameters. These parameters, which refer to the specific tool being used, are as follows:

where: F = Fasten
          L = Loosen
          C = Cut
          S = Surface treat
          M = Measure
          R = Record
          T = Think

Parameter Definitions

F Fasten

This parameter is used to establish the time for manually or mechanically assembling one object to another, using the fingers, a hand, or a hand tool.

L Loosen

This parameter is used to establish the time for manually or mechanically disassembling one object from another using the fingers, a hand, or a hand tool.

C Cut

This parameter covers the manual actions employed to separate, divide, or remove part of an object using a sharp-edged hand tool and related activities using
pliers.

S Surface Treat

This parameter covers the activities aimed at removing unwanted material or
particles from, or applying a substance, coating, or finish to, the surface of an
object.

M Measure

This parameter includes the actions employed in determining a certain physical
characteristic of an object by comparison with a standard measuring device.

R Record

This parameter covers the manual actions performed with a pencil, pen, chalk,
or other marking tool for the purpose of recording information.

T Think

This parameter refers to the eye actions and mental activity employed to obtain
information (read) or to inspect an object, including reaching to touch when
necessary to feel the object.

Parameter Indexing

With the exception of the special Tool Action parameters, the Tool Use Sequence Model contains only parameters from the General Move Sequence. Index values for these parameters are of course found on the General Move data card (Fig. 3.1). Two additional data cards are provided for the Tool Action parameters. Figure 3.19 contained index values for tools covered by the *Fasten* or *Loosen* parameters, and Figure 3.20 covers such activities as cutting, cleaning, gauging, reading, and writing. These tables for indexing the Tool Action parameters are used following the same procedure outlined in the General and Controlled Move sections.

Consider, for example, an assembly operation in which a bolt is used to fasten one object to another. The operator picks up a bolt from a bin located within reach, places it in the required location, and runs it down with three spins with the fingers. The sequence model would be indexed:

FASTEN BOLT AT ASSEMBLY WITH 3 SPINS USING FINGERS

$$A_1 \quad B_0 \quad G_1 \quad A_1 \quad B_0 \quad P_3 \quad F_6 \quad A_0 \quad B_0 \quad P_0 \quad A_0$$

$$(1 + 1 + 1 + 3 + 6) \times 10 = 120 \text{ TMU}$$

In this example, the "get" and "put in place" phases of the sequence model are used for getting and placing the bolt; placement of a threaded fastener will nearly always be a P_3 (with adjustments) unless it takes place in a blind or obstructed location (P_6). Since this is a fastening activity, the F parameter is chosen and inserted in the sequence model. The appropriate index value is determined by considering the body member performing the fastening activity (in this case, the fingers) and the number of actions performed. In Figure 3.19, we see that up to three finger actions requires an index value of 6. The remaining parameters in the sequence (A, B, P, and A) carry zero index values, since no activity was performed to set aside a tool or object.

In the second part of this example, let us say that after the fastening activity, the operator picks up a small box end wrench (lying on the workbench within reach) and tightens the bolt with three wrist actions. This second sequence model would be indexed

FASTEN BOLT WITH 3 WRIST—STROKES USING WRENCH FROM WORKBENCH AND LAY ASIDE

$$A_1 \quad B_0 \quad G_1 \quad A_1 \quad B_0 \quad P_3 \quad F_{10} \quad A_1 \quad B_0 \quad P_1 \quad A_0$$

$$(1 + 1 + 1 + 3 + 10 + 1 + 1) \times 10 = 100 \text{ TMU}$$

Again using the Fasten/Loosen data card, the index value is taken from the strokes column below wrist actions. Index values in this column reflect the way in which a wrench is normally used. That is, after each wrist action, the wrench

Basic MOST® System — FASTEN (F) or LOOSEN (L) — TOOL USE

Index X 10	Finger Action	Wrist Action				Arm Action				Tool Action	Index X 10
	SPINS	TURNS	STROKES	CRANKS	TAPS	TURNS	STROKES	CRANKS	STRIKES	SCREW DIAMETER	
	Fingers, Screw-driver	Hand, Screw-driver, Ratchet, T-Wrench	Wrench, Allen Key	Wrench, Allen Key, Ratchet	Hand, Hammer	Ratchet	Wrench, Allen Key	Wrench, Allen Key, Ratchet	Hand, Hammer	Power Wrench	
1	1	-	-	-	1	-	-	-	-	-	1
3	2	1	1	1	3	1	1	-	1	1/4" (6 mm)	3
6	3	3	2	3	6	2	-	1	3	1" (25 mm)	6
10	8	5	3	5	10	4	2	2	5		10
16	16	9	5	8	16	6	3	3	8		16
24	25	13	8	11	23	9	4	5	12		24
32	35	17	10	15	30	12	6	6	16		32
42	47	23	13	20	39	15	8	8	21		42
54	61	29	17	25	50	20	10	11	27		54

Figure 3.19 Tool Use data card for Fasten or Loosen. Values are read "up to and including."

Basic MOST® System — Cut(C), Surface Treat(S), Measure(M), Record(R), Think(T) — **TOOL USE**

INDEX ×10	C — Cut: CUTOFF (Pliers, WIRE)	C — CUT (Scissors, CUT(S))	C — SLICE (Knife, SLICE(S))	S — AIR-CLEAN (Nozzle, SQ.FT 0,1M²)	S — BRUSH-CLEAN (Brush, SQ.FT 0,1M²)	S — WIPE (Cloth, SQ.FT 0,1M²)	M — MEASURE (Measuring Device, IN.(CM) FT.(M))	R — WRITE (Pencil) DIGITS	R — WRITE (Pencil) WORDS	R — MARK (Marker) DIGITS	T — INSPECT (Eyes, Fingers) POINTS	T — READ (Eyes) DIGITS, SINGLE WORDS	T — READ (Eyes) TEXT OF WORDS	INDEX ×10
1	GRIP	1	-	-	-	-		1	-	CHECK MARK	1	1	3	1
3	SOFT	2	1	-	-	1/2		2	-	1 SCRIBE LINE	3	3	8	3
6	MEDIUM (TWIST BEND-LOOP)	4		1 SPOT POINT CAVITY	1 SMALL OBJECT	-		4	1	2	5 TOUCH FOR HEAT	6 SCALE VALUE DATE/TIME	15	6
10	HARD	7	3	-	-	1	PROFILE-GAUGE	6	-	3	9 FEEL FOR DEFECT	12 VERNIER-SCALE	24	10
16	BEND-COTTER PIN	11	4	3	2	2	FIXED SCALE CALIPER 12 IN. (30CM)	9	2	5 SIGNATURE, DATE		TABLE VALUE	38	16
24		15	6	4	3	-	FEELER-GAUGE	13	3	7			54	24
32		20	9	7	5	5	STEEL-TAPE 6 FT. (2M) / DEPTH MICROMETER	18	4	10			72	32
42		27	11	10	7	7	OD-MICROMETER 4 IN. (10CM)	23	5	13			94	42
54		33					ID-MICROMETER 4 IN. (10CM)	29	7	16			119	54

Figure 3.20 Tool Use data card for cutting, cleaning, gauging, reading, writing, and other activities. Values are read "up to and including."

must be repositioned on the fastener before any subsequent actions are made. In our example three wrist actions are performed with the wrench. The corresponding index value is therefore F_{10}.

In addition to the Use Tool Phase of the sequence model, the remaining parameters in this sequence apply to handling the tool. The P_3 prior to use tool in the example covers the initial placement of the wrench on the bolt. The parameters following the Use Tool Phase—A_1 B_0 P_1 A_0—indicate that the wrench is put aside following the fastening activity.

Use of the other Tool Action Card data (Fig. 3.20) can be demonstrated with a third example. Suppose that during a sewing operation a seamstress picks up a pair of scissors and makes three cuts to remove the excess material from around a stitch. This activity would be described as follows:

CUT MATERIAL 3 CUTS USING SCISSORS AND ASIDE

A_1 B_0 G_1 A_1 B_0 P_1 C_6 A_1 B_0 P_1 A_0

$(1 + 1 + 1 + 1 + 6 + 1 + 1) \times 10 = 120$ TMU

The appropriate Tool Action parameter for this example would be Cut, which is represented by the letter C. Looking down the column headed Cut in Figure 3.20, we see that "three cuts with scissors" carries the index value C_6. The initial placement of the scissors prior to the cutting action is assumed to be P_1 in this case.

The remainder of this section examines in detail each of the Tool Action parameters and discusses their application.

The Fasten/Loosen Data Card

Fasten or *Loosen* includes manually or mechanically assembling or disassembling one object to or from another using the fingers, a hand, or a hand tool. Index values for the F and L parameters are primarily grouped according to the body member (e.g., finger, wrist, or arm) performing the Tool Action. An additional category is provided for power-operated hand tools.

With the exception of power tools, all the data found in Figure 3.19 refer to the number of actions performed by the respective body member during either a Fasten (F) or Loosen (L) activity. An action is defined as the back-and-forth or up-and-down movement of the fingers, wrist, or arm to perform one "stroke," "pull," "turn," or "tap" with the tool. In the case of the crank data, action refers to one revolution of the tool.

Finger Actions (Spins or Cranks)   SPIN(S)

Finger spins include the movements of the fingers and thumb to run a threaded fastener down or out. These short finger movements are characterized by rolling or spinning an object between the thumb and index finger. Examples include running a nut down with the fingers or turning a machine screw with a small screwdriver. Because of the limited strength in the fingers, the muscular force (pressure) exerted on the fastener while performing spins is minimal. The Finger Spin data in Figure 3.18, however, includes a light application of pressure for seating and unseating of the fastener, as in replacing a cap on a bottle. This light pressure also includes one or two wrist turns (see next section), which often occur at the end of a finger spin activity when the resistance increases. If more than two wrist turns occur, the appropriate index value for wrist turns should be applied separately.

In some situations, the finger spin action converts into a finger crank action typified by turning a wing nut on a bolt with the forefinger held straight and pivoted at the base joint. Each 360° turn would be counted as one SPIN.

Wrist Actions

A wrist action refers to the twisting motion of the wrist about the axis of the forearm or the pivoting of the hand from the wrist with either a circular or back-and-forth motion. Wrist actions normally include hand movements up to 6 inches (15 cm) in length as measured from the knuckle at the base of the index finger. As Figure 3.19 indicates, data are classified according to the manner in which the wrist actions are performed.

Wrist Turn(s)   WRIST-TURNS(S)

Tool actions covered under the heading *wrist turns* include using the hand, screwdriver, ratchet, or small T-wrench. These tools are not removed from the fastener during use and are not repositioned on the fastener after an action. The time for wrist turns includes the time for repositioning the hand or tool handle after each action. Also, as a result of the added strength possible when using the larger muscles of the hand and forearm, a final tighten or initial loosen can be accomplished with a wrist turn. Therefore, the index values assigned from the wrist turn column also include the time for final tightening or initial loosening of a fastener.

Wrist Stroke (with reposition)   WRIST-STROKE(S)

The wrist stroke column covers the method normally employed when using a wrench. That is, after each stroke with the tool and before making each subsequent stroke, the wrench must be removed from and repositioned on the fastener. Index values in this column apply to the number of power strokes (actions) performed with the wrench (*not the number of repositions of the wrench*). Included also is the time for the wrench to be removed from and repositioned on the fastener between the strokes. Like wrist turn, the data for wrist stroke(s) also allow for the final tightening or initial loosening activity. Tools covered by this parameter include fixed end, adjustable, and Allen wrenches (tools that are normally *repositioned* on a fastener during use).

Wrist Crank WRIST-CRANK(S)

Data from the wrist cranks column apply to tools that are spun or rotated around a fastener while remaining affixed to it. They are guided with a circular movement of the hand as it is pivoted from the wrist (Fig. 3.21). This type of wrist action is sometimes used with either wrenches or ratchets when there are no obstructions in the path of the tool. After the initial placement of the tool, the fingers and hand are used to push or *crank* the tool completely around the fastener. However, these wrist actions are employed by operators only when little or no resistance is encountered; therefore, data in the wrist crank column *do not include* the time for final tightening or initial loosening of a fastener. If, after a number of wrist cranks, a fastener is final tightened, the normal type of tool action (wrist turn or wrist stroke) will be used to analyze the final tighten-

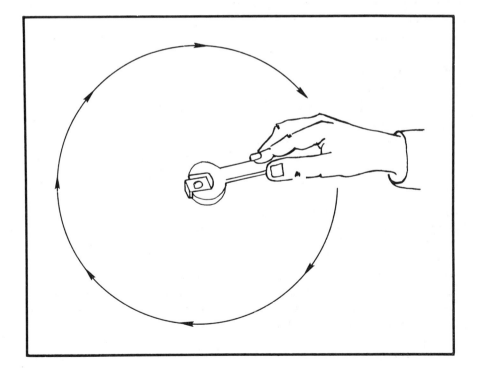

Figure 3.21 Wrist Crank.

ing activity. Usually, one or several of these actions will be needed. Index values for wrist cranks cover the number of revolutions performed with the tool.

Fasten/Loosen with continuous cranking motions is the most economical way of running down a screw, because one cranking motion results in running down one thread on the screw but other methods produce only one-third to one-sixth thread per action.

Tap   TAP(S)

The use of a small hammer, or other similar tools, is covered by the data under the heading TAPS. Index values from the tap column refer to the short tapping motions performed with the hand as it is pivoted at the wrist. Data in this column include the number of tapping actions made with the hand.

Arm Actions

Arm actions include the motions of the hand requiring elbow and shoulder movements. With the wrist relatively rigid, the forearm is pivoted from the elbow with an up-and-down, circular, or back-and-forth motion. These forearm motions may be assisted by the pivoting of the upper arm from the shoulder. Arm actions cover hand movements of between 6 and 18 inches (15–45 cm) in length or a circular motion with a diameter up to 24 inches (60 cm).

Arm Turn(s)   ARM-TURN(S)

In the first column, the tools covered under the heading Arm Turns include only the use of a ratchet. Arm actions of this type are employed when the ratchet is held near the end of the handle, resulting in a pulling action on the tool. Index values from the arm turn column include time for the final tightening or initial loosening that may occur in the complete fastening or loosening activity.

Arm Stroke(s) (with Reposition)   ARM-STROKE(S)

Similar to the Wrist Stroke data, the Arm Stroke column applies to the normal method of using a wrench. That is, following each stroke or pull with the tool, the wrench must be removed and repositioned again on the fastener before making a subsequent pull. Index values in this column apply to the number of arm actions (pulls) performed with the wrench (not the number of repositions). Index values for arm strokes allow for the final tightening or initial loosening activity that may occur in the complete fastening or loosening activity. Tools covered by this parameter include fixed end, adjustable, and Allen wrenches.

Arm Crank(s)   ARM-CRANK(S)

The data from the Arm Crank column apply to tools used with a circular move-ment of the forearm as it is pivoted at the elbow or the shoulder. Arm actions of this type are occasionally used with either wrenches or ratchets when there are no obstructions in the path of the tool. The hand is used to push or crank the tool around the fastener. Like the wrist actions under the same heading, this type of action is employed only when resistance is minimal; therefore, the values in the arm crank column *do not* include the time for final tightening or initial loosening of a fastener. The data in this column refer to the number of revolutions performed with the tool; if a partial revolution is observed, round to the nearest whole number.

Strike   STRIKE(S)

The use of a hammer with arm action is accounted for under the heading Strike. The data in this column refer to the up-and-down motions performed with the hand as it is pivoted from the elbow.

T-wrench (Two Hands)   TWO-ARM-TURN(S)

The following supplementary data (not found on the Fasten/Loosen data card) are provided to analyze the use of a large T-wrench with two hands (see Fig. 3.22). Each arm action involves a 180° turn of the T-wrench. All subsequent two-handed arm actions include the reach for each hand to the opposite handle before making the next turn. The data for two hands also allow for the final tightening or initial loosening involved in the complete fastening or loosening activity. This would also be appropriate for turning a large valve or other such item with both hands.

Power Tools   INCH(ES), CM

Power Tools include the use of power-operated hand tools. The data provided in Figure 3.18 cover electric and pneumatic power wrenches. Index values are based on the time required to run a standard threaded fastener down or out, a length equal to one or two times the bolt diameter of the fastener (Fig. 3.23), the distance to hold a nut securely. Two values are found in Figure 3.19: F_3 or L_3 for a screw diameter of $1/4$ inch (6 mm) or smaller, and F_6 or L_6 for larger screws up to and including 1 inch (25 mm) in diameter. Therefore, to apply F or L to a power tool, simply choose the fasten or loosen value based on the diameter of the fastener. *Note:* This applies to standard fasteners (where the length of holding threads is one to two times the diameter) only.

When running down or out longer fasteners, where more threads are needed to hold the item or threads are fine, a frequency can be applied to the F or L value chosen. For example, run in a $3/8$ inch (1 cm) diameter bolt 1 inch (2.5 cm). Normally, the bolt would be run in approximately $3/4$ inch (1.5 cm), or two times its diameter, and an F_6 would be appropriate. However, in this case it is being run in three to four times its diameter. An F_6 times two (F_6) (2) is now appropriate.

T - WRENCH (2 HANDS)	
INDEX VALUE	NUMBER OF ARM ACTIONS
F_1	-
F_3	-
F_6	1
F_{10}	-
F_{16}	3
F_{24}	6
F_{32}	8
F_{42}	11
F_{54}	15

Figure 3.22 Supplementary data card for T-wrench (two hands).

Also it must be remembered that the basic values for Fasten/Loosen with a power tool must be compared to the time required by the brands of power tools used in the plant. Should there be a difference in the Basic MOST values for Fasten/Loosen with a power tool and those studied, new index values for the tools on hand must be created using the *Index Value Determination Form* (the procedure for developing index values is outlined in Sec. E).

Supplementary values for special tools or special situations not found on the data card (Fig. 3.19) have been developed and are presented below.

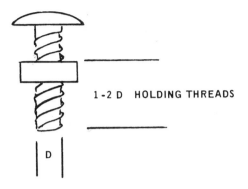

1-2 D   HOLDING THREADS

Figure 3.23   The index values in Figure 3.19 are based on the time required to run a standard threaded fastener down or out, a length equal to one or two times the bolt diameter of the fastener.

F_6 Torque Wrench   ARM-TURN

Tighten a bolt or nut with a torque wrench having a handle length of up to 10 inches (25 cm). The value is for one arm action and includes the time either to align the dial or to await the click.

F_{10} Torque Wrench   LONG-ARM-TURN

Tighten a bolt or nut with a torque wrench having a handle length of 10–15 inches (25–38 cm). The value is for one arm action and includes the time either to align the dial or to await the click.

F_{16} Torque Wrench   EXTRA-LONG-ARM-TURN

Tighten a bolt or nut with a torque wrench having a handle length of 15–40 inches (38 cm to 1 m). The value is for one arm action and includes the time either to align the dial or to await the click.

Tool Placement

The P parameter preceding the Tool Action parameter is used to analyze the placement of a tool or object in the working position prior to the tool action. The index value for P (placement of the tool) should be selected using the guidelines set forth in the General Move section. However, as a general rule, the P parameter for the Fasten/Loosen tools will carry the index values indicated in Figure 3.24. Notice that the placement of the fingers or hands used as a tool is considered a P_1. This is, of course, a G_1 Gain Control in actuality. However,

TOOL	INDEX VALUE
HAMMER	P_0 (1)
FINGERS OR HAND	P_1 (3 or 6)
KNIFE	P_1 (3)
SCISSORS	P_1 (3)
PLIERS	P_1 (3)
WRITING INSTRUMENT	P_1
MEASURING DEVICE	P_1
SURFACE TREATING DEVICE	P_1
SCREWDRIVER	P_3
RATCHET	P_3
T - WRENCH	P_3
FIXED END WRENCH	P_3
ALLEN WRENCH	P_3
POWER WRENCH	P_3
ADJUSTABLE WRENCH	P_6

Figure 3.24 Index values for tool placement.

since the fingers or hands are used in the same way as a fastening or loosening tool, the activity is considered the placement of a tool instead of a grasp. For example,

Get tool	Put tool in place	Use tool	Aside tool	Return	
A_0 B_0 G_0	A_1 B_0 P_1	F_6	A_0 B_0 P_0	A_0	**80 TMU**

If the fingers or hands are concerned with placing a fastener, such as a nut or bolt, immediately preceding the action to fasten it, the P parameter refers to the placement of the fastener. The placement of a threaded fastener nearly always requires a P_3 placement unless the placement occurs in a blind or obstructed location; under those conditions, a P_6 would be appropriate, for example,

Get fastener	Place fastener	Use tool	Aside tool	Return	
A_1 B_0 G_1	A_1 B_0 P_3	F_6	A_0 B_0 P_0	A_0	**120 TMU**

Notice also from Figure 3.24 that the placement of an adjustable wrench occurs with a P_6. This larger index value is required to cover the additional actions necessary to adjust the jaws of the wrench (with intermediate moves) to the size of the fastener. A value of P_3 would be sufficient if the wrench had been previously adjusted to the proper fastener size.

There may or may not be an initial placement of a hammer prior to any tapping or striking actions. Normally, if a hammer is being used to drive small nails or tacks, the hammerhead will be positioned over the nail (P_1) prior to performing any actions. In many cases, however, no initial placement of the hand or hammer is necessary (P_0), for example, before simply tapping or striking a larger object or surface area.

Tool Use Frequencies

Occasionally an activity may involve the fastening or loosening of several fasteners in succession using the same tool. By using a "special convention," the entire activity can normally be described using only one Tool Use Sequence Model. For example, an operator picks up a screwdriver within reach and tightens two screws with six wrist turns each and then sets aside the screwdriver. The first step in making an analysis of this activity is to analyze the situation as if only one screw were fastened and then repeat the appropriate parameters to tighten the second screw for example,

$$A_1 \quad B_0 \quad G_1 \quad A_1 \quad B_0 \quad P_3 \quad F_{16} \quad A_1 \quad B_0 \quad P_1 \quad A_0 \quad \text{(For one screw)}$$

What must be repeated to fasten the second screw? First, there is a reach over to the second screw, then the tool must be positioned, and then fastened; therefore, the placement and the fastening or loosening must be repeated.

To cover the action distance of the tool to each fastener requires that an A parameter be written into the sequence model between the P and either the F or L parameters. For example,

Add an "A" to cover the Reach between the fasteners

$$A_1 \quad B_0 \quad G_1 \quad A_1 \quad B_0 \quad P_3 \quad A \quad F_{16} \quad A_1 \quad B_0 \quad P_1 \quad A_0$$

Parentheses are then placed around all those parameters to be repeated (e.g., then P, A, and F or L). For example,

Add parentheses

$$A_1 \quad B_0 \quad G_1 \quad A_1 \quad B_0 \quad (P_3 \quad A \quad F_{16}) \quad A_1 \quad B_0 \quad P_1 \quad A_0$$

If the distance between the screws is $\leq$ 2 in. (5 cm), an A_0 is placed between the P and F or L parameters. For example, using a screwdriver, tighten two screws with six wrist turns each. The distance between the screws is $\leq$ 2 in. (5 cm).

$$A_1 \quad B_0 \quad G_1 \quad A_1 \quad B_0 \quad (P_3 \quad A_0 \quad F_{16}) \quad A_1 \quad B_0 \quad P_1 \quad A_0 \quad (2) = 430 \text{ TMU}$$

Note: "A" must be added to the use tool section to account for the distance between the screws.

If the distance between the screws is > 2 in. (5 cm), an A_1 must be placed in the parentheses. Since the action distance to each fastener is covered by the A parameter within the parentheses, *the A following Gain Control will now carry a zero index value.* This is to avoid counting an "extra" action distance value. For example, using a screwdriver, tighten two screws with six wrist turns each. The distance between the screws is 5 in. (12.5 cm).

The *incorrect* time calculation is:

$$A_1 \quad B_0 \quad G_1 \quad A_1 \quad B_0 \quad (P_3 \quad A_1 \quad F_{16}) \quad A_1 \quad B_0 \quad P_1 \quad A_0 \quad (2) = 450 \text{ TMU}$$

Note: When the distance between fasteners is > 2 in. (5 cm) you must drop the placement A_1 value since it will be included in the frequency value. As illustrated below, there are two action distances, one to the first screw and one to the second. The number in the frequency column times the A in the parentheses will account for all the reaches needed.

The multiplier for these parameters (the number of fasteners included in the fastening or loosening activity) is then placed in the frequency column of the MOST calculation sheet, also within parentheses. Therefore, the *correct* index allocation is:

$$A_1 \quad B_0 \quad G_1 \quad A_0 \quad B_0 \quad (P_3 \quad A_1 \quad F_{16}) \quad A_1 \quad B_0 \quad P_1 \quad A_0 \quad (2)$$

The time calculation for the fastening or loosening activity is performed by simply adding all index values contained within the parentheses and multiplying this sum by the number of fasteners involved (the partial frequency). The sequence model total is obtained by adding to this the index values from the remaining parameters. The conversion to TMU is obtained in the usual way by multiplying the total by 10. For example,

$A_1 \quad B_0 \quad G_1 \quad A_0 \quad B_0 \quad (P_3 \quad A_1 \quad F_{16}) \quad A_1 \quad B_0 \quad P_1 \quad A_0 \quad (2) = 440$ TMU

$(3 + 1 + 16) = 20 \times 2 = 40 + 1 + 1 + 1 + 1 = 44 \times 10 = 440$ TMU

Multiple Tool Actions

The data found in Figure 3.19 are classified according to the body member predominantly performing the tool action, not by the tool itself, since the tool can be used with more than one type of tool action. In fact, an operator may employ a combination of different finger, wrist, or arm actions during a fastening or loosening activity with a single tool. This may be found quite often when one or two finger actions (spins) and wrist or arm cranks are involved, for the values in those columns on the Fasten/Loosen data card *do not include* the time for final tightening or initial loosening of a fastener. Therefore, as previously explained, when a fastener is finally tightened or initially loosened in conjunction with any of the above activities, another activity (e.g., wrist or arm turn) is performed and should be analyzed.

For example, when using a screwdriver, the initial tool actions to run down a screw may be performed with finger spins if no resistance is encountered. But the final tightening (more than the finger pressure to seat the screw) may require the use of wrist actions. As another example, a ratchet may first be used with cranking actions followed by wrist turns to finally tighten the fastener.

These and other similar fastening or loosening activities can be described in one sequence model by placing the appropriate index values for each of the tool actions on a single F or L parameter. Index values for these multiple tool actions are separated by a plus ($+$) sign. Consider the above example with the screwdriver in which 18 finger actions (which include one to two wrist turns as explained under "Finger Actions") plus four additional wrist turns are employed to fasten a machine screw. *Note:* This convention applies to Manual MOST only. MOST computer systems require that two sequence models are used.

Examples: A screw is fastened with a screwdriver. A total of 18 spins and 4 wrist turns are necessary.

$A_1 \quad B_0 \quad G_1 \quad A_1 \quad B_0 \quad P_3 \quad F_{24 + 10} \quad A_1 \quad B_0 \quad P_1 \quad A_0$

$(1 + 1 + 1 + 3 + 24 + 10 + 1 + 1) \times 10 = 420$ TMU

Using the ratchet example, let us say that a nut is run down three revolutions with a wrist crank followed by six wrist turns. The sequence model is indexed:

A nut is fastened with a ratchet wrench. Following 3 wrist cranks, 6 wrist turns are applied.

$A_1 \quad B_0 \quad G_1 \quad A_1 \quad B_0 \quad P_3 \quad F_{6+16} \quad A_1 \quad B_0 \quad P_1 \quad A_0$

$(1 + 1 + 1 + 3 + 6 + 16 + 1 + 1) \times 10 = 300$ TMU

Note: This Manual MOST procedure should be used only when two different types of action are performed with the same tool.

Tool Use Examples for Fasten/Loosen

1. Obtain a nut from a parts bin located within reach, place it on a bolt, and run it down with seven finger actions.

FASTEN NUT ONTO BOLT WITH 7 SPINS USING FINGERS

$A_1 \quad B_0 \quad G_1 \quad A_1 \quad B_0 \quad P_3 \quad F_{10} \quad A_0 \quad B_0 \quad P_0 \quad A_0$

$(1 + 1 + 1 + 3 + 10) \times 10 = 160$ TMU

2. Pick up a small screwdriver that lies within reach and fasten a screw with six finger actions, and set aside the tool.

FASTEN SCREW WITH 6 SPINS USING SCREWDRIVER AND ASIDE

$A_1 \quad B_0 \quad G_1 \quad A_1 \quad B_0 \quad P_3 \quad F_{10} \quad A_1 \quad B_0 \quad P_1 \quad A_0$

$(1 + 1 + 1 + 3 + 10 + 1 + 1) \times 10 = 180$ TMU

3. Obtain a power wrench that lies within reach, run down four $3/8$-inch (10-mm) bolts located 6 inches (15 cm) apart, and set aside wrench.

FASTEN 4 BOLTS $3/8$ INCH (I CM) DIAMETER USING POWER WRENCH AND LAY ASIDE

$A_1 \quad B_0 \quad G_1 \quad A_0 \quad B_0 \quad (P_3 \quad A_1 \quad F_6) \quad A_1 \quad B_0 \quad P_1 \quad A_0 \quad (4)$

$[(3 + 1 + 6) \times (4) + 1 + 1 + 1 + 1] \times 10 = 440$ TMU

4. From a position in front of an engine lathe, obtain a large T-wrench located five steps away and loosen one bolt on a chuck on the engine lathe with both hands using five arm actions. Set aside the T-wrench from the machine (but within reach).

LOOSEN BOLT ON LATHE 5 ARM-CRANKS USING T-WRENCH AND ASIDE

$A_{10} \quad B_0 \quad G_1 \quad A_{10} \quad B_0 \quad P_3 \quad L_{24} \quad A_1 \quad B_0 \quad P_1 \quad A_0$

$(10 + 1 + 10 + 3 + 24 + 1 + 1) \times 10 = 500$ TMU

5. Obtain a $1/4$-inch (6-mm) ratchet located within reach and run a bolt down by rotating the ratchet with eight wrist cranks. Final tighten the bolt with four wrist turns and set aside the ratchet.

FASTEN BOLT WITH 8 WRIST-CRANKS USING RATCHET AND ASIDE

A_1 B_0 G_1 A_1 B_0 P_3 F_{16} A_1 B_0 P_1 A_0

$(1 + 1 + 1 + 3 + 16 + 1 + 1) \times 10 = 240$ TMU

6. Walk five steps to a tool cabinet and get a 12-inch (30-cm) fixed end wrench. Return to the workplace and loosen two bolts located 12 inches (30 cm) apart using four arm actions. Set the wrench aside, within reach.

LOOSEN 2 BOLTS 12 INCHES (30 CM) APART WITH 4 ARM-TURNS USING WRENCH AND ASIDE WITHIN REACH

A_{10} B_0 G_1 A_{10} B_0 $(P_3$ A_1 $L_{24})$ A_1 B_0 P_1 A_0 (2)

$[(3 + 1 + 24) \times (2) + 10 + 1 + 10 + 1 + 1] \times 10 = 790$ TMU

The Data Card for Cut, Surface Treat, Measure, Record, and Think

On this data card are found the index values for common activities found within the parameters of Cut, Surface Treat, Measure, Record, and Think. The list of values given are not meant to be comprehensive. In fact, should special or supplementary activities (tools or operations) be required to analyze a particular situation, the analyst is encouraged to develop those values under the guidelines set forth in Section E. With this, the analyst tailors the data card to his or her particular situation or industry.

Cut

Cut describes the manual actions employed to separate, divide, or remove part of an object using a sharp-edged hand tool. As Figure 3.20 indicates, index values for the C parameter cover the use of pliers, scissors, or knife for general cutting and related activities. These cutting tools and their use are described as follows.

Pliers

Three different methods may be employed to cut through wire using pliers. The particular method employed largely depends on the hardness of the wire material and the diameter or gauge of the wire. Small-gauge copper wire, for instance, requires only a squeezing of the hand to simply snip off the wire (soft wire). However, with larger gauge wire or harder material, such as steel, two separate cuts may be required to completely sever the wire (medium wire). That is, following an initial cut, the pliers are rotated around the wire and repositioned over the cut before completely cutting through the wire. A third method may be encountered with the largest gauge and hardest wire (hard wire). In addition to requiring two cuts, both hands are needed to apply sufficient force to cut through the wire.

C_3 Soft   CUTOFF SOFT

This parameter applies to cutting a soft steel, copper, or other small-gauge wire. Recognized by using the pliers with one hand and making one cut.

C_6 Medium   CUTOFF MEDIUM

This parameter applies to cutting a steel wire or cable and can be recognized by using the pliers with one hand and making two cuts.

C_{10} Hard   CUTOFF HARD

This parameter applies to cutting a heavier wire (approximately 10 gauge) and can be recognized by using two hands and making two cuts.

The data (Fig. 3.20) for using cutting pliers therefore include three index values for cutting wire. The value used most often in small electrical assembly work would be C_3 (cutoff soft wire). In heavier assembly work or electrical maintenance, for instance, the appropriate value may be C_6 (cutoff medium wire) or even C_{10} (cutoff hard wire). Placement of the pliers is normally a P_1.

Also included in the column for pliers are three common activities performed with pliers.

C_1 Grip   GRIP

Following the initial placement of the pliers, the operator squeezes the pliers to simply hold an item and subsequently releases the pressure on the item.

Example: Using pliers, hold a wire in place for soldering.

C_6 Twist   TWIST

Following the placement of the pliers on two wires, the jaws are closed and two twisting motions of the pliers join the wires together. Should more than two twisting actions need to be analyzed, break the number observed into groups of two and apply a frequency to the C_6.

Example: Using pliers, twist the ends of two wires together.

C_6 Form Loop   FORM-LOOP

Following the initial placement of the pliers, the operator closes the jaws and using two actions bends a loop or eye in the end of a wire.

Example: Using pliers, form an eye in the end of a wire to fit over a terminal in a junction box.

C_{16} Secure Cotter Pin

Following the initial placement, an operator bends both legs on a cotter pin to hold it in position.

Example: Using pliers, bend legs on a cotter pin to secure it through a small shaft.

Scissors

These data apply to cutting paper, fabric, light cardboard, or other similar material using scissors. Index values are selected according to the number of cuts or scissors actions employed during the cutting activity. To cut off a piece of thread, for example, only one cutting action is required. Accordingly, the appropriate index value from Figure 3.20 is C_1 (one cut with scissors). Likewise, the actions of a seamstress in cutting through a piece of fabric with four cutting actions would be indexed C_6 (four cuts with scissors). Placement of scissors is normally a P_1 (P_3 if exact placement is required).

Knife

The use of a sharp knife for cutting string or light cord or to cut through corrugated material or cardboard carries the index value C_3. This value also applies to the activities aimed at slicing open a corrugated box. The length of the cut can be up to 32 inches (80 cm). If the box is wrapped with string or cord, the initial cutting activity involves removing the cord (C_3, one slice). After this cord has been removed, the next activity involves cutting through the box (C_3, one slice). To slice three sides of the box so that the lid can be lifted, the analyst selects the index value based on the number of strokes (in this case 5).

$$A_1 \quad B_0 \quad G_1 \quad A_1 \quad B_0 \quad P_1 \quad C_{10} \quad A_1 \quad B_0 \quad P_1 \quad A_0 \quad \textbf{160 TMU}$$

The criterion for selecting the index value to account for the initial placement of a knife is the same as that discussed in the General Move section for Placement. However, as a general rule, a P_1 will be sufficient. If the cut must be exact, P_3 will be appropriate.

Tool Use Examples for Cut

1. An operator picks up a knife from a workbench two steps away, makes one cut across the top of a cardboard box, and sets aside the knife on the workbench.

SLICE BOX 1 SLICE USING KNIFE AND LAY ASIDE

$$A_3 \quad B_0 \quad G_1 \quad A_3 \quad B_0 \quad P_1 \quad C_3 \quad A_3 \quad B_0 \quad P_1 \quad A_0$$

$$(3 + 1 + 3 + 1 + 3 + 3 + 1) \times 10 = 150 \text{ TMU}$$

2. During a sewing operation, a tailor cuts the thread from the machine before setting aside the finished garment. The scissors are held in the palm during the sewing operation.

CUT THREAD 1 CUT USING SCISSORS AND HOLD

A_0 B_0 G_0 A_1 B_0 P_1 C_1 A_0 B_0 P_0 A_0

$(1 + 1 + 1) \times 10 = 30$ TMU

3. Following a soldering operation, an electronic component assembler must cut off the excess small-gauge wire from a terminal connection. The pliers are located within reach.

CUTOFF EXCESS SOFT WIRE USING PLIERS AND ASIDE

A_1 B_0 G_1 A_1 B_0 P_1 C_3 A_1 B_0 P_1 A_0

$(1 + 1 + 1 + 1 + 3 + 1 + 1) \times 10 = 90$ TMU

4. An electrician working on transmission lines takes a pair of pliers from the tool belt and cuts off a piece of line. The line is heavy, such that two hands are needed to cut through the wire.

CUTOFF HARD LINE USING PLIERS FROM TOOL BELT AND RETURN

A_1 B_0 G_1 A_1 B_0 P_1 C_{10} A_1 B_0 P_1 A_0

$(1 + 1 + 1 + 1 + 10 + 1 + 1) \times 10 = 160$ TMU

Surface Treat

Surface Treat covers the activities aimed at cleaning material or particles from or applying a substance, coating, or finish to the surface of an object. Activities of many types may be included in the surface treat category, such as lubricating, painting, cleaning, polishing, gluing, coating, and sanding. However, the data found in Figure 3.20 under Surface Treat cover only general cleaning activities performed with a rag or cloth, an air hose, or a brush. Other kinds of surface treat activity, if encountered, may be treated as special tools (see Sec. E) and supplementary index values developed for those particular activities.

The cleaning tools covered by the S parameter from Figure 3.20 include

1. *Air hose* or *nozzle* for blowing small particles or chips out of a hole or cavity or from a surface.   AIRCLEAN
2. *Brush* for brushing particles, chips, or other debris from an object or surface.   BRUSHCLEAN
3. *Rag* or *cloth* for wiping light oil or a similar substance from a surface.
                                                                              WIPE

Index values for these cleaning tools are based primarily on the amount of surface area cleaned. In most cases, the number of square feet cleaned determines the appropriate value. To analyze cleaning a small area such as a hole or cavity in a part, jig, or fixture with an air hose, the value S_6 (point or cavity) is appropriate; if more than one cavity is cleaned in this manner, the value S_6 along with the P parameters, and an action distance (A) to account for the distance between cavities; multiply this distance by the number of cavities.

To brush clean a small object, an S_6 is appropriate. A small object refers to brushing a jig, fixture, or cavity. For example, air clean five holes with an air hose. The holes are >2 inches (5 cm) apart:

$$A_1 \quad B_0 \quad G_1 \quad A_0 \quad B_0 \quad (P_1 \quad A_1 \quad S_6) \quad A_1 \quad B_0 \quad P_1 \quad A_0 \quad (5) \quad \quad 440 \text{ TMU}$$

Tool Use Examples for Surface Treat

1. Before marking off a piece of sheet metal (4 square feet, 0.36 m²) for a cutting operation, the operator takes a rag from his or her back pocket and wipes an oily film from the surface.

WIPE METAL SHEET 4 SQ. FT. (0.36 m²) USING RAG FROM POCKET AND RETURN

$$A_1 \quad B_0 \quad G_1 \quad A_1 \quad B_0 \quad P_1 \quad S_{32} \quad A_1 \quad B_0 \quad P_1 \quad A_0$$

$$(1 + 1 + 1 + 1 + 32 + 1 + 1) \times 10 = 380 \text{ TMU}$$

2. Following a sanding operation, an operator standing at a workbench picks up a brush located within reach and brushes the dust and chips from the working area (approximately 6 square feet, 0.54 m²) and then sets aside the brush on the workbench.

BRUSHCLEAN WORKBENCH 6 SQ. FT. (0.54 m²) USING BRUSH AND LAY ASIDE

$$A_1 \quad B_0 \quad G_1 \quad A_1 \quad B_0 \quad P_1 \quad S_{42} \quad A_1 \quad B_0 \quad P_1 \quad A_0$$

$$(1 + 1 + 1 + 1 + 42 + 1 + 1) \times 10 = 480 \text{ TMU}$$

3. Before assembling three components to a casting, the operator obtains an air hose (located within reach) and blows the small metal filings left from the previous machining operation out of three cavities. The distance between each cavity is >2 inches (5 cm).

AIRCLEAN 3 CAVITIES IN CASTING USING NOZZLE AND ASIDE

$$A_1 \quad B_0 \quad G_1 \quad A_0 \quad B_0 \quad (P_1 \quad A_1 \quad S_6) \quad A_1 \quad B_0 \quad P_1 \quad A_0 \quad (3)$$

$$[(1 + 1 + 6) \times (3) + 1 + 1 + 1 + 1] \times 10 = 280 \text{ TMU}$$

Measure   MEASURE

Measure includes the actions employed to determine a certain physical characteristic of an object by comparison with a standard measuring device.

Index values for the M elements cover all actions necessary to place, align,
adjust, and examine both the measuring device and the object during the measuring activity. Therefore, the initial placement of the tool will normally be
analyzed with a P_1. The data from Figure 3.20 cover the following gauges.

M_{10} Profile Gauge   PROFILE-GAUGE

This value covers the use of an angle, radius, level, or screw-pitch gauge to
compare the profile of the object to that of the gauge. The M_{10} value includes
placing and adjusting the gauge to the object, plus the visual actions to compare
the configuration of the object with that of the gauge.

M_{16} Fixed Scale   FIXED-SCALE

This parameter covers the use of a linear [12-inch (30-cm) ruler, yardstick,
meter stick, etc.] or an angular (protractor) measuring device. The value M_{16}
includes adjusting and readjusting the tool to two points and the time to read the
actual dimension from the graduated scale.

M_{16} Calipers $\leq$ 12 inches (30 cm)   CALIPER

This parameter covers the use of Vernier calipers with a maximum measurement
capacity of up to 12 inches (30 cm). The M_{16} value includes setting the caliper
legs to the object dimension, locking the legs in place, and reading the Vernier
scale to determine the measurement.

M_{24} Feeler Gauge   FEELER-GAUGE

This parameter covers the use of a feeler gauge to measure the gap between two
points. The M_{24} value includes fanning out the blades, reading and selecting the
appropriate blade size, and positioning the blade to the gap to check for fit.

M_{32} Steel Tape $\leq$ 6 feet (1.5 m)   STEEL-TAPE

This parameter coves the use of steel tape to measure the distance between two
points. The M_{32} value includes pulling the tape from the reel, positioning the end
of the tape, adjusting and readjusting the tape between the two points, the time
to read the dimension from the scale, and finally pushing the tape back into the
reel. This value is confined to the use of a steel tape from a fixed position, and
includes *no walking* between the two points to adjust the tape.

M$_{32}$/M$_{42}$/M$_{54}$ Micrometers ≤4 inches (10 cm)

These three index values cover the use of three different micrometers: M$_{32}$ for measuring depth (keyword DEPTH-MICROMETER), M$_{42}$ for measuring outside diameter (NO. INCH-OD-MICROMETER), and M$_{54}$ for measuring inside diameter (NO. INCH-ID-MICROMETER). These values are based on micrometers designed for maximum dimensions of 4 inches (10 cm). The values include setting the micrometer to the part, adjusting the thimble for fit, locking the device, and finally reading the Vernier scale to determine the dimension.

Notice that for these index values, all the placing and adjusting motions are included in the measure data (the M parameter). The result is that the initial placement of the measuring device is covered by each index value for M. For this reason, the place parameter prior to use tool will normally carry an index value of P$_1$ whenever the measure parameter is involved.

Tool Use Examples for Measure

1. Before welding two steel plates, a welder obtains a square and checks the angle between the plates to see that it is correct. The square (a profile gauge) is located three steps away on a workbench.

MEASURE PLATE ANGLE USING PROFILE-GAUGE FROM WORKBENCH AND RETURN

$$A_6 \quad B_0 \quad G_1 \quad A_6 \quad B_0 \quad P_1 \quad M_{10} \quad A_6 \quad B_0 \quad P_1 \quad A_0$$

$$(6 + 1 + 6 + 1 + 10 + 6 + 1) \times 10 = 310 \text{ TMU}$$

2. Following a turning operation, a machinist checks the diameter of a small shaft with a micrometer. The micrometer is located on and returned to the workbench two steps away.

MEASURE SHAFT USING 2-IN.-OD-MICROMETER FROM WORKBENCH AND RETURN

$$A_3 \quad B_0 \quad G_1 \quad A_3 \quad B_0 \quad P_1 \quad M_{42} \quad A_3 \quad B_0 \quad P_1 \quad A_0$$

$$(3 + 1 + 3 + 1 + 42 + 3 + 1) \times 10 = 540 \text{ TMU}$$

Several supplementary values for various measuring devices have been developed that do not appear on the data card. They are as follows.

M$_6$ Snap Gauge   2-IN.-SNAP-GAUGE

Measure with a snap gauge an outer diameter up to 2 inches (5 cm).

M$_{10}$ Snap Gauge   4-IN.-SNAP-GAUGE

Measure with a snap gauge an outer diameter up to 4 inches (10 cm).

M₁₆ Plug Gauge   PLUG-GAUGE

Measure with a plug gauge, GO + NOGO ends, up to 1 inch (2.5 cm).

M₂₄ Thread Gauge   1-IN.-THREAD-GAUGE

Measure with a thread gauge, internal or external threads up to 1 inch (2.5 cm).

M₂₄ Vernier Depth Gauge   DEPTH-GAUGE

Measure with a Vernier depth gauge up to 6 inches (15 cm).

M₄₂ Thread Gauge   2-IN.-THREAD-GAUGE

Measure with a thread gauge, internal or external threads 1–2 inches (2.5–5 cm).

Record

Record covers the manual actions performed with a writing instrument or marking tool for the purpose of recording information. Three columns of data are found in Figure 3.20 for the Record parameter. The index values for Write apply to the normal-size handwriting operations (script or print) performed with a pen, pencil, or other writing instrument. The Mark data covers the use of such marking tools as a scribe, felt marker, or chalk, for the purpose of identifying or making a larger mark (1–3 inches, 2.5–7.5 cm) on an object.

Write   WRITE (NO.) DIGIT(S), WORD(S), SIGNATURE, DATE

These data are provided to cover the routine clerical activities encountered in many shop operations. These activities may include filling out time cards, writing out a part number, or writing brief instructions. Index values for the R parameter are selected primarily on the basis of the number of digits (letters or numerals) or the number of words written. Consider the values for writing the date (either in the form 07-04-89 or July 4, 1984) or writing one's signature as writing two words and assign an R_{16} for either.

Mark   MARK (NO.) DIGIT(S), CHECKMARK, SCRIBE-LINE

These data apply to marking or identifying an object or container using a marking tool, such as a scribe or felt marker. Each *mark* is counted as a "digit." The index values for marking digits apply to printed characters (letters and numerals) of 1–3 inches (2.5–7.5 cm) in size. Other common marking values include making a check mark (R_1) and a scribing line (R_3).

The initial placement of a recording instrument before writing or marking usually occurs as a P_1. A possible exception may be the placement of a marking device prior to scribing a line. If the beginning point of the line is critical, a P_3 is required to cover the necessary adjustment to place the tool accurately.

Tool Use Examples for Record

1. After finishing an assigned job, the operator picks up a clipboard and pencil (simo) from the workbench, fills out the completion date on the job card, and signs his name. He then returns the board and pencil to the workbench.

WRITE 2 WORDS (DATE AND SIGNATURE) ON JOB-CARD USING PENCIL FROM CUPBOARD AND ASIDE

A_1 B_0 G_1 A_1 B_0 (P_1 A_0 R_{16}) A_1 B_0 P_1 A_0 (2)

$[(1 + 0 + 16) \times (2) + 1 + 1 + 1 + 1 + 1] \times 10 = 390$ TMU

2. To order a part, a clerk takes a pencil from her shirt pocket and *writes* a six-digit part number on the requisition form on her desk. She then clips the pencil back in her pocket.

WRITE 6 DIGITS ON FORM USING PENCIL AND RETURN TO POCKET

A_1 B_0 G_1 A_1 B_0 P_1 R_{10} A_1 B_0 P_3 A_0

$(1 + 1 + 1 + 1 + 10 + 1 + 3) \times 10 = 180$ TMU

3. Part of a packing operation involves identifying the components in the carton. This involves picking up a felt marker (within reach) and marking a six-digit number on the container.

MARK 6 DIGITS ON CARTON USING MARKER AND ASIDE

A_1 B_0 G_1 A_1 B_0 P_1 R_{24} A_1 B_0 P_1 A_0

$(1 + 1 + 1 + 1 + 24 + 1 + 1) \times 10 = 300$ TMU

Think

Think refers to the use of sensory mental processes, particularly those involving visual perception, and may also include "reaching to feel an object." The *think* data in Figure 3.20 are designed to cover only those types of reading and inspection activities that occur as a necessary part of a worker's job. Although these operations usually occur internally to the manual work and therefore have no effect on the duration of the work cycle, on numerous occasions these activities must be considered in the overall work content of the job. The analyst should exercise care in determining the extent to which these activities affect the total operation time.

Inspect   INSPECT, TOUCH, FEEL

The data in this column apply to inspection work designed for making simple decisions regarding certain characteristics of the object under inspection. The activity involves first locating the inspection point (locations) and then making a quick yes-or-no decision concerning the existence of a defect. These mental processes presume that the inspector possesses a clear understanding of the characteristic being judged. In other words, the presence of any defect, such as a scratch, stain, scar, or color variance, is readily apparent to the inspector.

The index values for inspection refer to the number of inspection points examined on the object. For each point, a yes-or-no decision is made concerning the presence or absence of readily distinguishable defects.

Except for reaching to feel an object, these parameter values *do not cover* the manual handling of the object that may occur during the inspection. Caution should be exercised in using these or any inspection values. In practical work situations, inspection time is rarely limiting, but usually occurs during the manual handling of elements. Whenever possible, work should be designed to make inspections internal to other activities.

Along with inspecting a number of points, values are provided for activities of Touch for Heat (T_6), where the hand is moved to the object, moved over the surface of the object, and removed, and Feel for Defect (T_{10}), where the hand is moved to the object, moved over three surfaces of the object, and removed.

Read   READ (NO.) DIGIT(S), SINGLE-WORD(S), WORD(S)

To read is to locate and interpret characters or groups of characters. The data for Read are divided into two sections: Read "digits or single words" and Read "text of words."

The column Digits or Single Words is to be used for reading technical data such as part numbers, codes, quantities, and dimensions from a blueprint. A digit is considered a letter, a number, or a special character. To index the T parameter, simply count the number of digits or single words read and choose the appropriate index number from the data card (Fig. 3.20).

The column Text of Words is used when analyzing situations in which the operator is required to read words arranged in sentences or paragraphs. These data are based on an average reading rate of 330 words per minute or 5.05 TMU per word. These index values may be applied to reading a set of instructions in a work order set or gathering general information from reading the tabular data or text on a blueprint.

Additional values that apply to more specific reading activities, such as reading gauges, scales, and tables are also provided in Figure 3.20.

T₃ Gauge

Use when a device is checked to see if the pointer is within a clearly marked tolerance range.

Example: The pointer is in the range; the pressure is acceptable.

T₆ Scale Value

A specific quantity is read from a graduated scale, such as a measuring stick or a temperature-pressure gauge.

Example: The pressure is 38 psi.

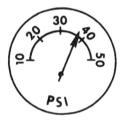

T₆ Date/Time

The month, day, and year are read from a document or calendar; the time of day is read from a clock or wrist watch.

T₁₀ Vernier Scale

Visually locate and read (only) an exact value from a micrometer, caliper, or similar device. This does not contain time for placing and setting the device to an object.

T₁₆ Table Value

A specific value is located and read from a table after scanning the table horizontally and vertically.

Example: The correct machine setting is read from a feed-speed table.

Tool Use Examples for Think

1. During a testing operation, an electronics technician picks up a meter lead, places it on a terminal, and reads voltage off the meter scale. The lead is then put aside.

READ METER SCALE-VALUE BY PLACING LEAD ON TO TERMINAL AND ASIDE LEAD

A_1 B_0 G_1 A_1 B_0 P_3 T_6 A_1 B_0 P_1 A_0

$(1 + 1 + 1 + 3 + 6 + 1 + 1) \times 10 = 140$ TMU

2. Prior to starting a turning operation, an operator picks up a work order set and reads a paragraph that describes the method to be followed; it contains an average of 30 words. The operator then places the set aside on the workbench.

READ WORK ORDER SET (30 WORDS) AND LAY ASIDE

A_1 B_0 G_1 A_1 B_0 P_0 T_{16} A_1 B_0 P_1 A_0

$(1 + 1 + 1 + 16 + 1 + 1) \times 10 = 210$ TMU

D. The Manual Crane Sequence

As stated in the introduction, the three sequence models covering the manual handling of objects constitute the Basic MOST Work Measurement technique. These sequence models, General Move and Controlled Move in particular, can be used to measure handling of heavy objects, with lifting or moving equipment as well. However, for reasons of simplicity, special sequences were developed to cover this equipment handling. (See also Chapter 5—Maxi MOST).

The values appearing on the data cards for equipment handling are based on a representative sample of equipment found in industry. Therefore, the data may be valid for the majority of situations as they stand. However, before applying the data, it is suggested that individual parameter values be reviewed and adjusted to local methods if necessary.

The *Manual Crane Sequence,* as does the manual handling sequence, indicates that a standard sequence of events must be considered when moving an object. The Manual Crane Sequence Model deals with the movement of objects using a manually traversed crane. The sequence model is appropriate for a crane that may resemble either a jib crane or an overhead bridge crane (Fig. 3.25), as long as the crane is moved laterally and longitudinally by hand, not under power.

As with the General Move Sequence, all manual operations can be identified with a certain sequence of events that repeats from cycle to cycle, regardless of the description, size, or name of the object being moved.

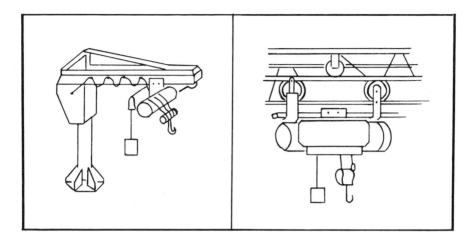

Figure 3.25 Manually traversed cranes: jib crane (left) and overhead crane (right).

1. The operator moves to the crane (Action Distance).
2. The crane is transported empty to the location of the object to be moved (Transport).
3. The object is hooked up and freed from its surroundings (Hook-up, Free).
4. The object is raised vertically using the crane (Vertical move).
5. The crane is moved, with the load, to the placement location (Loaded move).
6. The object is lowered vertically (Vertical move).
7. The object is placed in a fixture or container, for example (Placement).
8. The object is released from crane (Unhook).
9. The crane is transported empty to a rest position (Transport).
10. The operator returns to the original location (Action Distance).

The Manual Crane Sequence Model

The movement of an object with a manual crane is described by the sequence model

A   T   K   F   V   L   V   P   T   A

where: A = Action distance
         T = Transport empty crane
         K = Hook up and unhook
         F = Free object (from surroundings, pallet, fixture, etc.)

V = Vertical move
L = Loaded move
P = Placement

Parameter Definitions

A Action Distance

This is defined in the section on General Move and is indexed by the distance (in steps) the operator walks to or from the crane.

T Transport Empty Crane

Transport Empty Crane includes getting the empty crane and transporting it horizontally to the location of the object to be moved. Note that the movement is a result of the operator pulling or pushing the crane from one location to another. Vertical movement of the hook during the Transport empty parameter is an *internal* function.

K Hook up and Unhook

Hook up and Unhook includes both connecting and disconnecting the object from the holding device. The parameter begins at the point at which the transport of the empty crane ends and is complete when the object is fastened to the crane hook or sling, for example. The parameter also includes time to remove the holding device. Note that getting the hook or slings to the workplace will be analyzed separately with a General Move Sequence.

F Free Object

Free Object includes the actions necessary to work the object free from its surroundings (e.g., container or fixture) and raise the object, at a low speed, 2–3 inches (5–8 cm). This parameter is to include all actions necessary to position the load so that the next activity will be an unrestricted vertical move.

V Vertical Move

Vertical Move is the raising or lowering of the object at high speed following the F and L parameters. The hook is raised after the object is freed and lowered after the loaded crane is moved to the placement location. Note that if the hook is raised or lowered during the transportation of the crane, the time is covered by the T or L parameters.

L Loaded Move

Loaded Move covers the horizontal movement of the object with the crane. Note that the movement with a manual crane is a result of the operator pulling or pushing the crane from one location to another.

P   Placement

Placement covers the actions in lowering the object the last 2–3 inches (5–8 cm) at low speed and placing the object in the desired location. Index values are based on the degree of difficulty affecting placement, as follows.

1. No alignment: The object is simply lowered into position without any additional manual guidance from the operator. *Example:* Lower a small casting and place it by itself on a pallet.
2. Align with one hand: While lowering the last 2–3 inches (5–8 cm), the operator reaches out with one hand and steers or swings the load into position.
3. Align with two hands: During the placement activity, the operator must release the controls and steer or swing the object into position using two hands.
4. Align and place with one adjustment: To position an object, the operator must steer or swing the object into position, in addition to making one directional adjustment (longitudinally, laterally, or vertically).
5. Align and place with several adjustments: To position an object, an operator must steer or swing the object into position, in addition to making several directional adjustments (longitudinally, laterally, and/or vertically).
6. Align and place with several adjustments, in addition to exercising care in handling or applying pressure: To position an object, an operator must steer or swing the object into position, in addition to making several directional adjustments (longitudinally, laterally and/or vertically). A pause or hesitation must also be observed at the point of placement to indicate the application of heavy pressure required to seat the object, or an obvious slow motion is observed in placing the object carefully.

Figure 3.26 illustrates the sequence of events that occurs when an object is moved with a manual crane.

Use of the Manual Crane Data Card

The data card (Fig. 3.27) is divided into seven columns. Index values are selected either by the distance involved (the A, T, L, and V parameters) or by the holding device used or difficulty involved in moving an object (the F and P parameters).

Sequence Model Indexing

A   Action Distance

Choose the index value by the distance the operator walks to get to or move away from the crane.

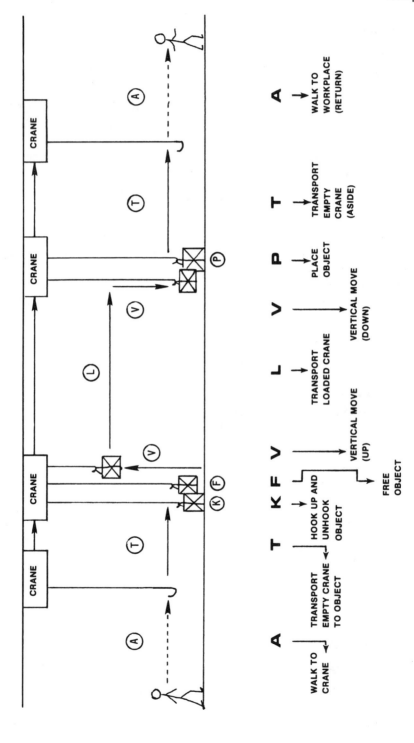

Figure 3.26 Illustration of Manual Crane Sequence Model.

Basic MOST® System

A T K F V L V P T A   MANUAL CRANE

INDEX X 10	A — ACTION DISTANCE STEPS	T — TRANSPORTATION UP TO 2 TON FEET (M) EMPTY	L — LOADED	K — HOOK-UP AND UNHOOK	F — FREE OBJECT	V — VERTICAL MOVE INCHES (CM)	P — PLACEMENT	INDEX X 10
3	2				Without direction change	9 (20)	Without direction change	3
6	4				With single direction change	15 (40)	Align with one hand	6
10	7	5 (1.5)	5 (1.5)		With double direction change	30 (75)	Align with two hands	10
16	10	13 (4)	12 (3.5)		With one or more direction changes, care in handling or apply pressure	45 (115)	Align and place with one adjustment	16
24	15	20 (6)	18 (5.5)	Single or double hook		60 (150)	Align and place with several adjustments	24
32	20	30 (9)	26 (8)	Sling			Align and place with several adjustments + apply pressure	32
42	26	40 (12)	35 (10)					42
54	33	50 (15)	45 (13)					54

Figure 3.27 Manual crane data card. Values are read "up to and including." Transportation times for the T and L parameters must be validated before application of the Manual Crane Sequence Model.

T Transport Empty

Select the proper index value by the distance (feet, meters) the operator moves the empty crane to or from the object moved. *Note:* The values for up to 2 tons include the use of $1/4$-ton, $1/2$-ton, 1-ton, and 2-ton cranes.

L Loaded Move

Select the proper index value by the distance (feet, meters) the operator moves the loaded crane.

K Hook up and Unhook

Choose the proper index value by the holding device used.

F Free Object

Choose the proper index value by the difficulty involved in freeing the object, in other words, raising the object 2–3 inches (5–8 cm) and positioning such that the next action will be an unobstructed vertical move.

V Vertical Move

Select the proper index value by the distance (inches, centimeters) the object is raised or lowered.

P Placement

Choose the proper index value by the difficulty involved in lowering the object the last 2–3 inches (5–8 cm) and placing it in the desired location.

Like the General Move, Controlled Move, and Tool Use Sequences, the index numbers are added for one sequence model and the total is multiplied by 10 to convert to TMU.

Manual Crane Data Card Backup Verification

The data provided on this data card are to be treated as sample data only. The methods represented on this card must be *verified* and the vertical speeds (process time) must be *validated* for the particular cranes in question.

Methods to be verified are the hook and unhook (K) and placement (P) subactivities. Backup data for methods other than specified on the data card can be developed and placed on the data card according to the procedure outlined in Section E. Equipment data to be verified and validated are loaded and unloaded transportation speeds and vertical speeds (T, L, V).

The transportation time per traveled distance and the corresponding index values can be calculated using the following formula:

$$t = c + (s \times n)$$

where: t = time (TMU)

  n = distance variable (number of feet or meters moved)

  c = fixed manual time (TMU), including grasping of control and crane acceleration and deceleration times

  s = crane horizontal speed (TMU/foot or meter).

Manual Crane Sequence Examples

1. A machine operator walks 10 feet (3 m) to a crane and manually transports it to a fixture (66 pounds, 30 kg) located 7 feet (2 m) away. The fixture, which is lying by itself on a pallet, is hooked up to the crane with a single hook and moved 14 feet (4.5 m) to a workbench 3 feet (1 m) higher than the pallet. The fixture is then lowered 4 inches (10 cm) and placed on top of the workbench. The operator transports the empty crane 3 feet (1 m) away and returns to the workbench.

TRANSPORT FIXTURE FROM PALLET TO WORKBENCH USING JIB CRANE WITH SINGLE-HOOK AND TRANSPORT EMPTY CRANE ASIDE AND RETURN TO WORKBENCH

A_6 T_{16} K_{24} F_3 V_{16} L_{24} V_3 P_3 T_{10} A_3

$(6 + 16 + 24 + 3 + 16 + 24 + 3 + 3 + 10 + 3) \times 10 = 1080$ TMU

2. The activity involved in exchanging the workpiece in the three-jaw chuck of an engine lathe requires the use of a jib crane. The operator first gets the jib crane from two steps away and transports it back to the machine where the operator hooks up the 300-pound (136-kg) workpiece with a sling. The operator then raises the crane 6 inches (15 cm) and moves the load 16 feet (5 m) away and then lowers the crane 3 feet (1 m) to place the workpiece on a pallet. From another pallet located 6 feet (2 m) from the first, the operator gets a new workpiece, moves it back to the machine (22 feet, 7 m) and places it in the chuck, then puts the crane aside, two steps away, and returns.

TRANSPORT 300-LB (136-KG) WORKPIECE FROM 3-JAW CHUCK TO PALLET USING JIB CRANE WITH ONE SLING

A_3 T_{10} K_{32} F_{16} V_3 L_{24} V_{16} P_3 T_0 A_0 **1070 TMU**

TRANSPORT WORKPIECE FROM PALLET-2 TO 3-JAW CHUCK ON LATHE USING JIB CRANE WITH ONE SLING AND RETURN TO LATHE

A_0 T_{16} K_{32} F_3 V_{16} L_{32} V_3 P_{32} T_{10} A_3 **1470 TMU**

                                                                                  2540 TMU

E. Application of Basic MOST Work Measurement Technique

MOST for Methods Improvement

Preliminary to the actual MOST analysis, the analyst should study the operation
with the objective of establishing the most effective method of accomplishing the
task. Although the "best" method will not always be apparent, every job should
be approached with the attitude that "any method can be improved."

The starting point for a study is the information-gathering (operation analysis) phase. All important facts concerning the job, such as the workplace layout,
tools and equipment, materials, and shop conditions, should be collected and
studied in detail. All data should be clearly documented and made easily accessible for future reference. This activity alone should point out many improvement possibilities.

In terms of parameter index values, MOST sequence models give a quantitative description of distances, types of placing activity, tool use frequencies, and
so on. During the course of filling out sequences, these index values can serve
as indicators for evaluating potential improvements or comparing different methods. All indexes above 3 for A, B, G, and P parameters should be investigated
for possible method improvements. For the Tool Use Sequence, index values
should reflect the optimum time value based on the choice of tool.

Standard Form for Basic MOST Calculations

Analysis with MOST is simplified by the use of standard calculation forms (Fig.
3.28). The standard MOST calculation form contains the following six main
sections:

1. Identification (Code, Date, Signature, and Page number)
2. Area
3. Activity/conditions
4. Method description
5. Basic sequence model analysis section (General Move, Controlled Move,
   and Tool Use)
6. Total time

All information necessary to *identify, describe* and *calculate* the standard time
for an operation or a suboperation is included on the MOST calculation form.

At the top of the form (see Section 1 of Fig. 3.28), space is provided for the
10-digit *data bank code* (for additional manual coding information, see Chap.
7), the date, the analyst's name, and the number of pages in the analysis.
Section 2 of Figure 3.28 is used for indicating the area in which the subopera-

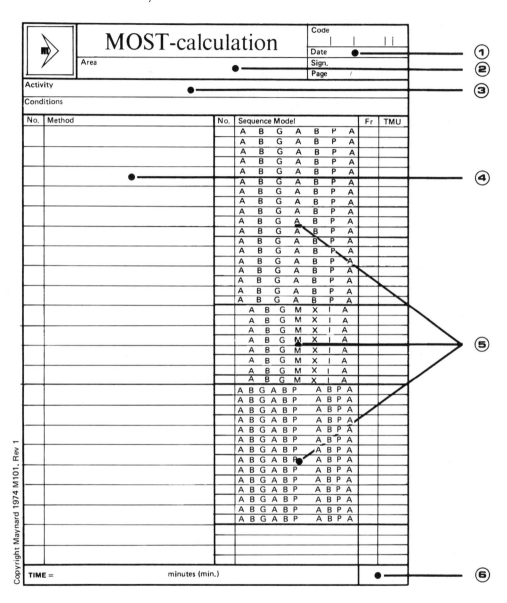

Figure 3.28 MOST calculation form.

tion analyzed below is found. This could be a general geographical plant area (such as building or department) or work area (such as final assembly, fabrication, or turret lathes).

Section 3 of Figure 3.28 is a very important section on the form; it is headed Activity. The words inserted here determine the size and scope of the suboperation data unit analyzed below. These same words, when manually coded, would appear as the 10-digit code under which the data unit will be filed and retrieved from the data bank. In MOST Computer Systems, these words alone act as the vehicle by which a suboperation data unit is filed and retrieved from the data base (see Chap. 8 for more details). It is very important that the words placed in the activity section of the MOST calculation form accurately describe the contents of the suboperation and be uniform and complete. It is suggested that even though suboperations may be manually coded and filed, the title (activity) sentence format for the computer filing system be used; this ensures a consistent and thorough description of the suboperation. The conditions section of the heading allows the analyst to record any additional descriptive data concerning the suboperation and will aid others in properly identifying it. Examples of special conditions might be:

- For Model X231 only
- Operator must wear special clothing
- For parts up to and including 5 pounds (2 kg)

The left side of the form (section 4 of Fig. 3.28) is used to record the *method description* of the activity in a plain-language, logical, and chronological sequence. This description can be as detailed or as brief as required. The amount of information placed in the method description section is usually a function of its eventual use; that is, the description can be used for detailed operator instructions or for an outline of the manual work for time computation only. It is important to note that each method step has *only one* corresponding sequence model (section 5 of Fig. 3.28). Therefore, the method description should be phrased in terms of moving an object(s) or using a tool(s) using *keywords*.

The form also contains provisions for applying *frequencies* to individual sequence models and for the total time calculation for each sequence model. The time for an activity (operation or suboperation) is calculated simply by adding the totals for all the individual sequence models. The grand total is placed in the bottom right-hand corner of the form (section 6 of Fig. 3.28); this total time (in TMU) can be converted to decimal minutes, hours, or millihours, and so on.

Note: The total time value reflects the "normal time" for the activity *without allowances*. Therefore, the time value on the MOST calculation form must be multiplied by the appropriate allowance factor (PRD) in order to produce a complete time standard. Also, below the section containing the preprinted sequence models (section 5 of Fig. 3.28) are four blank lines. These lines are provided for additional sequence models if required. Should one of the pre-printed sections above be filled, or should a Manual Crane Sequence Model be required, the additional sequence model(s) would be placed in these four lines. A sample of completed MOST calculation forms can be found in Appendix B.

Analyst Consistency

Since each parameter or variable pertaining to the Basic MOST sequence models is shown on the calculation form, the analyst will not easily omit or "forget" motions. Each parameter must be filled in or indexed. This forces the analyst to decide which index value to assign. Even nonoccurring motions (index value 0) require a decision. For this reason, the analyst error of omitting motions is for all practical purposes eliminated. The result is a high level of consistency in the application of MOST Systems.

Summary of the Basic MOST Calculation Procedure

The Basic MOST calculation sheet is filled out as follows.

1. Indicate at the top of the form: code number (from data bank coding system); area of work; activity.
2. Document the *method* to be analyzed by dividing it into a number of successive steps corresponding to the "natural" breakdown of the activity. Number each step in chronological order. Use *keywords*.
3. Select *one appropriate sequence model* for each method step.
4. Indicate the correct *index value* for each parameter within each sequence model.
5. Add parameter index values together, multiply by 10, and insert the result in right-hand column to arrive at the time for the sequence model in TMU.
6. For the total activity time in TMU, add all sequence times together and insert the result in the bottom right-hand corner. If desired, these time values may be converted to hours, minutes, seconds, or millihours in the bottom left-hand corner of the sheet.

Practical Analysis Procedures

Ideally, observation of two cycles in slow motion will be sufficient to make a Basic MOST analysis. If conditions permit, the operator should first perform the activity from start to finish, allowing the analyst to document the method description. On the next slow-motion cycle, the analyst selects the appropriate sequence model(s) for the corresponding method steps and places index values on each parameter. This procedure requires that the analyst be fully trained, have experience with Basic MOST application, and be thoroughly familiar with the operation.

This approach is, of course, not always possible or even practical. Quite often such calculations have to be made well in advance of the performance of the actual operation in the shop. However, if the method is well established and the analyst possesses complete knowledge of the operation and conditions, the Basic MOST calculations can be made from the office. This requires the use of workplace layouts that include the location and distances of tools, equipment, and parts. The completed analysis should be checked, if possible, by observing the actual operation along with the completed Basic MOST analysis sheet. This procedure is particularly useful for cost estimates of new components and products.

Another analysis procedure that is becoming more common is based on the videotaping of operations. Since the MOST Work Measurement Technique is a simple system and a fast measurement method that does not require collection and specification of extremely detailed information, the Basic MOST analysis can often be made directly from observing the operation on a TV monitor. However, the quality of the videotape has to meet specific needs, which will require some practice in the filming of operations or the use of professionals in this phase of the project.

The most efficient approach to documenting methods on the shop floor is dictation. With a hand-held tape recorder, work area data and methods can quickly be recorded and transcribed. Since it is quite possible to describe a process or method by talking faster than an operator can perform that work, one cycle may often be enough for the study. On the other hand, documenting a method by writing will take two or more cycles to complete.

The dictation procedure is particularly efficient for entering work measurement data into MOST Computer Systems. The structured format for the descriptions of work areas and methods, in combination with the use of keywords, simplifies the work measurement task considerably. In some situations, the dictation procedure can be used to save time for setting standards.

Obviously, the dictation method will become even more efficient when a suitable voice-recognition system replaces the tape recorder. The industrial engineer will then be able to enter data directly into the computer from the shop floor.

General Rules for Using Basic MOST

Each sequence model is fixed; *no letter may be added or omitted,* except as indicated in the sequence model for tool or equipment use.

Index values are fixed; no parameter may carry any index other than 0, 1, 3, 6, 10, 16, 24, 32, 42, 54, and so on. For example, there is *no* index number 2.

Each parameter variant must be supported by backup analysis. No index value for any parameter may be used unless this backup exists. All elements in the Basic MOST system presented in this book are backed up by MTM-1 or MTM-2 analyses.

Updating the Basic MOST Calculation

When evaluating alternative methods or updating existing analyses for correction, methods improvement, or the adaptation of these data units to other company divisions or plant situations, it is not necessary to make a completely new analysis each time. Variations from the documented method can be noted on a copy of the original Basic MOST analysis from the data bank simply by changing index values, inserting additional method steps, or eliminating method steps. The new method can then be rewritten or typed on a clean calculation sheet and inserted in the data bank. Naturally, a major advantage of MOST Computer Systems is the capability to edit, update, and mass update rapidly and consistently.

To illustrate the updating procedure, the following clerical activity will be used. An operator, seated at a desk, stands, picks up a letter, and walks 13 steps to a photocopy machine. The cover is raised and the original placed on the glass. The cover is closed. The operator then sets the dial to make one copy. The start button is depressed, and a copying process time of 6 seconds follows. During the process time, the operator gains control of the cover and when the ready light appears, lifts the cover. The original is removed, the cover lowered, and the operator picks up the copy, returns 13 steps to the desk, places the original and the copy on the desk, and sits down.

Figure 3.29 provides the "original" analysis for this operation. An analyst in another plant observes the method of a similar copying activity and retrieves the original analysis (Fig. 3.29) from the company's central data bank. A quick review of the original analysis (Fig. 3.29) tells the analyst that the method for the operation he or she is interested in analyzing differs from the original.

The analyst then makes a copy of Figure 3.28 and replaces the original in the data bank. The copy of the original analysis is used as a starting point for updating the calculation to fit his or her particular circumstances. Figure 3.30, which illustrates the updating process, reflects the following methods changes.

- The operator's desk is only six steps from the photocopy machine (steps 1 and 10)
- Two dials are manipulated so that 12 copies can be made (step 5).
- The process time is increased to 9 seconds (step 6).
- A method step is added to the analysis (step 9).
- A new total time is generated
- A new title is applied.

After making all the corrections on the copy of the original analysis, the analyst makes a smooth copy of the updated analysis (Fig. 3.31) and places it in the

◢	MOST-calculation		Code 8 0 9 0 0 1 4 2 0 1
			Date 10/15/78
	Area CLERICAL		Sign. WMY
			Page 1 / 1

Activity COPY ONE ORIGINAL AT PHOTOCOPY MACHINE

Conditions ONE COPY PRODUCED MACHINE MODEL NO. 12345

No.	Method	No.	Sequence Model	Fr	TMU
1	PICK-UP ORIGINAL AND MOVE TO MACHINE	1	A_1 B_{10} G_1 A_{24} B_0 P_0 A_0		360
		3	A_0 B_0 G_0 (A_1) B_0 P_3 A_0		30
2	OPEN COVER AT MACHINE	8	A_1 B_0 G_1 A_1 B_0 P_0 A_0		30
		10	A_1 B_0 G_1 A_{24} B_{10} P_1 A_0		370
3	PLACE ORIGINAL ON GLASS		A B G A B P A		
			A B G A B P A		
4	CLOSE COVER		A B G A B P A		
			A B G A B P A		
5	SET DIAL FOR 1 COPY		A B G A B P A		
			A B G A B P A		
6	PUSH BUTTON TO START COPYING - PROCESS TIME 6 SEC.		A B G A B P A		
			A B G A B P A		
7	OPEN COVER		A B G A B P A		
			A B G A B P A		
8	REMOVE ORIGINAL		A B G A B P A		
			A B G A B P A		
9	CLOSE COVER		A B G A B P A		
			A B G A B P A		
10	PICK-UP COPY, RETURN TO DESK AND PLACE	2	(A_1) B_0 G_1 M_3 X_0 I_0 A_0		40
		4	A_0 B_0 G_0 M_3 X_0 I_0 A_0		30
	ORIGINAL AND COPY ASIDE	5	A_1 B_0 G_1 M_1 X_0 I_0 A_0		30
		6	A_1 B_0 G_1 M_1 X_{16} I_0 A_0		190
		7	$(A_1$ B_0 $G_1)$ M_3 X_0 I_0 A_0		30
		9	A_0 B_0 G_0 M_3 X_0 I_0 A_0		30
			A B G M X I A		
			A B G M X I A		
			A B G A B P A B P A		
			A B G A B P A B P A		
			A B G A B P A B P A		
			A B G A B P A B P A		
			A B G A B P A B P A		
			A B G A B P A B P A		
			A B G A B P A B P A		
			A B G A B P A B P A		
			A B G A B P A B P A		
			A B G A B P A B P A		
			A B G A B P A B P A		
			A B G A B P A B P A		
			A B G A B P A B P A		
TIME = .68	minutes (min.)				1140

Figure 3.29 Original analysis.

	MOST-calculation			Code	
m▷				$8\,0\,9\,0\,0\,1\,3\,2\,0\frac{2}{1}$	
	Area CLERICAL			Date 10/15/78	
				Sign. WMY	
				Page 1 / 1	

Activity COPY ONE ORIGINAL AT PHOTOCOPY MACHINE

~~TWELVE COPIES~~

Conditions ~~ONE COPY~~ PRODUCED MACHINE MODEL NO. 12345

No.	Method	No.	Sequence Model	Fr	TMU
1	PICK-UP ORIGINAL AND MOVE TO MACHINE	1	$A_1\ B_{10}\ G_1\ A_{24}^{12}\ B_0\ P_0\ A_0$		~~360~~ 212
		3	$A_0\ B_0\ G_0\ (A_1)\ B_0\ P_3\ A_0$		30
2	OPEN COVER AT MACHINE	8	$A_1\ B_0\ G_1\ A_1\ B_0\ P_0\ A_0$		30
		10	$A_1\ B_0\ G_1\ A_{24}^{10}\ B_{10}\ P_1\ A_0$		~~270~~ 230
3	PLACE ORIGINAL ON GLASS		A B G A B P A		
			A B G A B P A		
4	CLOSE COVER		A B G A B P A		
			A B G A B P A		
5	SET ~~DIAL~~ FOR ~~1 COPY~~ DIALS 12 COPIES		A B G A B P A		
			A B G A B P A		
6	PUSH BUTTON TO START COPYING - PROCESS TIME $\frac{9}{8}$ SEC.		A B G A B P A		
			A B G A B P A		
7	OPEN COVER		A B G A B P A		
			A B G A B P A		
8	REMOVE ORIGINAL		A B G A B P A		
			A B G A B P A		
9	CLOSE COVER		A B G A B P A		
			A B G A B P A		
10	PICK-UP ~~COPY~~ COPIES, RETURN TO DESK AND PLACE	2	$(A_1)\ B_0\ G_1\ M_3\ X_0\ I_0\ A_0$		40
		4	$A_0\ B_0\ G_0\ M_3\ X_0\ I_0\ A_0$		30
	ORIGINAL AND ~~COPY~~ COPIES ASIDE	5	$A_1\ B_0\ G_1\ M_1\ X_0\ I_0\ A_0$	2	~~30~~ 60
		6	$A_1\ B_0\ G_1\ M_1\ X_{15}^{10}\ I_0\ A_0$		~~100~~ 270
9'	SET DIALS BACK TO ZERO	7	$(A_1\ B_0\ G_1)\ M_3\ X_0\ I_0\ A_0$		30
		9	$A_0\ B_0\ G_0\ M_3\ X_0\ I_0\ A_0$		30
		9'	$A_1\ B_0\ G_1\ M_1\ X_0\ I_0\ A_0$	2	60
			A B G M X I A		
			A B G A B P A B P A		
			A B G A B P A B P A		
			A B G A B P A B P A		
			A B G A B P A B P A		
			A B G A B P A B P A		
			A B G A B P A B P A		
			A B G A B P A B P A		
			A B G A B P A B P A		
			A B G A B P A B P A		
			A B G A B P A B P A		
			A B G A B P A B P A		
			A B G A B P A B P A		
			A B G A B P A B P A		

TIME = ~~.69~~ .62 ~~16~~ ──────── minutes min. ~~1260~~ ~~1150~~ 1030

Figure 3.30 Updated analysis, by hand.

	MOST-calculation		Code $\;$ $8,0,9\,\vert\,0,0,1,4\,\vert\,2\,\vert\,0,2$
≫			Date $\quad$ 11/20/78
	Area $\quad$ CLERICAL		Sign $\quad$ AB
			Page $\quad$ 1 / 1

Activity $\quad$ COPY ONE ORIGINAL AT PHOTOCOPY MACHINE

Conditions $\quad$ TWELVE COPIES PRODUCED, MACHINE MODEL NO. 12345

No.	Method	No.	Sequence Model	Fr	TMU
1	PICK-UP ORIGINAL AND MOVE TO MACHINE	1	$A_1\ B_{10}\ G_1\ A_{10}\ B_0\ P_0\ A_0$		220
		3	$A_0\ B_0\ G_0\ \widehat{A_1}\ B_0\ P_3\ A_0$		30
2	OPEN COVER AT MACHINE	8	$A_1\ B_0\ G_1\ A_1\ B_0\ P_0\ A_0$		30
		11	$A_1\ B_0\ G_1\ A_{10}\ B_{10}\ P_1\ A_0$		230
3	PLACE ORIGINAL ON GLASS		A $\;$ B $\;$ G $\;$ A $\;$ B $\;$ P $\;$ A		
			A $\;$ B $\;$ G $\;$ A $\;$ B $\;$ P $\;$ A		
4	CLOSE COVER		A $\;$ B $\;$ G $\;$ A $\;$ B $\;$ P $\;$ A		
			A $\;$ B $\;$ G $\;$ A $\;$ B $\;$ P $\;$ A		
5	SET DIALS FOR 12 COPIES		A $\;$ B $\;$ G $\;$ A $\;$ B $\;$ P $\;$ A		
			A $\;$ B $\;$ G $\;$ A $\;$ B $\;$ P $\;$ A		
6	PUSH BUTTON TO START COPYING - PROCESS TIME 9 SEC.		A $\;$ B $\;$ G $\;$ A $\;$ B $\;$ P $\;$ A		
			A $\;$ B $\;$ G $\;$ A $\;$ B $\;$ P $\;$ A		
7	OPEN COVER		A $\;$ B $\;$ G $\;$ A $\;$ B $\;$ P $\;$ A		
			A $\;$ B $\;$ G $\;$ A $\;$ B $\;$ P $\;$ A		
8	REMOVE ORIGINAL		A $\;$ B $\;$ G $\;$ A $\;$ B $\;$ P $\;$ A		
			A $\;$ B $\;$ G $\;$ A $\;$ B $\;$ P $\;$ A		
9	CLOSE COVER		A $\;$ B $\;$ G $\;$ A $\;$ B $\;$ P $\;$ A		
		2	$\widehat{A_1}\ B_0\ G_1\ M_3\ X_0\ I_0\ A_0$		40
10	SET DIALS BACK TO ZERO	4	$A_0\ B_0\ G_0\ M_3\ X_0\ I_0\ A_0$		30
		5	$A_1\ B_0\ G_1\ M_1\ X_0\ I_0\ A_0$	2	60
11	PICK-UP COPIES, RETURN TO DESK AND PLACE	6	$A_1\ B_0\ G_1\ M_1\ X_{24}\ I_0\ A_0$		270
		7	$\widehat{A_1}\ B_0\ \widehat{G_1}\ M_3\ X_0\ I_0\ A_0$		30
	ORIGINAL AND COPIES ASIDE	9	$A_0\ B_0\ G_0\ M_3\ X_0\ I_0\ A_0$		30
		10	$A_1\ B_0\ G_1\ M_1\ X_0\ I_0\ A_0$	2	60
			A $\;$ B $\;$ G $\;$ M $\;$ X $\;$ I $\;$ A		
			A B G A B P $\;$ A B P A		
			A B G A B P $\;$ A B P A		
			A B G A B P $\;$ A B P A		
			A B G A B P $\;$ A B P A		
			A B G A B P $\;$ A B P A		
			A B G A B P $\;$ A B P A		
			A B G A B P $\;$ A B P A		
			A B G A B P $\;$ A B P A		
			A B G A B P $\;$ A B P A		
			A B G A B P $\;$ A B P A		
			A B G A B P $\;$ A B P A		
			A B G A B P $\;$ A B P A		
			A B G A B P $\;$ A B P A		
			A B G A B P $\;$ A B P A		
	TIME = .62 $\qquad$ minutes (min.)				1030

Figure 3.31 Final "smooth" copy of the updated analysis.

data bank behind the original analysis. The updating of a Basic MOST calculation is then complete.

The ease with which Basic MOST calculations can be updated and/or new methods determined is one of the greatest assets of the MOST Work Measurement Technique. It makes simulation and comparison easy and the concept of a data bank of sharable data units a reality.

Method Levels and Simultaneous Motions

Method level refers to the degree of coordination between the right and left hands during two-handed work. We say that a *high method level* exists when a large percentage of manual and body motions are performed simultaneously. Obviously it is desirable to have as much work as possible performed at high method levels because of the reduction in time for accomplishing a given amount of work.

The method level at which an activity is performed is determined by its occurrence frequency, that is, the practice opportunity available to the operator. The more often the activity occurs, the greater the operator's opportunity to improve the method level. If the activity is seldom performed, the short learning period prevents any development of simultaneous skills. For example, with mass production and large batch size operations, which allow ample training and practice opportunity, one would expect to find operators using a high percentage of simultaneous motions. On the other hand, job shop and setup activities will most likely be performed with few simultaneous motions. Therefore, method level depends to a large extent on the type of work being performed. Three different method levels are defined for the application of Basic MOST.

1. *High method level* includes all possible simultaneous motions with the right and left hands. The analysis and time for the limiting (longest) hand is allowed. If the analysis for the other hand is shown, the time value must be circled, indicating that this value is not included in the total. The following activity occurs simultaneously with and is "limited out" by another activity:

A_1 B_0 G_1 A_1 B_0 P_1 A_0 (40)   Time: 0 TMU

In this case, the time for the sequence in the right column is circled to indicate that it is not included in the total.

2. *Low method level* involves no simultaneous motions. The analysis and time for both hands must be allowed:

RH	A_1	B_0	G_1	A_1	B_0	P_1	A_0	40 TMU
LH	A_1	B_0	G_1	A_1	B_0	P_1	A_0	40 TMU
								80 TMU

3. *Intermediate method level* refers to a method performed partially with simultaneous motions. For example, the action distance "within reach" to two objects may be performed simultaneously with both hands, but gaining control and placing two objects simultaneously may not be possible. In the Basic MOST analysis, the appropriate parameter(s) are circled to indicate that they are performed simultaneously and should be excluded from the sequence model time calculation. In the following activity, a portion of the sequence model (the reach to get the object) is performed simultaneously with another activity:

RH	A_1	B_0	G_1	A_1	B_0	P_1	A_0	40 TMU
LH	(A_1)	B_0	G_1	A_1	B_0	P_1	A_0	30 TMU
								70 TMU

In this case, the circled portion of the sequence model is not included in the time calculation because it is "limited" by another activity.

Examples

The activity "place two pins in assembly" is analyzed using three different method levels. A pin is picked up by each hand and placed in the assembly with adjustments.

1. *High method level:* both hands work simultaneously.

RH	A_1	B_0	G_1	A_1	B_0	P_3	A_0	60
LH	A_1	B_0	G_1	A_1	B_0	P_3	A_0	(60)
								60 TMU

2. *Low method level:* both hands work separately.

RH	A_1	B_0	G_1	A_1	B_0	P_3	A_0	60
LH	A_1	B_0	G_1	A_1	B_0	P_3	A_0	60
								120 TMU

3. *Intermediate method level:* only the "Get phase" occurs simultaneously.

RH	A_1	B_0	G_1	A_1	B_0	P_3	A_0	60
LH	$(A_1$	B_0	$G_1)$	A_1	B_0	P_3	A_0	40
								100 TMU

As the example shows, there is a wide variation in the total time for each method level; therefore, one of the analyst's most important considerations in a work measurement situation is to represent the *correct method level* in the analysis. This relationship between method and standard (time) should always be emphasized in Basic MOST analysis work and should be based on the theory that the greater the practice opportunity for the operator, the higher the method level.

Development of Elements (Index Values) for Special Tools or Situations

Another important feature of the Basic MOST system is the provision for developing special elements for activities unique to local conditions.

Special Tools

The Tool Use data cards were designed to provide accurate parameter values for a wide range of common tools found throughout industry. Although the majority of tools can be analyzed using the data from Figures 3.19 and 3.20 (either directly or by comparison), special tools used in an operation may not be covered by any of these Tool Use categories. If the tool is infrequently used, the basic sequence models (General and Controlled Move) can, of course, be used to analyze its use, but if the tool is frequently used, it may be desirable to develop special tool use parameters specifically for the tool.

Three alternatives are available to the analyst for describing the use of those tools *not found* in the Tool Use tables:

1. Identify the method employed, compare it with existing data, and select an appropriate index value from a similar Tool Use method. (It is always the *method of using a tool,* not the name of the tool, that determines the parameter value.)
2. Make a detailed Basic MOST analysis using a combination of General and Controlled Move Sequences.
3. For frequently used tools, develop a special parameter with index values based on a Mini MOST, MTM-1, MTM-2, or time study analysis.

Alternative 1: Compare Method and Use Existing Data Frequently, a special tool will resemble another tool in appearance as well as the method employed. A corkscrew, for example, which requires the use of wrist actions, also looks very much like a small T-wrench. Therefore, as this alternative suggests, the activity to "turn" a corkscrew into a cork (e.g., with six wrist actions) can be analyzed using the Fasten/Loosen data for a small T-wrench:

$$A_1 \quad B_0 \quad G_1 \quad A_1 \quad B_0 \quad P_3 \quad F_{16} \quad A_0 \quad B_0 \quad P_0 \quad A_0$$
$$(1 + 1 + 1 + 3 + 16) \times 10 = 220 \text{ TMU}$$

Since light pressure is needed to start the corkscrew, a P_3 is required for the tool placement. The removal of the cork is then described using the General Move Sequence. (Notice the G_3 for "disengage.")

$$A_0 \quad B_0 \quad G_3 \quad A_1 \quad B_0 \quad P_1 \quad A_0$$
$$(3 + 1 + 1) \times 10 = 50 \text{ TMU}$$

(The removal of the cork from the corkscrew will require another Tool Use Sequence Model.)

Alternative 2: Analyze the Method Using General and Controlled Move Sequences If an appropriate index value is not found after comparing a special tool method with the existing data, the activity can be analyzed using parameters from General and Controlled Move Sequences. For example, the method of using a crank-operated hand drill does not seem to fit any of the tools listed in Figure 3.19 or 3.20. However, a detailed Basic MOST analysis can be made by breaking down the complete drilling activity into its basic subactivities. The analysis for using a hand drill to make a hole in a wooden block with eight revolutions of the crank handle would require three sequence models as follows:

1. Get and place hand drill to a mark on the block:

$A_1 \quad B_0 \quad G_1 \quad A_1 \quad B_0 \quad P_3 \quad A_0$

$(1 + 1 + 1 + 3) \times 10 = 60$ TMU

2. Get hold of handle and drill hole with eight cranking actions:

$A_1 \quad B_0 \quad G_1 \quad M_{16} \quad X_0 \quad I_0 \quad A_0$

$(1 + 1 + 16) \times 10 = 180$ TMU

3. Remove and set hand drill aside:

$A_0 \quad B_0 \quad G_3 \quad A_1 \quad B_0 \quad P_1 \quad A_0$

$(3 + 1 + 1) \times 10 = 60$ TMU

Note: This alternative should be used for those tools *infrequently found* in use because of the analysis detail involved.

Alternative 3: Develop Element(s) (Index Values) for the Tool One of the most useful features of the MOST Work Measurement Technique is the provision for the development of index values for special parameters. This feature is particularly applicable when a *frequently used* tool (or applicable method) is not found in the Tool Use data. The index value determination procedure first requires that the tool use method be analyzed using Mini MOST, MTM-1, MTM-2, or time study. Index values are then assigned to the element according to the Basic MOST time interval table for the tool.

Consider, for example, an assembly operation in which a spiral screwdriver is frequently used. The MTM-2 analysis for this activity might be:

Analysis	TMU	Description
GW6	3	Accumulate muscle tension (6 pounds)
PA6	6	Power stroke
PW10	1	With 6-pound resistance
PA6	6	Return stroke
	16	TMU per tool action

With an additional 14 TMU (MTM-2, apply pressure) for final tightening, the tool use parameter for the spiral screwdriver can be expressed algebraically:

$t = 16N + 14$

where: t = time per tool action in TMU
                N = number of tool actions

This formula, representing the spiral screwdriver parameter, can be completed for various numbers of tool actions N and converted to the proper Basic MOST index values using the time intervals from Appendix A, Figure A.3.

Example: Using the formula, the time value for one tool action (30 TMU) falls within the interval between 18 and 42 TMU, which corresponds to the index number 3. This can be calculated individually for N actions. A less tedious way is to complete the formula for three separate values for N (e.g., $N = 1$, $N = 5$, $N = 11$) and to plot these values on an Index Value Determination Form (Fig. 3.32).

Steps to develop elements (index values) for the spiral screwdriver example using the Index Value Determination Form are as follows:

1. Perform Mini MOST, MTM-1 or MTM-2 analysis.
2. Develop algebraic formula: $t = 16N + 14$.
3. Choose three separate values for N and work the formula.

     $t_1 = 16(1) + 14 = 30$ TMU
     $t_2 = 16(5) + 14 = 94$ TMU
     $t_3 = 16(11) + 14 = 190$ TMU

4. Using an Index Value Determination Form, identify and supply the number of actions to the x axis of the form (Fig. 3.32).
5. Plot the TMU values calculated in step 3. (Use the TMU or seconds scale on the form; Fig. 3.32).
6. Connect the points plotted with a straight line. *Note:* Should the line curve or veer sharply, further detailed analysis should be performed to determine the variable influencing the shape of the line (Fig. 3.32).
7. Where the plotted line crosses one of the horizontal lines printed on the form (the upper limit for each index range), draw a vertical line. This vertical line divides the number of tool actions into various index ranges (Fig. 3.31). A simple matter of placing these values in tabular form results in the development of a supplementary index value table for a spiral screwdriver (Fig. 3.33).
8. Additional values can always be obtained by working the formula and assigning the index value from Figure A.2 of Appendix A.

If the spiral screwdriver were used to fasten a screw with ten tool actions, the Basic MOST analyst could now use one Tool Use Sequence Model and the table (Figure 3.33) that has been developed. The analysis would appear as

A_1 B_0 G_1 A_1 B_0 P_3 F_{16} A_1 B_0 P_1 A_0

$(1 + 1 + 1 + 3 + 16 + 1 + 1) \times 10 = 240$ TMU

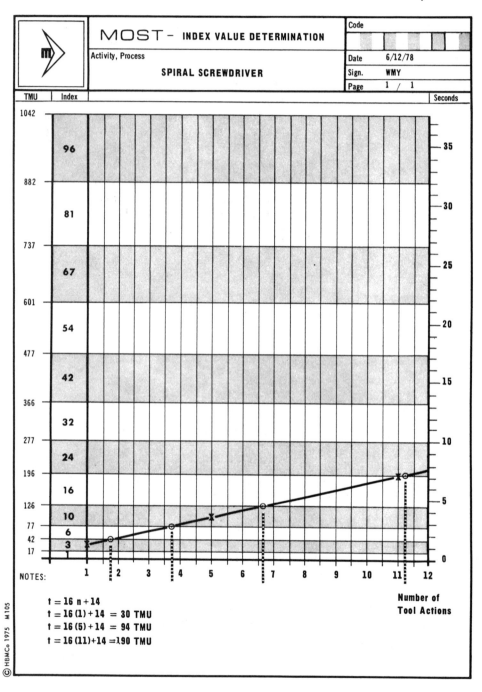

Figure 3.32 Index value determination form.

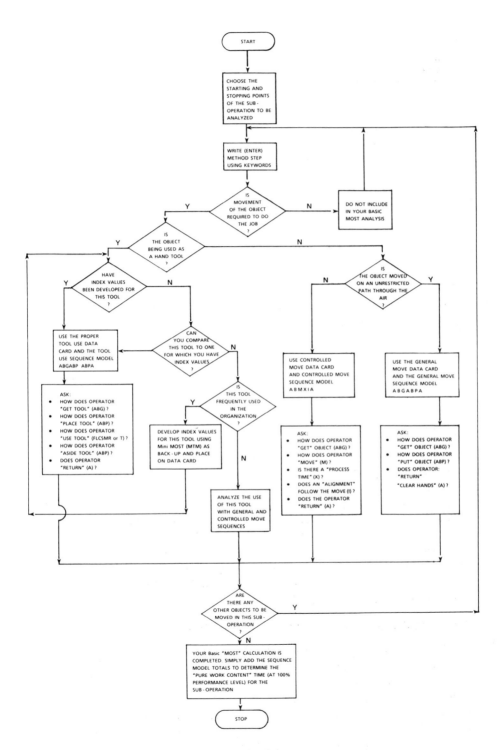

Figure 3.34 Basic MOST Analysis decision diagram.

SPIRAL SCREWDRIVER	
INDEX VALUE	NUMBER OF TOOL ACTIONS
F_1	-
F_3	1
F_6	3
F_{10}	6
F_{16}	11

Figure 3.33 Supplementary index values for a spiral screwdriver. Values are read "up to and including."

The preceding situation dealt with the development of index values for a spiral screwdriver based on a detailed MTM-2 backup analysis. Backup for index values can also be developed using time study. Situations that lend themselves to time study backup analyses are such activities as polishing, grinding, painting, gluing, or any other activity involving a short process time (i.e., using power tools or office machines). Index values should be developed for these situations when they occur frequently enough in the operation of a company or plant to justify the time taken to develop such values and when consistency of application is required.

To determine index values using time study, the unit of the variable should be specified, the proper time studies performed, and the results plotted on the Index Value Determination Form. For example, the times for polishing might be in seconds per square foot; this would be plotted, and a supplementary data table for polishing per square foot would be developed. To use the data, values from this table could then be applied to the Tool Use Sequence Model and placed under the Surface Treat (S) parameter.

Basic MOST Analysis Decision Diagram

To aid the MOST analyst, a Basic MOST Analysis decision diagram is provided (see Fig. 3.34). This diagram will lead the analyst through all the basic thought processes and decisions that need to be considered in order to arrive at a thorough and consistently applied Basic MOST analysis. In the diagram, the boxes indicate a process or operation and the diamonds indicate that a binary decision is required. Simply follow the process and your decisions through the diagram to properly complete an analysis of a suboperation. *Note:* The decision diagram does not include the use of the Manual Crane Sequence.

4

The Mini MOST System

The development project to create MOST sequence models and backup data for the analysis of highly repetitive operations was guided by the following goal:

- To develop a version of MOST Work Measurement Systems based on the MOST concept and format that can be applied to *identical cycles* (normally of short duration) with a high level of accuracy.

As indicated in a previous chapter, Mini MOST was developed to satisfy the more rigorous accuracy requirements associated with short-cycle and highly repetitive operations. Most often such operations are performed following an *identical* or almost identical motion pattern from cycle to cycle. Mini MOST is more detailed and takes more time to use than Basic MOST and should therefore be applied only to operations and activities that have been determined to be short-cycled and identically repeated. Guidelines for when to select Mini MOST as the appropriate measurement tool are contained in Chapter 2.

The Sequence Models

Following the basic philosophy of Basic MOST Work Measurement Systems, Mini MOST was designed to replace the more "detailed" systems, such as MTM-1 and Work Factor. It consists of two sequence models, the *General Move*

    A   B   G   A   B   P   A

and the *Controlled Move*

    A   B   G   M   X   I   A

with the parameters indexed according to the basic scale of 1, 3, 6, 10, 16, 24, etc., with a multiplier for the index numbers of one (1); that is, each number directly represents the time in TMU (Time Measurement Units). Mini MOST construction results in a consistent *theoretical* balance time of 501 TMU, which was calculated for all elements. MTM-1 backup data supports all entries on the data cards, and each such element is designed to an accuracy of ±5% with a 95% confidence level. (See Appendix A for further discussion on balance time.) For instance, the Gain Control value for Transfer was developed by considering the hand reaching to an object in the other hand. The MTM backup shows

R1A   2.5
G3   5.6   G3
        ───
        8.1

The time for holding the receiving hand stationary and moving the object to it is also 8.1 TMU (M1A + G3). The time of 8.1 TMU falls in the interval of 7.68–12.62. Therefore, an index 10 is used for "Transfer grasp" in Mini MOST.

The Mini MOST Analysis

Since the time interval represented by each index number is very small, Mini MOST provides a highly detailed system for measuring work while maintaining many of the benefits of the Basic MOST Work Measurement Technique. The desire to analyze very short cycle identical motion patterns has brought us to a level of detail somewhere between MTM-1 and Basic MOST. As a result, analysts must look at the work to be measured differently. When using the Mini MOST System, it is the task of every analyst to dissect the A_1 (Within Reach) of the Basic MOST sequence models and to ascertain more precisely the distance the hand moved in inches (cm) and/or whether it was rotated during the action. Analysts must now take the G_1 (Gain Control of light object) and determine the type of grasp or grasps employed and the physical surroundings in which the grasp took place. An action that might be analyzed with one parameter in the Basic MOST sequence models may well appear as one or two complete sequence models in Mini MOST.

The analyst's job becomes more difficult as the cycle gets shorter and the skill level of the operator increases. The sequence models for the *identical* cycles described in this chapter are designed to make the analyst's job as easy as possible while retaining the level of detail demanded by the work being measured.

The analyses represented in Figures 4.1, 4.2, and 4.3 provide a comparison of Basic MOST and Mini MOST (two alternative forms). The same operation is analyzed with Basic MOST and Mini MOST. Mini MOST analysis requires greater detail than Basic MOST analysis. Since there is no Tool Use Sequence in

MOST-calculation

Code | | | | | | | | | |

Date: 2/15/79
Sign.: J.T.B.
Page: 1 / 1

P.C. BOARD ASSEMBLY

Activity: STAKE 6 TERMINALS TO P.C. BOARD ON ARBOR PRESS

Conditions:

No.	Method	No.	Sequence Model	Fr	TMU
		1	$A_1 B_0 G_1 A_1 B_0 P_1 A_0$		40
1	MOVE P.C. BOARD TO PRESS	2	$A_1 B_0 G_1 A_1 B_0 P_3 A_0$	6	360
			A B G A B P A		
2	GET TERMINAL AND INSERT IN		A B G A B P A		
	UPPER PRESS FIXTURE		A B G A B P A		
			A B G A B P A		
3	GET PRESS HANDLE AND lower		A B G A B P A		
	PIN NEAR BOARD		A B G A B P A		
			A B G A B P A		
4	MOVE BOARD SLOWLY INTO		A B G A B P A		
	POSITION TO RECEIVE PIN		A B G A B P A		
			A B G A B P A		
5	PRESS IN PIN		A B G A B P A		
			A B G A B P A		
6	RAISE PRESS HANDLE		A B G A B P A		
		3	$A_1 B_0 G_1 M_1 X_0 I_0 A_0$	6	180
7	PICK UP P.C. BOARD, INSPECT	4	$A_0 B_0 G_0 M_3 X_0 I_0 A_0$	6	180
		5	$A_0 B_0 G_0 M_3 X_0 I_0 A_0$	6	180
	AND ASIDE	6	$A_0 B_0 G_0 M_1 X_0 I_0 A_0$	6	60
			A B G M X I A		
			A B G M X I A		
			A B G M X I A		
		7	$A_0 B_0 G_0 A_1 B_0 P_0 T_6 A_1 B_0 P_1 A_0$		90
			A B G A B P A B P A		
			A B G A B P A B P A		
			A B G A B P A B P A		
			A B G A B P A B P A		
			A B G A B P A B P A		
			A B G A B P A B P A		
			A B G A B P A B P A		
			A B G A B P A B P A		
			A B G A B P A B P A		
			A B G A B P A B P A		

TIME =   milihours (mh.)/minutes (min.)   1090

Figure 4.1 Basic MOST calculation form.

Mini MOST® SYSTEMS CALCULATION 1X

| Area | P.C. BOARD ASSEMBLY | | | | | | | | | Date 8/81 | Sign JTB | Page 1/1 |

Operation: STAKE 6 TERMINALS TO P.C. BOARD ON ARBOR PRESS

Title | Time with TMU 1053

Conditions | Per BOARD

STEP	LEFT HAND METHOD DESCRIPTION	SEQUENCE MODEL	FR.	SIMO KEY	TMU	FR.	SEQUENCE MODEL	RIGHT HAND METHOD DESCRIPTION	STEP
1	Slide P.C. Board from Stack	A B G A B P A — A₁₀ B₀ G₃ M₆ X₀ I₀ A₀			19		A B G A B P A — A B G M X I A		
2	Control P.C. Board, set on Press and Retain	A₀ B₀ G₆ A₁₀ B₀ P₃ A₀ — A B G M X I A			19		A B G A B P A — A B G M X I A		
3	Control P.C. Board to Hold	A₀ B₀ G₆ A₀ B₀ P₀ A₀ — A B G M X I A			6		A B G A B P A — A B G M X I A		
4		A B G A B P A — A B G M X I A			432	6	A₁₆ B₀ G₁₆ A₁₆ B₀ P₂₄ A₀ — A B G M X I A	Select (small) terminal & posi. to fix. (acc. ins.)	4
5		A B G A B P A — A B G M X I A			192	6	A B G A B P A — A₁₆ B₀ G₆ M₁₀ X₀ I A	Operate Press Handle to lower pin near board	5
6	Align Board to receive Pin (accurate)	A₀ B₀ G₀ A₆ B₀ P₁₀ A₀	6		96		A B G A B P A — A B G M X I A		6
7		A B G A B P A — A B G M X I A			156	6	A₀ B₀ G₀ M₁₀₊₁₆₀ X₀ I₀ A₀	Operate Handle 6 inches and seat pin	7
8		A B G A B P A — A B G M X I A			60	6	A₀ B₀ G₀ M₁₀ X₀ I₀ A₀	Raise Press Handle. (10 inches)	8
9	Lift Board	A₀ B₀ G₀ A₆ B₀ P₀ A₀ — A B G M X I A			6		A B G A B P A — A B G M X I A		
10	Check 6 Pins	A₀ B₀ G₀ M₀ X₀ I₆ A₀	6		36		A B G A B P A — A B G M X I A		
11	Set Board on Stack and Retain	A₀ B₀ G₀ A₆ B₀ P₃ A₀ — A B G M X I A			19		A B G A B P A — A B G M X I A		
12	Fingers out and slide Board in place.	A₀ B₀ G₆ M₆ X₀ I₀ A₀			12		A B G A B P A — A B G M X I A		
Total TMU					1053			Code	

Figure 4.2   Mini MOST calculation form, alternative 1.

Mini MOST, an analysis using one sequence model in Basic MOST may require several sequence models in Mini MOST.

Mini MOST Parameters

The following list provides a breakdown of the Mini MOST parameters:

A-Action Distance
Includes
    Hand moved through the air
    Object moved through the air
    Turn the hand in the air (loaded or empty)
    Leg + foot motions, walk (one or two steps)

				Code							

Mini MOST® SYSTEMS CALCULATION 1X

Area: P.C. BOARD ASSEMBLY

Operation: STAKE 6 TERMINALS TO P.C. BOARD ON ARBOR PRESS   Date 8/81   Sign JTB   Page 1/1

Title: STAKE TERMINALS TO BOARD   TMU 1053

Conditions   Per BOARD

No.	H	Method Description	Simo To	Sequence							Fr	TMU
1	L	SLIDE P.C. BOARD FROM STACK		A10	B0	G3	M6	X0	I0	A0		19
2	L	CONTROL P.C. BOARD, SET ON PRESS AND RETAIN		A0	B0	G6	A10 B0 P3			A0		19
3	L	CONTROL P.C. BOARD TO HOLD		A0	B0	G6	A0 B0 P0			A0		6
4	R	SELECT (small) TERMINAL AND POSITION TO FIXTURE (ACCURATE INSERT)		A16	B0	G16	A16 B0 P24			A0	6	432
5	R	OPERATE. PRESS HANDLE TO lower PIN NEAR. BOARD		A16	B0	G6	M16	X0	I0	A0	6	192
6	L	ALIGN BOARD TO RECEIVE. PIN (ACCURATE.)		A0	B0	G0	M6	X0	I10	A0	6	96
7	R	OPERATE. HANDLE 6 INCHES AND SEAT PIN		A0	B0	G0	M10+16	X0	I0	A0	6	156
8	R	RAISE. PRESS HANDLE 10 inches		A0	B0	G0	M10	X0	I0	A0	6	60
9	L	LIFT BOARD		A0	B0	G0	A6 B0 P0			A0		6
10	L	CHECK 6 PINS		A0	B0	G0	M0	X0	I6	A0	6	36
11	L	SET BOARD ON STACK AND RETAIN		A0	B0	G0	A16 B0 P3			A0		19
12	L	REGRASP AND SLIDE BOARD IN PLACE.		A0	B0	G6	M6	X0	I0	A0		12

ACTION DISTANCE A	BODY MOTION B	GAIN CONTROL G	PLACE OBJECT P	MOVE OBJECT CONTROLLED M	PROCESS TIME X	ALIGN OBJECT CONTROLLED I	Total TMU
							1053

©HBMCo 1980

Figure 4.3 Mini MOST calculation form, alternative 2.

Selection based on
> Distance the hand moves to a fixed location
> Distance the hand moves to any other location (empty or loaded)
> Distance leg or foot moves
> Steps taken
> Degrees rotated (turn)

B-Body Motion

Includes
> Vertical movement—Bend or arise
> Eye Travel

Selection based on
> Bend or arise
> Eye action

G-Gain Control

Includes
> One-inch reach
> Making contact or closing hand
> Differential for care in reaching
> Differential for accelerating and decelerating the hand
> Disengage and weight considerations
> Change in control of an object already in hand

Selection based on
> Type and size of object grasped
> Manner in which object is grasped
> Weight

P-Placement

Includes
> One-inch move
> The position variables (fit, orientation, handling, insertion)
> Differential care in moving object
> Differential acceleration and deceleration
> Exertion of force
> Relinquish control

Selection based on
> Whether hand stops
> Retain or release
> Precision required
>> Measured tolerance
>> Measured insertion

M-Move Controlled

Includes
> Rotate controlled object
> Exert force

    Crank
    Move in controlled path
    Leg and foot motions for pedals
    Release
  Selection based on
    Degrees turned
    Number of revolutions cranked
    Distance moved

X-Process Time
  Includes machine process times
  Selection based on actual clock or calculated time of cycle

I-Align
  Includes
    Alignment
    Eye use times
    Differential for care during moving
  Selection based on
    Type of alignment observed
    Points checked

A. The General Move Sequence

The *General Move Sequence* deals with the spatial displacement of one or several objects. Under manual control, the object(s) follows an unrestricted path through the air. If the object(s) are in contact with, or restrained in any way by, another object during the move, the General Move Sequence is not applicable.

Characteristically, General Move follows a sequence of subactivities identified by the following steps:

1. *Reach* with one or two hands a distance to the object, either directly or in conjunction with body motions.
2. *Gain* manual *control* of the object.
3. *Move* the object a distance to the point of placement, either directly or in conjunction with body motions.
4. *Place* the object in a temporary or final position.
5. *Return* to workplace or original location.

These five subactivities form the basis for the activity sequence describing the manual displacement of one or several object(s) freely through space. This sequence describes the manual events that can occur when moving an object freely through the air and is therefore, as in the Basic MOST system, known as a *sequence model.* The major function of the sequence model is to guide the attention of the analyst through an operation, thereby adding the dimension of having a preprinted and standardized analysis format. The existence of the sequence model provides for increased analyst consistency and reduced sub-activity omission.

The Sequence Model

The sequence model takes the form of a series of letters representing each of the various subactivities (called parameters) of the General Move Activity Sequence. With an additional parameter for body motions, the General Move Sequence follows the previous five-step pattern:

A   B   G   A   B   P   A

where: A = Action distance
         B = Body motion
         G = Gain control
         P = Placement

Parameter Definitions

A   Action Distance

This parameter covers all spatial movement or actions of the fingers, hands, and/or feet, either loaded or unloaded. Any control of these actions by the surroundings requires the use of other parameters.

B   Body Motion

This parameter is used to specify either vertical (up-and-down) motions of the body including body movements necessary to overcome an obstruction or impairment. The movement of the head to exercise eye travel is also part of the Body Motion parameter.

G   Gain Control

This parameter covers all manual motions (mainly by finger, hand, or foot) employed to obtain complete manual control of an object or objects. The G parameter can include one or several short motions whose objective is to gain full control or the object(s) before moving it to another location.

P   Placement

This parameter is used to analyze actions at the final stage of the displacement to align, orient, and/or engage the object(s) with another object or objects and subsequently relinquish control of the object(s).

Phases of the Sequence Model

The displacement of an object or objects through space occurs in three distinct phases, as shown by the following General Move Sequence breakdown.

Get		Put		Return
A B G	A B P	A

The first phase, referred to as *Get,* describes the actions to reach the object, with body motions (if necessary), and to gain control of the object. The A parameter indicates the distance the hand or body travels in order to reach the object(s); the B indicates the need for any body motion during this action. The degree of difficulty encountered in gaining control of the object(s) is described by the G parameter.

The *Put* phase of the sequence model describes the actions to move object(s) to another location. As before, the A and B parameters indicate the distance the hand or body travels with the object(s) and the need for any body motions during the move before the placement of the object(s) has been accomplished. The manner in which the object or objects are placed is described by the P parameter.

The third phase simply indicates a "forced" return or covers clearing a hand out of the way to permit the next activity. Normally "return" of the hand or fingers is accounted for as the first Action Distance of a subsequent sequence model.

The MOST analyst should strictly adhere to the three-phase breakdown of the General Move Sequence Model. Such adherence provides consistency in application and ease in communication. To acquire such consistency, the analyst should always ask these questions prior to indexing a sequence model:

1. What is the object (or objects) being moved?
2. How is it moved? (Determine the appropriate sequence model.)
3. Then, assuming the sequence model is a General Move, what did the operator do to Get the object? (Determine the index values for A, B, and G—first phase.)
4. What did the operator do to Put the object? (Determine the index values for A, B, and P—second phase.)
5. Did the operator use the Return? (Determine the final A index—third phase.)

Parameter Indexing

For manual application of Mini MOST, indexing each parameter of the General Move Sequence Model is accomplished by observing or visualizing the operator's actions during each phase of the activity and selecting the appropriate parameter variants from the data card (Fig. 4.4) that describes those actions. The corresponding index value for each parameter is taken from the extreme left- or right-hand column of the data card and is written just below and to the right of the sequence model parameter, for example, A_3.

For computer application of Mini MOST, MOST Computer Systems automatically determines the index values based on the method description entered in keyword language. (See Method Descriptions in Keyword Language in Chapter 3, Sec. A for an explanation of this technique.) In the text that follows, the Mini MOST keywords used for each parameter variant are printed in capital letters, as well as examples of method descriptions in keyword language as they appear at the end of the sections covering the General and Controlled Moves.

Index Value Definitions

Action Distance covers all spatial movements or actions of the hand or fingers and of the foot or leg. Any control of these actions by the surroundings requires the use of another parameter. Action Distance also includes horizontal transportation of the body up to two steps.

Action Distance (A)

The value for a hand Action Distance is determined by the total net distance (inches or centimeters) the hand travels. This distance must be measured. It is necessary to trace the arc the hand travels in measuring the distance. Do *not* use the straight-line distance, since the hand follows an arc. The keyword designation for all hand and finger distances greater than 1 inch (2.5 cm) is a whole number followed by the keyword INCHES (CM). With MOST Computer Systems, the number of inches does not need to be included in the method description if Action Distances were previously entered in the work area data.

A_0 ≤1 inch (2.5 cm)   Any displacement of the fingers and/or hands a distance of up to 1 inch (2.5 cm) will carry a 0 index value. Time for performing these short distances are included within the Gain Control and Placement parameters. Placing the fingers to a key on a keyboard is usually an action distance of 1 inch (2.5 cm) or less.

A_1 ≤2 inches (5 cm)   Any displacement of the fingers and/or hands a distance greater than 1 inch (2 cm) and less than or equal to 2 inches (5 cm).

A_3 ≤4 inches (10 cm)   Any displacement of the fingers and/or hands a distance greater than 2 inches (5 cm), less than or equal to 4 inches (10 cm).

A_6 ≤8 inches (20 cm)   Any displacement of the fingers and/or hands a distance greater than 4 inches (10 cm), less than or equal to 8 inches (20 cm).

A_{10} ≤ 14 inches (35 cm)   Any displacement of the fingers and/or hands a distance greater than 8 inches (20 cm), less than or equal to 14 inches (35 cm).

A_{16} ≤ 24 inches (60 cm)   Any displacement of the hand greater than 14 inches (35 cm), less than or equal to 24 inches (60 cm).

A_{24} > 24 inches (60 cm)   Any displacement of the hand greater than 24 inches (60 cm), but within reach.

Reaching to a Fixed Location or to the Other Hand   FIXED, OTHER-HAND

There is a note on the data card (Fig. 4.4) instructing you to use the next lower index value when the hand reaches a distance of more than 8 inches (20 cm) to an object in a fixed location or in the other hand. These reaches can be accomplished with no visual attention, which significantly reduces the time required for their completion. If, however, the hand must make a sharp change of direction in reaching to the object, the time reduction does not occur and the time in the hand column is allowed without adjustment. Reaches to a fixed location frequently occur when reaching to machine controls, such as buttons or levers. Reaches to the other hand apply to any object held in the hand or on which the hand is resting. This applies, provided the new grasping point is within 3 inches (7.5 cm) of the hand previously in contact with the object.

Occasionally, a reach is observed that does not require visual attention but does not meet the fixed location or other hand location criteria. This may occur when there is unusually high practice in performing the motion. If this is the case, the time should be reduced one index value when the length of the reach is greater than 8 inches (20 cm). When this occurs, make sure that the absence of visual control is possible because of the nature of the work, not due to unusual skill or coordination on the part of the individual operator. It should be noted that the rule for reducing the time applies only to reaches performed by the hand. It does not apply to placing an object or to any action of the foot or leg. This adjustment, when required, is made to the first A index in the sequence model.

The criteria for making this adjustment are as follows:

1. Hand Action Distance
2. Reaching to object or location (first A)
3. No visual control required.
   a. Object in fixed location (practice necessary)
   b. Other hand (object grasped within 3 inches (7.5 cm) of other hand)
4. Net distance exceeds 8 inches (20 cm)

All four of the numbered criteria must be present to adjust the time. Criteria 3a or 3b indicates the absence of visual control.

Mini MOST® System								GENERAL MOVE	
						A B G A B P A			
	A			**B**	**G**		**P**		
	ACTION DISTANCE			BODY MOTION	GAIN CONTROL		PLACEMENT		INDEX X I
	HAND		LEG						
INDEX X I	Degrees	Inches (cm)	Inches (cm)						
0	30	1 (2.5)				SWEEP		DROP, PICK UP, KEEP	0
1	60	2 (5)							1
3	120	4 (10)				CONTACT (hand or foot)		TOSS SET AND RETAIN	3
6	180	8 (20)	8 (20)			GRASP REGRASP		SET ASIDE; SET AND SLIDE; PLACE	6
10		14 (35)	12 (30)	EYE - MOTION		TRANSFER SELECT		POSITION	10
16		24 (60)	18 (45) 1 STEP			DISENGAGE SELECT - SMALL		ORIENT	16
24		>24 (60)	26 (65)						24
32			>26 (65) 2 STEPS	BEND ARISE					32

NOTES:

(1) When hand reaches more than 8 inches (20 cm.) to an object in a fixed location or to the other hand, use the next lower index value

(1) ENW = Effective Weight (max. 2.5 lbs., 1 kg.)

(2) For an ENW of 2.6 - 10.0 lbs. (1 - 5 kgs.) use the next higher index value accept for "Grasp"

(1) For accurate positioning (ACCURATE) or difficult handling (DIFFICULT) or insertion 1/8" - 1" (.3 - 2.5 cm) (ENTER, INSERT) use the next higher index value.

(2) For binding or applying pressure go up two index values per occurence (BIND, DOUBLE BIND).

(3) For insertions > 1" (2.5 cm) use an additional Controlled Move Sequence Model.

Figure 4.4 General Move Sequence Model data card.

Hands-Degree

Aside from linear movements, the Action Distance parameter covers rotational movements of the hand. This refers to the revolving of an empty or loaded hand about the long axis of the forearm. The rotation of the hand would be estimated to the nearest 15° and the appropriate index value selected. Estimate the rotation from the thumb knuckle or the base knuckle of the little finger.

A_0 ≤30°
A_1 ≤60°
A_3 ≤120°
A_6 ≤180°

Example: Rotate arm to read wristwatch: A_3.

When a linear action distance occurs simultaneously with a rotational action distance, both values must be located on the action distance table and the greater time value or the limiting action allowed.

Example: Take a book lying flat on the table, and turn it upright while moving it 12 inches (30 cm) to the bookshelf: 90°, A_3; 12 inches (30 cm), A_{10}. Allow the A_{10}.

Note: These data are for rotation of the hand with or without an object while moving freely through the air. If rotating a dial or other attached object, use the Move Controlled (M) parameter.

Leg Action Distance

This column applies to Action Distances of the leg or foot. These actions are for displacements of the leg or foot, not for leg and foot actions that transport the body. Leg actions are pivoted at the knee or at the hip and are measured at the ankle. Measurements are taken to the nearest inch (cm) and the index value located on the data card. Foot actions move the ball of the foot, with either the heel or the instep acting as a fulcrum. Foot actions are by their nature quite short. The index value for a foot action is 6.

This type of Action Distance is commonly limited by movements made by other body members (i.e., fingers and hands). Table values are as follows:

A_6 ≤8 inches (20 cm)
A_{10} ≤12 inches (30 cm)
A_{16} ≤18 inches (45 cm)
A_{24} ≤26 inches (65 cm)
A_{32} >26 inches (65 cm)

Examples: While seated, reach 14 inches (35 cm) to contact a foot-operated pedal: A_{16}. With both feet on the ground, raise the right foot 24 inches (60 cm) and put on bicycle pedal: A_{24}. Reach from the soft pedal to the damper pedal on a piano, keeping heel on the floor: A_6.

Sometimes there is confusion about when to allow a step as opposed to a leg action. To make this decision, determine the primary purpose of the action. If the primary purpose is to *locate the foot,* such as on a pedal, allow a leg action of the appropriate distance. If the primary purpose is to *locate the body,* such as preparing to read a gauge, allow a step. *Note:* The trunk of the body is shifted or displaced during a step.

An Action Distance performed by the foot in locating the foot on the block is shown here:

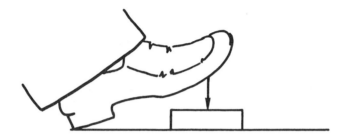

An A_6 would be allowed.

Action Distance: Steps   (NO.) STEP(S)

Steps refer to horizontal displacement of the body. For convenience they are shown in the Leg Action Distance column.

A_{16} **One Step** The trunk of the body is shifted or displaced by walking, sidestepping, or turning the body around taking one step (the foot hits the floor once).

A_{32} **Two Steps** The trunk of the body is shifted or displaced by walking, sidestepping, or turning the body around. The number of steps is equal to the number of times the foot hits the floor (twice).

Because of the repetitiveness of the activities that are analyzed with Mini MOST, the need for values for more than two steps seldom arises. If it does occur in practice, the layout should be reviewed and the distance shortened. However, in the rare cases calling for these values, the procedure should be to use the one-step data and the frequency column for the number of steps needed.

Example: Take three steps to get a part

(A_{16}) B_x G_x A_x B_x P_x A_x (3)   **48 TMU**

Basic MOST is usually the preferred technique for analyzing operations including more than two steps.

Body Assistance to Hand Action

When the operator takes only one step, caution must be exercised in deciding whether to allow the step or to treat it as body assistance. Normally, a step that displaces the body to the side less than 12 inches (30 cm) or turns the body less than 45° for the purpose of extending the reach is considered body assistance. However, such body assistance does not have to be analyzed separately as a step because the time will be included in the Action Distance for the hand. Longer steps and those steps that must be completed prior to the next action in the operation are usually time limiting and must be recorded in the analysis to account for their time.

Movement of the Hand with Steps   (NO.) INCH(ES), CM

When steps are involved in the getting or the placing of object(s), the hand(s) usually begin the required movement as the steps are being taken. When the step(s) are complete, the hand(s) will typically have moved 5 inches (12.5 cm) closer to the object(s); therefore, a 5 inch (12.5 cm) action distance is already included in the step data. When an Action Distance for step(s) is included in a Mini MOST analysis, any additional distance the hand moves after the conclusion of the step(s) is analyzed as a separate hand Action Distance.

Example 1: Take a side step, then reach 9 inches (22.5 cm) over an obstruction to get a part ("reach" begins at the conclusion of the step).

Sidestep: A_{16}
Reach 9 inches (22.5 cm): A_{10}

To simplify the expression and reduce the number of sequence models needed, this analysis could be shown as

$$A_{16 + 10} \quad B_x \quad G_x \quad A_x \quad B_x \quad P_x \quad A_x$$

In exceptional situations, it is permissible to show more than one type of Action Distance for the same A parameter. Remember to separate the index value by a plus (+) sign. Do not add them together (i.e., A_{26}. This designation shows that more than one action occurs. Use this notation only when the two index values are required for *the same activity* and only with manual Mini MOST.

Example 2: Grasp a part 25 inches (62 cm) from the edge of a table two steps away (reach begins during the second step).

2 steps: A_{32}
20 inches (50 cm) of the reach: A_{16}

$$A_{32 + 16} \quad B_x \quad G_x \quad A_x \quad B_x \quad P_x \quad A_x$$

The following is a list of examples of Action Distances:

1. Reach 6 inches (15 cm) to a part jumbled with others in a tote pan: A_6

2. Reach 4 inches (10 cm) to a needle lying on the table: A_3
3. Place a bolt in a parts bin located 9 inches away (22.5 cm): A_{10}
4. Reach a net distance of 20 inches (50 cm) with both hands to a suitcase on a bench: A_{16}
5. Move a checker piece to the next square through the air: A_1
6. Step to a telephone receiver: A_{16}
7. Move index finger to next key on a calculator: A_0
8. Place an object on a table two steps away: A_{32}
9. Place nuts on bolts located 1 inch (2.5 cm) apart: A_0

The following are *not* Action Distances because the action does not occur over an unrestricted path in space:

1. Slide a book across the desk.
2. Operate a foot pedal.
3. Rub a sheet of paper to force the air out from under it.
4. Depress a key on a calculator.

The analysis of such activities is covered under Move Controlled (M parameter).

Body Motion (B)

Body Motion refers primarily to vertical (up or down) motions of the body.

B_{32} Bend or Arise   BEND, ARISE

From an erect standing position, the body is lowered to allow the hands to reach below the knees, *or* the subsequent return to an upright position. It is not necessary for the hands to actually reach below the knees, only that the body is lowered sufficiently to allow the reach. Note that this value is only for bend *or* arise, not both bend and arise.

Note: Care must be exercised to distinguish between body assistance and body motion. Leaning, which does not lower the shoulders enough to permit the hands to reach below the knees, is body assistance. The time for this body movement is covered by the Action Distance parameter by measuring the hand movement. However, when the body is lowered far enough to permit the hands to reach below the knees, Body Motion rather than an Action Distance is allowed.

Normally when a Body Motion occurs, any accompanying Action Distance is completed during the Body Motion and only the Body Motion is allowed. However, there are times when both the Body Motion and the Action Distance must be accounted for because the latter occurs before or after the Body Motion because of some obstruction in the workplace, or it may be necessary to help an operator to maintain balance.

Example: Bend to clear shelving and reach 10 inches (25 cm) to an object at the back of the shelf:

A_{10} B_{32} G_x A_x B_x P_x A_x

The Action Distance had to take place after the Body Motion was completed.

Example: With a 15-pound (7-kg) object supported by both hands, bring the object 12 inches (30 cm) nearer to the body for balance and arise from a bending position. Here the Action Distance had to take place prior to the start of the Body Motion.

When combinations of this type occur, care must be taken to allow *only* that length of Action Distance that *must* be done before or after the Body Motion. Action Distances that may be performed during a Body Motion are not allowed.

B_{10} Eye Travel   EYE-MOTION

Eye travel, when required, may be allowed as a body motion. *Eye travel* is the basic eye motion employed to shift the axis of vision from one location to another. Eye travel rarely occurs as a limiting motion and is allowed only when the next manual motions depend upon its completion. To assign a B_{10} for Eye Travel, a necessary recognizable pause must occur. This pause occurs only when the items requiring attention are not within the "area of normal vision;" that is, the distance between the items is greater than one-quarter the perpendicular distance from the eyes. For objects 16 inches (40 cm) from the eyes, the area of normal vision is a circular area 4 inches (10 cm) in diameter.

Examples: With a peg held in each hand, place one in a hole located 20 inches (50 cm) from the first. The openings are on a board located 16 inches (40 cm) from the operator's eyes. Eye travel is needed before the placement of the second peg can occur. Had the distance between the openings been 4 inches (10 cm) or less, no eye travel would have been allowed.

Supplementary Body Motion Values

Additional Body Motion values that are not on the data card (Fig. 4.4) have been developed and are presented here.

B_{32} **Sit**   The keyword SIT includes lowering the body to a seated position on a chair. It does not include any adjustments to the chair.

B_{42} **Stand**   The keyword STAND includes raising the body out of a chair to an erect position. It does not include any adjustments to the chair.

Operations requiring a detailed Mini MOST analysis do not usually include sitting or standing. Therefore, these values are not shown on the data card.

Gain Control (G)

The Gain Control parameter covers all motions of the fingers, hand, or foot required to obtain control of one object or group of objects when they are arranged so that they may be handled as one object. The index value selected should reflect the motions necessary for obtaining control due to the nature of the object, its surroundings, and its size. The G parameter includes the time for up to 1 inch (2.5 cm) hand movement prior to or in combination with the grasp of the object(s).

Note: Only when several objects are grouped together or arranged in such a way that they can be picked up as one object, does one G value sufficiently cover the grasp involved. Picking up several objects separately requires a series of Action Distances and Gain Control considerations.

G_0 Sweep   SWEEP

The object is obtained (controlled) without interrupting the flow of the Action Distance—the hand does not stop. Closing the fingers around the object occurs internally to the action distance; therefore no hesitation or pause is seen. An object obtained in this manner is necessarily of nominal weight and size and can be located by itself on the surface with no interference at the grasping point.

Example: Wiping erasure remains from a page with the side of the palm (with an open hand).

G_3 Contact   CONTACT

Control is gained simply by touching the object with the fingers, hand, or foot.

Examples: Gain control of an on/off button, light switch, telephone dial, calculator key, or sewing machine pedal. Gain control of a coin to slide it out of the way when counting. In the illustration below, the hand is brought to the ruler, rests on the ruler, and pulls the ruler away with no closing of the fingers.

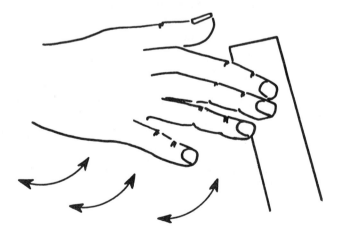

When the hand is already on the object and one or more fingers are closed on the object, use a G_3 *contact grasp.*

Example: Close thumb on sheet of paper that has just been slid off a stack.

G₆ Grasp

This is the usual case of gaining control. The grasp is a simple pickup, with closing of the fingers around the object prior to the next action. The object can be of any size; it can be lying close against a flat surface or by itself. A G_6 also includes gaining control of an object with a recoil up to and including 1 inch (2.5 cm).

Examples: Grasp soft drink can. Grasp telephone receiver. Grasp pencil from table, lying by itself (grasp is complete with pencil held between thumb and index fingertips). Grasp aspirin from table. Grasp paper clip from table. Grasp emery board.

The value for Grasp allows the last 1 inch (2.5 cm) of the hand motion to the object, closing the fingers on the object, and when required, a short scraping or digging in of the fingers, or a slight recoil of not more than 1 inch (2.5 cm). A Grasp motion is illustrated below. A G_6 would be allowed.

G₆ Regrasp

Regrasp differs from the other forms of Gain Control in that the object is already controlled by the operator but the grip is shifted to improve or change the control. While control of the object is maintained, the grasp is shifted slightly for the purpose of improving control or bringing the object into position for use. Regrasp is characterized by two or three short finger actions and can occur repetitively when a major repositioning is required.

Examples: After writing several words, shift pencil in fingers before continuing (G_6). After cutting a piece of paper, readjust scissors by removing thumb, then forefinger from the handle to hold scissors in palm (G_6).

Note: Because of restrictions imposed on the initial gain control, it is common for a regrasp to immediately follow a grasp. Therefore, analysts should be on the watch for these adjustments to control and train their eyes to detect this motion.

Example: Pick up pencil from desk, and control to write:

Grasp G_6 =   6
Regrasp G_6 =   6
                    ――――――
                    12 TMU

Regrasps also frequently occur during an Action Distance while transporting the object and are normally limited. In applying regrasp, it will be of assistance to remember that the motion requires more than one finger action and fewer than four finger actions. Shifting one finger with one motion to a new location on on object is *not* a regrasp. The regrasp motions must also be short.

G_{10} Transfer   TRANSFER

Control of the object is exchanged from one hand to the other. This includes the brief holding period required by the fingers of both hands before release of the giving hand can occur. This hesitation or pause highlights a *transfer grasp*.

Examples: Transfer a book from the right hand to the left. After cutting a piece of meat, transfer the fork held in the left hand to the right hand to eat. Transfer a telephone receiver from one hand to the other.

The layout should be arranged in such a way that transfer grasps are reduced to a minimum. The following illustration shows the hands at the "pause" position during a transfer grasp:

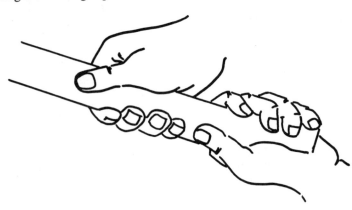

A transfer takes place only when one hand is closed on the object and then the other hand opened. For instance, picking up a nut lying in the palm of the left hand by closing the fingers of the right hand is not a transfer. There was no opening of the left hand to relinquish control of the object.

G_{10} Select   SELECT

Normally, search and select occurs when the object is not by itself in an open area and the grasp is accomplished after overcoming some restriction or impairment encountered at the grasping point due to the surroundings. Short motions are involved to locate the fingers around an object jumbled with other objects or to "roll out" a cylindrical object to separate it from others. To aid in choosing a G_{10} (Select) instead of a G_{16} (Select, Small), the size of the object comes into play. To qualify for a G_{10}: (1) if jumbled with other objects, the object must be larger than $1 \times 1 \times 1$ inch ($2.5 \times 2.5 \times 2.5$ cm), or (2) if nearly cylindrical and restricted on the bottom and one side, the diameter must be greater than or equal to $1/4$ inch (0.6 cm).

Examples: Obtain a $1^1/2$ inch (4 cm) nut from a bin filled with nuts. Get a piece of chalk (located against other pieces of chalk) from a chalkboard tray. Get a $1/4$ inch (0.6 cm) dowel from a neat row.

The requirement of restriction or impairment is necessary for a Gain Control to have the Select value. Getting a softball from a basket of balls does not require a Select Gain Control. Here the object is quite large, no restriction exists, and Gain Control can be accomplished with a Grasp (G_6).

G_{16} Select, Small   SELECT-SMALL

The criteria for Select Small are the same as for Select in that the object is restricted or impaired by other objects. As with Select, the objects may be jumbled or, if cylindrical, restricted on the bottom and one side. The distinguishing factor for Select, Small is the size of the object. The object size is $1 \times 1 \times 1$ inch ($2.5 \times 2.5 \times 2.5$ cm) or smaller if jumbled, or if cylindrical, the diameter is less than $1/4$ inch (0.6 cm).

Examples: Get small flat washer located in bin with others. Get $3/32$ inch (0.2 cm) diameter plastic tube from stack of tubes. Get one paper clip from a collection of paper clips (the paper clips are not tangled or interlocked).

G_{16} Disengage   DISENGAGE

The application of muscular force is needed to free the object from its surroundings. *Disengage* is characterized by the application of pressure (to overcome resistance) followed by the sudden movement and recoil of the object greater than 1 inch (2.5 cm) up to and including 5 inches (12.5 cm).

Note: Recoil of the object must follow an unrestricted path through the air (not to be confused with unseating a lever, crank, or other controlled device).

Examples: Remove tightly fitted cap from pen. Remove electric plug from socket.

The Disengage index value includes time to bring the hand the last inch (2.5 cm) to the object, to gain control of the object, to build up muscular force to free the object, and to recover from the recoil when the object breaks free. Occasionally, additional rocking or twisting motions may be required to free the object from its surroundings. These additional activities are not included in the

Disengage value and must be separately analyzed, usually with the Controlled Move Sequence Model.

Should the recoil in freeing an object exceed 5 inches (12.5 cm), consider whether method improvements might reduce the recoil. A recoil of more than 5 inches (12.5 cm) suggests that Basic MOST would be the preferred work measurement technique. The additional distance (>5 inches or 12.5 cm) can also be measured and included in the Action Distance in the beginning of the Put phase.

Consideration of Effective Net Weight (ENW)

The preceding discussions of index value selection for Gain Control (G) are based on an object of nominal weight not more than 2.5 pounds (≈ 1 kg). For objects with an Effective Net Weight (ENW) of 2.6–10.0 pounds (1–5 kg), the next higher index value should be used. This rule applies to all gain control activities except Grasp (G_6) for which no consideration of weight is necessary and no adjustment to the index value is necessary. The determination of the Effective Net Weight of an object depends upon the way the object is being moved. To measure the handling of object(s) with an ENW of more than 10 pounds (5 kg), Basic MOST is the preferred analysis technique.

Weight Consideration for the General Move Sequence   If an object is being moved freely through the air, the actual weight of the object is allocated to each body member performing the work based on the portion of the weight supported by that body member. If the object is being moved by one hand, the actual weight of the object is the Effective Net Weight. If two hands are moving the object, the Effective Net Weight is equal to the weight of the object divided by 2 if the weight is evenly distributed.

Examples: Get an 8 pound (4 kg) tool kit with one hand: 8/1 = 8 pounds (4 kg) ENW. Get a 10 pound (5 kg) tool kit with two hands: 10/2 = 5 pounds (2 kg) ENW.* Get a 5 pound (2 kg) tool kit with two hands: 5/2 = 2.5 pounds (1 kg) ENW.*

Therefore, when moving an object through space, the actual weight per hand must exceed 2.5 pounds (1 kg) before an adjustment to the G parameter is considered for weight purposes. On occasion an operator will support most of an object's weight in one hand while the other hand guides the object to its destination. This is often seen in the use of power tools. Typically, the right hand bears the weight of the tool, the left hand guides the tool to the proper location for use, and the right hand activates the tool. In this case, the ENW is calculated for one hand only.

The keyword used to indicate that the weight of the object(s) affects the analysis is the suffix -WT added to the appropriate G keyword. For example,

---

*Assuming that the weight is distributed equally to each hand.

DISENGAGE-WT is used when a force of 6 pounds (3 kg) is needed to free a part from a retainer.

Placement (P)

Placement includes the motions in the final stage of the displacement of object(s) moved for the purpose of bringing the object(s) to the final destination. The time for a 1-inch (2.5-cm) move prior to making contact with a surface in combination with the placement of the object(s) is included in the placement value except in the case of P_0 "drop," "hold," "toss," and "set and retain." Also, the time for relinquishing control of the object(s) is included whenever appropriate.

P_0 Drop   DROP

No deceleration or placing motions occur; the object is released with the hand in motion, and the hand continues in motion into the next action.
Example: Drop part in chute, and continue to get the next part.

P_0 Indefinite Location/Hold   PICKUP, KEEP

A part is retained in space where its location is unimportant. This can occur as a preliminary step to another motion or to clear the part from an area. In many cases, this P_0 to an indefinite location is followed by a pause or waiting time. This value is not found on the data card. (The keyword KEEP is used when there is no Action Distance after Gain Control.)
Examples:

1. Pick up part with left hand and hold in space while positioning a part with the right hand.
2. Move a part clear of a machine prior to operating the machine.

P_3 Toss   TOSS

The object is tossed or thrown but the hand stops or reverses direction prior to the next action.
Examples: Deal cards to players sitting around table. Toss scrap into scrap bin.

Notice that the distinction between Drop and Toss is whether the hand must stop or reverse directions. For Toss, the hand stops or reverses direction. For Drop, the hand continues.

P_3 Set and Retain   SET AND RETAIN

The object is moved to a location, usually on a surface, and remains under control for subsequent work.

Note: If the retained object(s) were subsequently released with no further Placement or Controlled Move of the object(s), the correct analysis would be P_6 (Set Aside), to account for the release.

Example: Set base on bench and hold while assembling additional part.

P_6 Set Aside   SET ASIDE

The object is moved to a location and control is relinquished. The object may be moved to a stop, to a general location, or to an exact location with a radial tolerance greater than 0.350 inch (approximately 3/8 inch, 1 cm). Precise and predetermined placement is *not* required.

Examples: Place pencil on desk. Place paper clip on table. Set egg in wire basket.

P_6 Set and Slide   SET AND SLIDE (NO.) INCH(ES)

The object is brought to a preliminary location and the object or hand is slid up to 1 inch (2.5 cm) to a secondary location. The object may be retained or released. For placements where the object must be slid more than 1 inch (2.5 cm), the additional distance will be analyzed on the M parameter in the Controlled Move Sequence. *Example:* An object is placed and slid 6 inches (15 cm). The initial placement is shown with a P_6. The slide distance is shown as an M_{10}. This concept will be more clearly understood once you have studied the Controlled Move sequence.

Examples: Place 3/4 inch (2 cm) piece of tape on envelope. Set part near a stop, and slide 1 inch (2.5 cm) to a stop. Put pencil to paper and make a checkmark in a general location. *Note:* When drawing longer lines in a defined location, the pencil placement is analyzed by using the P parameter, while the drawing of the line is covered by the M parameter in the Controlled Move Sequence Model.

Position

Position involves locating an object or point on an object to a *precise* and *predetermined* destination. Position includes all incremental motions necessary subsequent to an Action Distance to locate an object in a predetermined destination and to seat the object in or on this destination. Position provides time for alignment (linear and tilting), orientation, contact at the destination, and insertion. Alignment is always present in placements that require "Position."

Alignment includes linear adjustments to bring the object to the desired location with the required accuracy, plus any tilting of the object that may be required.

P₆   Simple Position   PLACE

An object or point on an object is placed to a predetermined location. Time is
included for linear and tilting alignment and for making contact with the destination. Insertions of ¹/₈ inch (0.3 cm) or less are considered a part of making
contact. There is no significant orientation* required because the object can be
placed in more than 10 ways about the contact axis. The tolerance does not
demand a high degree of accuracy. A radial clearance from 0.150 inch (approximately ⁵/₃₂ inch, 0.4 cm) to 0.350 inches (0.8 cm) is present with this placement. Control of the object may be retained or relinquished.

Example: Place pencil to paper in preparation for writing. Place a round
object into a hole ¹/₁₆ inch (0.15 cm) deep; the tolerance is loose.

P₁₀   Position with Some Orientation   POSITION

An object or a point on the object is placed at a predetermined location on the
surface. In addition to allowing time for a simple position of the object, time is
allowed for a rotational ($\leq 90°$) adjustment of the object about the contact axis.
The criterion is that the object is rotated about its axis, regardless of the manual
motion made to accomplish that rotation. Objects needing this type of classification are those that could be placed in 2–10 possible ways about the axis and that
have not been preoriented. That is, the object must be rotated at the point of
placement. Again, an insertion of up to ¹/₈ inch (0.3 cm) is considered part of
bringing the object into contact and tolerances are loose enough [from 0.150–
0.350 inch (0.4–0.8 cm) radial clearance] so that a high degree of accuracy is
not required. Release of the object may or may not occur.

Example: Place a metal band through a slot in a bracket with an insertion of
¹/₈ inch (0.3 cm).

P₁₆   Position with Complete Orientation   ORIENT

An object or a point on the object is placed at a predetermined location on the
surface. In addition to allowing time for a simple position, time is allowed for a
rotational ($>90°$, $\leq 180°$) adjustment of the object about the contact axis.
Objects needing this type of classification are those that can be placed in one
and only one possible way around its axis and that have not been preoriented;
the rotational adjustment must occur during the "place" activity. Again, the
manual motion made to accomplish the rotation is not the deciding factor; it is
essential only that the object require rotation. Insertions of up to ¹/₈ inch (0.3

---

*Orientation refers to the rotation of the object about its axis, alignment, and contact in order to
properly engage the object with another. It takes into account the shape of the object at the surface
of contact or insertion.

cm) are considered part of bringing the objects to the surface. This placement does not require a high degree of accuracy [clearance from 0.150 to 0.350 inch (0.4–0.8 cm) radially]. Release of the object may or may not occur.

As noted previously, the orientation values apply only at the point of placement. In many cases, the object may be prepositioned or preoriented either prior to or during the Action Distance. This preorientation normally reduces the orientation required at the point of placement. As a result, the Placement index value is reduced accordingly.

Adjustments to the Values for Position

Any keyword in this section may be used following the P keywords PLACE, POSITION, and ORIENT as a placement condition.

Accuracy   ACCURATE

The previous discussions deal with the positioning of an object or point on the object that can be accomplished without slowdown, tension, or corrective motions, because the tolerances involved are loose. However, if an object's positioning demands a more exact placement, the next higher index value should be selected (see data card notes to Fig. 4.4). The increased precision may be observed as a sequential adjustment or as light pressure. The tolerance associated with this accurate positioning is a radial clearance of less than 0.150 inch (0.4 cm) at the plane of initial insertion or at the point of contact if no insertion occurs.

Insertion   ENTER, INSERT

The three classes of position previously described all allow an insertion of the object up to $1/8$ inch (0.3 cm). If the object or point on the object must be inserted more than $1/8$ inch (0.3 cm), the next higher index value should be selected. By so doing, an insertion of up to 1 inch (2.5 cm) is allowed. For an insertion greater than 1 inch (2.5 cm), use a separate Controlled Move Sequence Model (M parameter).

Examples: Position object with some orientation—insertion of $1/16$ inch (.15 cm): P_{10}. Position object with some orientation—insertion of $3/4$ inch (2 cm): P_{16}. Position object with some orientation—insertion of 3 inches (7.5 cm): P_{16} (General Move) and M_6 (Controlled Move).

Example: Place key in lock:

P_{16} Complete orientation
   • go to next index value for

P_{24} Accuracy
   • go to next index value for
P_{32} Insertion of $3/4$ inch (2 cm)

Difficult to Handle   DIFFICULT

At times during the positioning of an object, a regrasp, hesitation, or pause is
required because the object is difficult to handle (hard to control). This can be
due to the nature of the object (flexible items such as yarn, paper, and cloth) or
to the type of grip that has to be employed, or to distance, if the object is
grasped a distance from the point being positioned. In other cases, the handling
difficulty is observed as a shifting of the grip during positioning. If difficulty in
handling is observed, the next higher index value is selected to account for this
additional adjusting motion.

Examples: Position hand drill to center of block:

P_6 Placement to surface with no orientation
   • go to next higher index value for
P_{10} Accurate placement
   • go to next higher index value for
P_{16} Difficult to handle: drill bit at considerable distance from point of
      control, drill handle, and crank

Binding   BIND, DOUBLE-BIND

At times, when an object is being inserted, a part of the object will catch or
snag. This will result in the application of muscular force to overcome the
obstruction. This can be seen as the snapping action to seat an object during the
placing activity. Little or no movement of the object occurs as the bind is freed.
For each observation of a bind, go up *two index values*.

Binding will occur only when dealing with an insertion. This allowance for
binding should be applied after all others.

Example: Place key in lock (two occurrences of binding), insert 2 inches
(5 cm):

P_{16} Complete orientation
   • go to the next higher index value for
P_{24} Accuracy
   • go to next higher index value for
P_{32} Insertion up to 1 inch (2.5 cm)
   • go up two index values for
P_{54} First bind
   • go up two index values for
P_{81} Second bind

Example: Place cap on end of mechanical pencil

P_6 No orientation
   • go to next higher index value for
P_{10} Accuracy
   • go to next higher index value for
P_{16} Insertion up to 1 inch (2.5 cm)

   Example: Place paper clips on papers

P_6 No orientation (if preoriented before the start of the action distance to papers)
   • go to next higher index value for
P_{10} Accuracy
   • go to next higher index value for
P_{16} Insertion up to 1 inch (2.5 cm)

Special Case: In some instances, an application of muscular force may occur without insertion. If the application of force occurs as a part of placement without insertion, go up two index values for each application of pressure.

   Example: Firmly push a drill to drill a hole.

Position to a Point in Space

On occasion, an object or point on an object is located in a precise manner to a predetermined point in space with no contact made with any surface. When this occurs, allow the position time for the appropriate accuracy and handling. Do not allow any orientation, regardless of whether orientation occurs. All considerations except orientation are the same as for position where contact is made.

   Examples: Locate an eyedropper near the eye. Locate an oil can spout over a small turning shaft.

Is a Position Value Required?

A Position value is required when the object or point is brought into a *precise* and *predetermined* relationship with another object or point. The placing actions require high care and visual attention. However, not all placing activities requiring high care and visual attention are Position placements. For instance, placing an egg in a wire basket requires high care and visual attention to avoid breaking the egg, but a Set Aside value is assigned because the egg may be placed anywhere in the basket.

General Move Application

Each of the General Move parameters (A, B, G, and P) has been discussed in detail with respect to function and index values.

The General Move Sequence is broken into three components: These are

Get	Put	Return
A B G	**A B P**	**A**

When analyzing an operation, you must first determine the activities necessary to Get the object, then the activities necessary to Put the object, and finally, you must consider any Return possibilities.

The sequence is read:

A   Action Distance to Get an Object
B   Body Motions Required to Get an Object
G   Gain Control of the Object
A   Action Distance to Move or Put an Object
B   Body Motions Required to Put an Object
P   Place an Object in Its Required Location
A   Action Distance to Return or Clear

Using the techniques previously described under Parameter Indexing, each phase and parameter is analyzed to determine index values, which are then assigned and added to establish the total time in TMUs (multiplier = 1).

Return (Final A)

The Return or Final A in the sequence may be used for only three activities:

1. Hand Action Distance to an indefinite location where the purpose is not to get or put an object.
2. Disengage greater than 5 inches (12.5 cm).
3. Clear hand out of the way to permit the next activity.

General Move Examples

1. Reach 8 inches (20 cm) to a pencil lying on the table, move it 10 inches (25 cm), and set aside on the table.

   LH REACH 8 INCHES (20 CM) AND SET PENCIL FROM TABLE ASIDE 10 INCHES (25 CM) TO TABLE

   A_6 B_0 G_6 A_{10} B_0 P_6 A_0 28 TMU

2. Reach 8 inches (20 cm) to the same pencil, gain control, and move the pencil 16 inches (40 cm) to write, regrasping it while moving. The placement is a simple position.

   RH REACH 8 INCHES (20 CM) AND GRASP PENCIL AND PLACE TO PAPER 16 INCHES (40 CM)

A_6 B_0 G_6 A_{16} B_0 P_6 A_0 **34 TMU**

Note: The regrasp is limited by the Action Distance to move the pencil.

3. An operator reaches 12 inches (30 cm) to a cotter pin, gains control of the pin, and places it into a hole 16 inches (40 cm) away with a 0.2 inch (0.5 cm) radial clearance. The pin is inserted 2 inches (5 cm) and released.

RH REACH 12 INCHES (30 CM) AND PLACE COTTER PIN ACCURATE AND INSERT IN TO HOLE 16 INCHES (40 CM) AWAY

A_{10} B_0 G_6 A_{16} B_0 P_{10} A_0 42
A_0 B_0 G_0 M_6 X_0 I_0 A_0 $\underline{6}$

                                                          48 TMU

4. An assembly worker reaches 10 inches (25 cm) to a $3/4$ inch (2 cm) washer jumbled with other washers, gains control of the washer, moves it 8 inches (20 cm), and positions it onto a bolt with $1/8$ inch (0.3 cm) radial clearance. The washer is moved down $1/2$ inch (1 cm) and released.

LH SELECT-SMALL WASHER FROM BIN 10 INCHES (25 CM) AWAY AND PLACE ON TO BOLT ACCURATE AND INSERT

A_{10} B_0 G_{16} A_6 B_0 P_{16} A_0 **48 TMU**

B.   The Controlled Move Sequence Model

The Controlled Move Sequence describes the manual displacement of object(s) over a controlled path. That is, movement is restricted in at least one direction by contact with or an attachment to another object or the nature of the work demands that the object(s) be deliberately moved on a specific path.

Similar to the General Move Sequence, Controlled Move proceeds according to a fixed sequence of subactivities identified by the following steps:

1. *Reach* with one or two hands a distance to the object(s), either directly or in conjunction with body motions.
2. *Gain* manual *control* of the object(s).
3. *Move* the object(s) over a controlled path.
4. Allow time for a *process* to occur.
5. *Align* the object(s) following the controlled move or at the conclusion of the process time.
6. *Return* to workplace.

These six subactivities form the basis for the activity sequence describing the manual displacement of object(s) over a controlled path.

The Sequence Model

The sequence model takes the form of a series of letters representing each of the various subactivities (called parameters) of the Controlled Move Activity Sequence.

A B G M X I A

where: A = Action distance
        B = Body motion
        G = Gain control
        M = Move controlled
        X = Process time
        I = Alignment

Parameter Definitions

Only three new parameters are introduced: the A, B, and G parameters were discussed with the General Move Sequence and remain unchanged.

M Move Controlled

This parameter is used to analyze all manually guided movements or actions of object(s) over a controlled path.

X Process Time

This parameter applies to the portion of work controlled by a process or machine, not by manual actions.

I Alignment

This parameter is used to analyze manual actions following the controlled move or at the conclusion of process time to achieve the alignment of objects.

Phases of the Sequence Model

A Controlled Move is performed under one of three conditions. The object or device (1) is restrained by its attachment to another object, such as a push button, lever, door, or crank; (2) is controlled during the move by the contact it makes with the surface of another object, as in pushing a box across a table; or (3) it must be moved on a controlled path to accomplish the task, such as folding a cloth, coiling a rope, winding a spool, moving a balanced item, or to avoid a hazard, such as electricity, sharp edges, or running machinery. If the object can be moved freely through the air unaffected by any of these conditions, its movement must be analyzed as a General Move.

A breakdown of the Controlled Move Sequence Model reveals that, like the General Move, three phases occur during the Controlled Move activity.

$$
\begin{array}{c|c|c}
 & \text{Move} & \\
 & \text{or} & \\
\text{Get} & \text{Actuate} & \text{Return} \\
\text{A \quad B \quad G} & \text{M \quad X \quad I} & \text{A}
\end{array}
$$

The Get and Return phases of Controlled Move carry the same parameters as in the General Move Sequence Model and therefore describe the same subactivities. The fundamental difference between these two sequence models is the activity immediately following the G parameter. This (second) phase describes actions either to simply Move an object over a controlled path or to Actuate a control device. Normally, Move implies that the M and I parameters of the sequence model are involved, but Actuate usually applies to situations involving the M and X parameters. Of course, for either situation (Move or Actuate), any or all the parameters in the sequence model could be used, and should be considered. A Move, for example, would occur when opening a tool cabinet door or sliding a box across a table. Engaging the clutch on a machine or flipping an electrical switch to start a process are examples of Actuate.

Parameter Indexing

Like General Move, parameters in the Controlled Move Sequence Model are indexed by referring to an index value data card (Fig. 4.5). Since the A, B, and G parameters can be found on the General Move data card, the Controlled Move data card includes only the M, X, and I parameters.

Parameter indexing is accomplished by selecting from the data card (Fig. 4.5) the parameter variant that appropriately describes the observed or visualized Controlled Move and then applying the corresponding index value to the sequence model. In computerized Mini MOST applications, the system automatically assigns appropriate index values based on the method description entered in keyword language and computes the time for the sequence model in TMU.

Index Value Definitions

Move Controlled (M)

Move Controlled includes all manually guided movements or actions of object(s) over a controlled path. That is, movement of the object is restricted in at least one direction by contact with or attachment to another object. Time for relinquishing contact with the object(s) is included.

Mini MOST® System   A B G M X I A   **CONTROLLED MOVE**

INDEX X 1	M MOVE CONTROLLED					X PROCESS TIME	I ALIGNMENT		INDEX X 1
	PUSH,PULL,SLIDE,ROTATE			SMALL CRANK,CRANK			TO POINT OR LINE		
	HAND		FOOT OR LEG	SMALL-CRANK ≤ 5 INCHES (13 cm)	CRANK ≤ 20 INCHES (50 cm)		WITHIN AREA OF NORMAL VISION	OUTSIDE AREA OF NORMAL VISION	
	INCHES (cm)	DEGREES	INCHES (cm)	REVOLUTIONS	REVOLUTIONS	TMU			
0									0
1	1 (2.5) BUTTON					1.7			1
3						4.2			3
6	4 (10)	90				7.7	ALIGN, CHECK INSPECT		6
10	10 (25)	180	10 (25)			12.6	ALIGN-ACCURATE ALIGN-POINTS		10
16	18 (45) SEAT,UNSEAT		16 (40) FOOT-PRESS	1		19.6	ALIGN-POINTS-ACCURATE	ALIGN-OUT, CHECK-OUT INSPECT-OUT	16
24	30 (75)		22 (55)		1	27.7		ALIGN-ACCURATE-OUT ALIGN-POINTS-OUT	24
32			30 (75)	2		36.6		ALIGN-POINTS-ACCURATE-OUT	32
42				3	2	47.6			42
54				4	3	60.1			54

Figure 4.5   Controlled Move Sequence Model data card. Values are real "up to and including."

Push, Pull, Slide, Rotate

The object(s) or device may be hinged or pivoted at some point (e.g., door, lever, or dial) or restricted due to guides, slots, friction from surface, or other components of the surroundings as described by the following M parameter variants.

Hand-Inches (cm)

The object(s) are displaced over a controlled path using the hand or fingers. Distance is measured to the nearest inch (2.5 cm) as described in the Action Distance section.

M_3 ≤ 1 inch (2.5 cm)   Object displacement is achieved by a movement of the fingers or hands not to exceed 1 inch (2.5 cm). *Examples:* Push coin $^3/_4$ inch (2 cm) to count. Increase volume on radio with fingers.

M_6 ≤ 4 inches (10 cm)   Object displacement is achieved by a movement of the fingers or hands greater than 1 inch (2.5 cm) but less than or equal to 4 inches (10 cm).

M_{10} ≤ 10 inches (25 cm)   Object displacement is achieved by a movement of the fingers or hands greater than 4 inches (10 cm) but less than or equal to 10 inches (25 cm).

M_{16} ≤ 18 inches (45 cm)   Object displacement is achieved by a movement of the fingers or hands greater than 10 inches (25 cm) but less than or equal to 18 inches (45 cm).

M_{16} Seat/Unseat   Object is "snapped" into or out of place with pressure being applied by hand, or a pushing or pulling force is exerted on an object and little or no motion occurs. *Keyword:* SEAT, UNSEAT. In the *unseating* of an object, the recoil must follow a restricted path (not to be confused with a G_{16} Disengage, which allows for the recoil of a object freely through the air). *Examples:* Pull on ring to open three-ring binder. Pull on string ends to secure a knot that was just tied. Pull lever to seat. Apply pressure to stamp already on envelope. Press on stapler to staple pages together.

M_{24} ≤ 30 inches (75 cm)   Object displacement is achieved by a movement of the fingers or hands greater than 18 inches (45 cm) but less than or equal to 30 inches (75 cm).

Hand-Degrees

The object is displaced over a controlled path with the hand rotating about the long axis of the forearm. Rotations are estimated using the thumb knuckle or the base knuckle of the little finger as a reference point and the appropriate index value selected. (Rotations of less than 15° are treated as linear actions.)

M_6 $\leq 90°$ Object is displaced over a controlled path with the hand rotating greater than 15° but less than or equal to 90° about the long axis of the forearm. *Examples:* Turn latch on suitcase. Fasten screw with screwdriver, one turn less than 90° (performed as a wrist turn).

M_{10} ≤ 180° Object is displaced over a controlled path with the hand rotating greater than 90° but less than or equal to 180° about the long axis of the forearm. *Example:* Turn off shower nozzle.

Should a rotation of less than 15° occur, treat it as linear Move Controlled. Measure the distance the hand or fingers move to rotate the device, and select the proper value from the distance column.

Foot or Leg Motion   (NO.) INCHES (CM)

Object is displaced over a controlled path using the *foot* or *leg*. Distance is measured as discussed in the Action Distance section. Leg distances are measured at the ankle. Foot distances are always less than 10 inches (25 cm).

M_{10} ≤ 10 inches (25 cm) Object is displaced over a controlled path with the leg or foot not to exceed 10 inches (25 cm) in movement. *Examples:* Depress an electric sewing machine pedal with the foot. Depress a clutch pedal (action hinged at hip).

M_{16} ≤ 16 inches (40 cm) Object is displaced over a controlled path with leg movement greater than 10 inches (25 cm), but less than or equal to 16 inches (40 cm).

M_{16} Foot with Pressure A foot motion when muscular force is needed to overcome friction or resistance due to the nature of the surroundings. This includes time to overcome the resistance and to complete the motion. *Keyword:* FOOT-PRESS. *Example:* Push foot-pedal with 35 pounds (16 kg) resistance. FOOT-PRESS PEDAL.

M_{24} ≤ 22 inches (55 cm) Object is displaced over a controlled path with the leg movement greater than 16 inches (40 cm) but less than or equal to 22 inches (55 cm).

M_{32} ≤ 30 inches (75 cm) Object is displaced over a controlled path with the leg movement greater than 22 inches (55 cm) but less than or equal to 30 inches (75 cm).

Note: There is no index value provided for overcoming resistance when the leg is used. This is because of the strength of the leg. The leg commonly exerts great force and does not require added time to overcome the resistance normally encountered in industrial settings.

Crank   CRANK, SMALL-CRANK, (NO.) REVOLUTIONS

With the forearm pivoting at the elbow, the object or device is moved in a circular or nearly circular path by the fingers, hand, and forearm. Index values are based on the diameter of the crank, the method of cranking—continuous or intermittent—and the number of cranking revolutions rounded to the nearest whole number. For less than half a revolution, use Push-Pull index values.

In Mini MOST, Crank applies only to those specific motions with the hand following a circular path, pivoting at the wrist and/or the forearm pivoted at the elbow, with the upper arm essentially fixed. Crank values are not used for any activity in which there is significant motion of the elbow.

Continuous Cranking The object is moved in a circular path without pause or interruptions between revolutions. It begins with the object at rest, allows for the number of revolutions needed, and ends when the cranking stops completely.

Example: Activate towel dispenser.

Intermittent Cranking The object is moved in a circular path with noticeable pauses occurring between revolutions. The cranking begins with the object at rest, allows for one revolution, and ends when the pause occurs before the succeeding revolution(s).

Example: Crank handle to review movie film, stopping after each crank.

For intermittent cranking, the index value per revolution is selected based on the crank diameter. For cranking multiple revolutions, a frequency must be employed.

M_{16} Crank diameter less than or equal to 5 inches (12.5 cm): one revolution
M_{24} Crank diameter greater than 5 inches (12.5 cm), up to and including 20 inches (50 cm): one revolution

Continuous Cranking The index value is selected based on the total number of revolutions and the crank diameter.

Crank diameter less than or equal to 5 inches (12.5 cm):

M_{32} two revolutions
M_{42} three revolutions
M_{54} four revolutions

Crank diameter greater than 5 inches (12.5 cm), up to and including 20 inches (50 cm):

M_{42} two revolutions
M_{54} three revolutions

Examples: Continuously wrap a piece of yarn around a spool with 15 revolutions—10 inch (25 cm) crank diameter. Frequency:

(M_{54})   (5)   270 TMU

Intermittently crank three revolutions—12 inch (30 cm) crank diameter:

M_{24} 3   72 TMU

Open louvered window panes four revolutions—2 inch (5 cm) crank diameter (continuous):

M₅₄   54 TMU

Caution should be exercised to apply crank appropriately. Crank is determined by the motions employed, not the device being used. If the elbow is displaced, crank is not the motion being used.

Examples: Winding a car window up or down is *not* a cranking motion when the elbow moves back and forth. The following illustrate crank motions:

The following is *not* a crank motion.

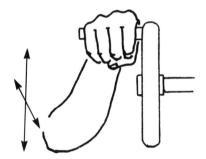

Here the elbow moves with the action pivoted at the shoulder. Turning the wheel is analyzed as a series of push-and-pull motions.

Effective Net Weight in the Controlled Move Sequence

If an object is being pulled, pushed, or slid across a horizontal surface, the body member(s) do not support all the object weight and must supply only enough force to overcome friction. This amount of force depends on surface texture and composition, but it has been calculated that the ENW (Effective Net Weight) of an object being slid on a solid surface is approximately 40% of its spatial ENW. Therefore, when sliding an object, the ENW must exceed 2.5 pounds (1 kg) before an adjustment to the G parameter is considered for weight purposes.

When an object such as a lever requires muscular force to overcome resistance, a spring scale can be employed to determine the amount of force needed.

Example: Push a 15-pound (7-kg) carton across a table using both hands (contact grasp):

Actual weight: 15 pounds (7 kg)

ENW (spatial): 15/2 = 7.5 pounds (3.5 kg)

ENW (sliding): 40% of 7.5 = 3.0 pounds (1.5 kg)

For general application of this theory, the following table is provided. Similar tables can be developed to suit local demands.

Type of move	Number of hands	Actual weight of object, pounds (kg)
General Move	1	2.6–10.0 (1–5)
(spatial)	2*	5.2–20.0 (2–10)
Controlled Move	1	6.5–25.0 (3–12)
(sliding)	2*	13.0–50.00 (6–24)

*Equal distribution of weight is assumed.

See the Gain Control in Section A for the appropriate adjustment for Effective Net Weight.

Process Time (X)

Process time occurs as that portion of work controlled by a process or machines, not by manual actions. Index values for process time are based on the calculated or actual clock time for a machine-controlled process to occur. All time values are converted to TMU. Then the index value is selected for that number of TMU and placed on the X parameter.

Note: Actual clock time is never placed on the X parameter.

The X parameter covers short machine cycle times up to 10% of the total time for the activity. When a process time exceeds 10% of the total cycle time, record the observed process time in TMU on a separate line on the form.

Examples: Press button to start machine:

A_{10} B_0 G_3 M_3 X_0 I_0 A_0 **16 TMU**

Process time, 20-second cycle   556 TMU

572 Total TMU

Note: MOST Computer Systems performs these conversions automatically based on the keyword: PTIME (NO.) TMU, SECONDS or MINUTES.

Alignment (I)

Alignment includes manual actions following the controlled move or, at the conclusion of a process time, to achieve alignment of an object to a point or line or to check for a single characteristic.

Area of Normal Vision

At a distance of 16 inches (40 cm) from the eye, an area 4 inches (10 cm) in diameter can be covered with a single eye focus. Within this 4 inches (10 cm) the alignment of an object can be performed easily without any special "eye times" (time for the eye to travel to the point of alignment). If an object must be aligned to a point or line outside the area where the eyes are directed or with two points more than 4 inches (10 cm) apart, an additional eye travel (ET) time is required because of the inability of the eyes to focus on both points at the same time.

Index values for aligning an object are selected from the Within Area of Normal Vision column if no eye travel is required to shift the eye to the point of alignment; that is, if one point is ≤ 4 inches (10 cm) from the current focal point of the eyes at a 16 inches (40 cm) distance from the eye. A value from the outside Area of Normal Vision column is used when the eyes must shift more than 4 inches (10 cm) from their current focal point to assist the alignment.

In the alignment of a second or any sequential point, the alignment time includes movements of the object being aligned of up to, but not including, 1 inch (2.5 cm). Movements of 1 inch (2.5 cm) or more require an additional Controlled Move. The alignment values, which follow, are defined for alignments or checks *within* the area of normal vision. For an alignment or check *outside* the area of normal vision, the I parameter index value is two index values higher.

Normal alignment is characterized by one manual adjustment of the object to move it into a predetermined relationship to one location (point to point, object to location) where radial clearance from 0.15 inch (0.3 cm) to .50 inch (1 cm) is considered normal. *Keyword:* LOCATE, LOCATE + ADJUST (outside area of normal vision).

An accurate alignment is characterized by adjustments of the object to move it into a more precise relationship than a normal alignment. A radial clearance less than 0.15 inch (0.3 cm) is considered accurate. *Keyword:* GUIDE, GUIDE + ADJUST.

Check (I_6) includes the eye and mental activities utilized in the determination of a single easily recognized physical characteristic of an object. It is a simple binary recognition of a trait; a yes-or-no decision. *Keyword:* CHECK, CHECK + ADJUST, INSPECT, INSPECT + ADJUST.

A common accurate alignment to two points may be analyzed by applying an index value of I_{24} *within* and I_{54} *outside* area of normal vision. Several eye motions are included in the latter case. *Keyword:* ALIGN, ALIGN+ADJUST.

   Examples: Align ruler to two points, 3 inches (7.5 cm) away from each other to draw a line (accurate): I_{24}. Align ruler to two points, 7 inches (17.5 cm) away from each other to draw a line (accurate): I_{54}. After checking off Mary Smith's name on the class roll attendance record, look up to see if John Doe is present at his assigned desk. (check): I_{16}. Fold a piece of paper 3×4 inches (7.5×10 cm) in half so that the bottom edge of the paper is within $1/2$ (1 cm) of the top edge: I_{10}.

Selection of Position (General Move) or Align (Controlled Move)

Position and Align are similar in that both involve moving an object to a precise and predetermined location. Position (in General Move) provides for locating an object in space, bringing an object in contact with a surface, and, when necessary, inserting one object into another. Align (in Controlled Move) provides only for locating an object on the same surface. For instance, in writing, bringing the pencil to the paper is a Position. Reversing direction at a precise point, as at the top of a written "c" is an Align. Normally, the nature of the preceding movement, spatial or controlled, is the determining factor behind the selection of a sequence model. Remember also that P is to A as I is to M. For accurate position of the object(s) with insertion < 1 inch (2.5 cm) or difficult handling, use the next higher index value for the I parameter. If the insertion is > 1 inch (2.5 cm), use the M parameter in a separate Controlled Move Sequence Model. For binding or pressure, go up two index values per occurrence.

Position (General Move) Followed by Align (Controlled Move)

Sometimes after an object is positioned it may require a subsequent alignment. The Controlled Move sequence is used to provide for the alignment. First allow the position (P value), and then use a Controlled Move sequence to allow the alignment (I value).

   Example: Insert a round pin in a hole (0.050 inch [0.1 cm] radial clearance), and insert precisely 2 inches (5 cm). There is a mark on the pin that must be aligned to within 0.200 inches (0.5 cm) of the surface. The alignment (I) is to insert the pin to the exact depth of 2 inches (5 cm) (Fig. 4.6). Allow P_{16} and M_6 for insertion and an I_6 for aligning the mark.

A_x B_x G_x A_x B_x P_{16} A_0
A_0 B_0 G_0 M_6 X_0 I_6 A_0

Controlled Move Examples

A machine operator reaches 20 inches (50 cm) to the start button on a machine and presses the button. Process time is $1/2$ second.

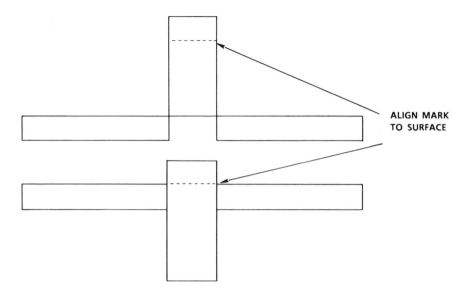

Figure 4.6 Alignment to insert pin.

RH REACH 20 INCHES AND PUSH BUTTON AT MACHINE PTIME .5 SECOND

A_{16} B_0 G_3 M_3 X_{16} I_0 A_0 **38 TMU**

An operator releases a part from a fixture by moving a handle 8 inches (20 cm). The handle is 10 inches (25 cm) away.

RH REACH 10 INCHES AND PULL HANDLE 8 INCHES

A_{10} B_0 G_6 M_{10} X_0 I_0 A_0 **26 TMU**

A person reaches 18 inches (45 cm) to the inside mirror of a car and adjusts it by turning it 30° in two directions.

RH GRASP MIRROR 18 INCHES AWAY AND ROTATE 30 DEGREES AND CHECK POSITION PF 2(4)

A_{16} B_0 G_6 (M_6) X_0 I_6 A_0 (2)   **40 TMU**

C. The Application of the Mini MOST System
Calculation Forms

There are two forms available for applying Mini MOST. The forms are constructed to reflect the status of Mini MOST as a MOST subsystem while providing for the special requirements of a Mini MOST application. The headings, like the Basic MOST heading, provide for the identification of the work being measured, the analyst, and the date.

Form with One Column of Sequence Models

The form with one column of sequence models resembles the Basic MOST form (see Fig. 4.2). There are, however, important differences for Mini MOST applications. There is a column headed H between the No. (number) column and the Method Description column. The hand performing the work is identified in this column. An "L" is entered for the left hand, an "R" for the right, or a "B" for both hands.

The Method Description column has two lines for each methods step. This is because Mini MOST work requires a precise definition of the method. It is essential that you describe the method completely and in detail. The sequence model shows the time for the method step, but only the method description can account for the decisions made to arrive at the index values. It should also be noted that in highly repetitive work a small change in method can result in a large percentage change in the time required for the operation. The method description must therefore be thorough and detailed enough to identify such method changes.

The fourth column is headed "Simo To." It is used to designate *simultaneous motions*. The sequence models are printed in the column headed "Sequence." There are only two sequence models used in Mini MOST. Select the appropriate sequence model, and fill in the index values on the preprinted sequence model beside the method description for that step.

The use of the frequency column is identical to that for Basic MOST. Both partial frequencies and total frequencies are shown in this column.

The time is posted to the TMU column. The proper frequencies are applied to the index values, but no other multiplication is required as the sum of the index values appears directly in TMU. The column total is shown at the bottom of the sheet. The total may then be converted to the time unit normally used to express standards in your application. The time is then posted to the "Time" block at the upper right of the form and the appropriate unit of measure indicated. In the block labeled Per, show the *count unit* for which the analysis was written.

Form with Two Columns of Sequence Models

The form with two sequence model columns is provided for more exact detailing of two-handed methods and motion combinations (Fig. 4.2). The left hand activities are described and analyzed on the left side of the form. Right hand activities are shown on the right side of the form.

The method steps are sequentially numbered using the columns at the edges of the form.

Write the method description in the method description column provided for the hand doing the method steps. Simultaneous activities are shown on opposite sides of the form. As stated earlier about the other form, it is essential that the method step be described in exact detail. The method description provides the detail that accounts for your decisions in selecting index values. Exact details of the method also enable you to recognize any changes that may be made in the method.

A Frequency column (FR) is provided for each hand. It is used in the same way as the frequency column in Basic MOST. Both partial frequencies and complete frequencies are written in this column.

This form also has a column headed "Simo To." It is used to provide details concerning simultaneous motions and is discussed below.

Finally, the allowed index values are totaled for each method step, multiplied by the appropriate frequencies, and posted to the "TMU" column. No other multiplication is required since the index values are in TMU. The column total is shown at the bottom of the sheet. The total may then be converted to the time unit normally used to express standards in your application. The time is posted to the "Time" block at the upper right of the form and the appropriate unit of measure indicated. In the block labeled "Per," show the count unit for which the analysis was written. "Per" might show "occurrence," "piece," "pound," "pot," "pair," "set," "blank," or any count unit you consider appropriate and convenient.

Motion Combinations

Motion combinations occur when two or more motions are performed at the same time either by the same body member or by different body members. These motion combinations often occur in industry and are especially prevalent in operations for which Mini MOST is being applied.

Motion Combinations Performed by the Same Body Member

Those motion combinations performed by one body member, hand or foot, are referred to as "combined motions." The analyst's task is to completely document the method and allow index values for the controlling or time-limiting motions. For example, an operator reaches 12 inches (30 cm) to a part on the bench, grasps the part, and sets it 10 inches (25 cm) to the front of the bench. While moving the part, the operator regrasps the part for an easier hold and rotates the part 90° to make assembly easier. Assuming the work is done with the left hand, the analysis will show

STEP	LEFT–HAND METHOD DESCRIPTION	SEQUENCE MODEL	FR.	SIMO TO	TMU
1	Set part to front of bench, hold for assembly	$A_{10}\ B_0\ G_6\ A_{10}\ B_0\ P_6\ A_0$ A B G M X I A			32
2	New grip for holding	$A_0\ B_0\ G_6\ A_0\ B_0\ P_0\ A_0$ A B G M X I A		1 - 4	-
3	Turn 90° to receive next part	$A_0\ B_0\ G_0\ A_3\ B_0\ P_0\ A_0$ A B G M X I A		1 - 4	-

The A_{10} (for a 10-inch action to place the object), G_6 (regrasp), and A_3 (rotate) are combined motions. The A_{10} is the controlling or limiting motion, and its index value is included in the total time. A circle indicates that the parameter(s) are combined with one or more parameters having a greater index value. If the index values are equal for combined motions, allow only one of the parameters.

Motion Combinations Performed by Different Body Members

Motion combinations performed by different body members are referred to as "simultaneous motions." When simultaneous motions occur, record the sequence model for each body member (usually the hands) and enter the appropriate index value for each parameter. After completely recording each method step, decide which parameters are performed simultaneously and circle the parameter with the lower index value for each pair of simultaneous parameters.

Example: Start with the hands at the edge of your desk and reach 10 inches (25 cm) with the left hand to a box of paper clips and place it near the edge of the desk while the right hand reaches 6 inches (15 cm) to a gum eraser and places it near the edge of the desk. This is an example of simultaneous motions. It can be analyzed as follows:

STEP	LEFT HAND METHOD DESCRIPTION	SEQUENCE MODEL	FR.	SIMO TO	TMU	FR.	SEQUENCE MODEL	RIGHT HAND METHOD DESCRIPTION	STEP
1	Place box near edge of desk	$A_{10}\ B_0\ G_6\ A_{10}\ B_0\ P_6\ A_0$ A B G M X I A		1 - 1 1 - 7	32 (24)		$\boxed{A_6\ B_0\ G_6\ A_6\ B_0\ P_6\ A_0}$ A B G M X I A	Place eraser near edge of desk	2

The simultaneous. pattern can also be analyzed on the one sequence model column form, as follows:

STEP	HAND	METHOD DESCRIPTION	SEQUENCE MODEL	FR.	SIMO TO	TMU
1	L	Place box near edge of desk	$A_{10} B_0 G_6 A_{10} B_0 P_6 A_0$ A B G M X I A			32
2	R	Place eraser near edge of desk	$A_6 B_0 G_6 A_6 B_0 P_6 A_0$ A B G M X I A		1 - 1 1 - 7	(24)

In this case the "Simo To" for the right hand will indicate a "1" (=step 1). The entire sequence model *and* the time value for the right hand activity will be circled.

The left hand requires a greater time. The right hand sequence is "limited out" by the activity of the left hand, which is indicated by writing a "1" (=step 1) in the Simo To column for the left hand. The Simo To column will therefore be used to identify the controlling method step. If the controlling motion consists of a part of a sequence model, for instance, the first three parameters (A, B, and G) the Simo To box will show 1 (1–3), which denotes that parameters 1–3 of step 1 are controlling the time for the simultaneous motions.

Since each sequence model consists of seven parameters, they can be numbered as follows:

A   B   G   A   B   P   A

1   2   3   4   5   6   7   parameter number

Consequently, if the left hand parameters A, B, and G are performed simultaneously with the right hand activity (parameters 4–7) the Simo To for the left hand will show 2 (1–3). And, as in the examples below, if the right hand parameters A, B, and P are being performed simultaneously with the left hand activity (parameters 1–3), the Simo To will indicate 1 (4–6).

Example: Suppose an operator is seated at a workbench with his hands resting on a fixture in front of him. A triangular block is located 6 inches (15 cm) to the left of the fixture. A tote pan of wood screws is located 12 inches (30 cm) to the right of the fixture. The left hand gets the block and positions the block to a loose-fitting triangular hole in the fixture (the block will only fit one way), inserting the block to a depth of $5/8$ inches (1.5 cm). Simultaneously, the right hand selects a screw from a tote pan and lays it on the bench approximately 3 inches (7.5 cm) from the tote pan. The analysis may be done as follows:

STEP	LEFT HAND METHOD DESCRIPTION	SEQUENCE MODEL	FR.	SIMO TO	TMU	FR.	SEQUENCE MODEL	RIGHT HAND METHOD DESCRIPTION	STEP
1	Place block into triangular hole	$\boxed{A_6 B_0 G_6}$ $A_6 B_0 P_{24} A$ A B G M X I A		2 - 1 2-3 1-4 1-6	30 20		$A_{10} B_0 G_{10}$ $\boxed{A_3 B_0 P_6}$ A_0 A B G M X I A	Lay screw from tote pan to bench	2

The same designation is used on both forms. However, the numbering is different and the hand performing the work must be entered on the single sequence model form. The two sequence model column form shows the hand and time relationship of the method steps by their location on the form.

Simultaneous Motion Guide

Figure 4.7, a simultaneous motion guide, has been prepared to indicate when activities of various levels of control may and may not be performed simultaneously. The guide is reproduced here as a reference for the following discussion of control levels.

The *control level* refers to the mental and visual control the operator must exercise to complete the activity or motion parameter. *Low* control level activities require little mental control and little or no visual control. *Medium* control level activities require mental and visual attention during the activity but not at

CONTROL LEVEL		HIGH	MEDIUM	LOW
LOW		USUALLY	USUALLY	USUALLY
MEDIUM	WITHIN*	PRACTICE	USUALLY	USUALLY
	OUTSIDE*	RARELY	PRACTICE	USUALLY
HIGH		RARELY	PRACTICE	USUALLY

*Refers to "Area of Normal Vision."

Figure 4.7 Simultaneous motion guide.

the completion of the activity. *High* control level activities require mental and visual attention during the activity and on completion of the activity.

An examination of the simultaneous performance chart will show that activities with a low control level can usually be simultaneously performed with an activity of any control level. On occasion, it may not be possible to perform a low control level activity simultaneously with another activity because of some constraint imposed by the parts or workplace. Medium control level activities can usually be performed simultaneously with low control level activities and may or may not be performed simultaneously with other medium or with high control level activities depending on the practice opportunity and whether the activities are within the same area of normal vision. One high control level activity can rarely be performed simultaneously with another high control level activity. Time for both high control level activities should be allowed even though you may occasionally see an unusually skilled or coordinated operator perform them as simultaneous motions.

The simultaneous motion guide also includes a listing of the control level of common activities. It shows the control level normally associated with these activities (see Fig. 4.8). The left column lists the parameters. Common activities within each parameter are listed in the three Control Level columns by the control they most commonly require. It should be noted that the workplace, parts, or tools may impose conditions changing the control level of an activity.

To use the simultaneous motion guide, the activities are first located in the table showing the control level of common activities and the control level determined for those activities. Then use the simultaneous performance chart to determine if the activities can be performed simultaneously. Allow the longer time when the activities can be performed simultaneously. Allow both times (index values) when the activities must be performed sequentially.

Analysis of Activities Involving Tools

There is no sequence model for tool use in Mini MOST. Since the use of a tool can vary from operation to operation, it is necessary to individually analyze each occurrence of tool use with General and Controlled Move Sequences for those operations that require the detailed analysis of Mini MOST.

Example: An operator reaches 12 inches (30 cm) to a screwdriver, grasps the handle, moves the screwdriver 10 inches (25 cm) to a screw, and fits the blade to the slot. The operator shifts control of the handle and, rotating the forearm, turns the screw 120° and then opens the fingers, and, holding the palm to the handle, rotates the hand to get a new grip on the handle for four additional 120° turns. Thus to tighten the screw a total of five 120° turns are made by rotating the hand about the forearm. The hand is rotated about the forearm for each of the four reaches back. The palm of the hand is always in contact with the

PARAMETER	CONTROL LEVEL		
	LOW	MEDIUM	HIGH
GAIN CONTROL G	SWEEP CONTACT GRASP (NORMAL) REGRASP FIXED LOCATION INDEFINITE LOCATION OTHER HAND	GRASP SMALL OBJECT GRASP WITH CARE DISENGAGE VARYING LOCATION FOOT OR LEG	GRASP VERY SMALL OBJECT SELECT
PLACEMENT P	DROP TO OTHER HAND TO STOP	TOSS SET AND RETAIN SET ASIDE SIMPLE POSITION GENERAL LOCATION	POSITION - NORMAL POSITION - ACCURATE EXACT LOCATION
MOVE CONTROLLED M	TO STOP TO OTHER HAND	GENERAL LOCATION	EXACT LOCATION
ALIGNMENT I		ALIGN WITHOUT ORIENTATION CHECK	ALIGN WITH ORIENTATION ALIGN - ACCURATE

Figure 4.8   Control level of common activities.

screwdriver handle. It requires a force of about $1^1/_2$ pounds (0.7 kg) for the first three turns and a force of about 3 pounds (1.4 kg) for the last two turns. The example of using the screwdriver is analyzed as shown in the chart on page 171.

This method description may be written in keyword language as follows:

1. REACH 12 INCHES (30 CM), GRASP HANDLE AND POSITION ACCURATE AND DIFFICULT SCREWDRIVER TO SCREW
2. REGRASP AND ROTATE SCREWDRIVER 120 DEGREES
3. REACH BACK 120 DEGREES, GRASP AND ROTATE SCREWDRIVER 120 DEGREES F 2
4. REACH BACK 120 DEGREES, GRASP-WT AND ROTATE SCREWDRIVER 120 DEGREES F 2
5. SET SCREWDRIVER TO BENCH 10 INCHES (25 CM)

This analysis applies only to the example described. Another use of the screwdriver may differ in distance turned, finger moves instead of hand rotations,

TMU	SIMO TO	FR.	SEQUENCE MODEL	RIGHT–HAND METHOD DESCRIPTION	STEP
50			$A_{10}\ B_0\ G_6\ A_{10}\ B_0\ P_{24}\ A_0$ A B G M X I A	Grasp screwdriver by handle and position to slot	1
16			A B G A B P A $A_0\ B_0\ G_6\ M_{10}\ X_0\ I_0\ A_0$	Regrasp handle rotate 120°	2
38		2	A B G A B P A $A_3\ B_0\ G_6\ M_{10}\ X_0\ I_0\ A_0$	Rotate hand back, close fingers, rotate 120°	3
38		2	A B G A B P A $A_3\ B_0\ G_6\ M_{10}\ X_0\ I_0\ A_0$	Rotate hand back, close fingers, rotate 120°, resist 3 lbs (1.4 kg)	4
16			$A_0\ B_0\ G_0\ A_{10}\ B_0\ P_6\ A_0$ A B G M X I A	Set screwdriver aside, 10 inches (25 cm)	5
158					

number of turns, resistance, or even the method of placing the screwdriver. Each occurrence of tool use must be separately analyzed.

The Hand Used as a Tool

There are times when the hand is used in a manner similar to use of a tool. This occurs when an object is rubbed by hand or turned by hand (nut). For rubbing, a controlled move is allowed. Sometimes, when an extremely accurate grasp is required, it is necessary to Position the hand or fingers. When this occurs, use the A   B   P portion of the sequence model and consider the same variables as in placing an object.

Striking

Striking, either with the hand or with a tool, requires attention to the Placement value selected. The General Move Sequence is used for striking. The Placement for the blow is almost always a P_3, Set and Retain. Normally the Placement value for the backswing is also a P_3, Set and Retain. At a first glance, the backswing for striking may appear to be a P_0, Indefinite Location, but a closer examination will usually reveal that a general location is required at the end of the backswing in order to start a blow that can be properly directed to the target. In a few cases of pounding a general surface requiring very little control of the blow, a P_0, Indefinite Location, is adequate, but normally the P_3, Set and Retain, is required.

Also, care must be taken to accurately determine the Action distance in striking, especially for tapping blows delivered with a hammer. The distance the hammer head moves is often much farther than the hand moves. The measurement must be taken at the hand. Typically, wrist assistance occurs in using a hammer so the Action Distance must be further reduced for the assistance. Often the Action distance for normal hammering, such as driving a nail, is as little as 1 or 2 inches (2.5–5 cm). The sequence model for each hammer blow with a 2 inch (5 cm) Action Distance is

$$A_0 \quad B_0 \quad G_0 \quad A_1 \quad B_0 \quad P_3 \quad A_0$$

This gives a total of 4 TMU per blow. The backswing sequence model is also

$$A_0 \quad B_0 \quad G_0 \quad A_1 \quad B_0 \quad P_3 \quad A_0$$

The backswing is also 4 TMU per occurrence.

Development of Special Elements

In Basic MOST a procedure is available for the development of special elements primarily for tools that may be generally unique but commonly used in a particular company. Since there is no tool use sequence model in Mini MOST, there is no need to develop special elements for tools. Nor is it recommended that General Move or Controlled Move elements be added to the Mini MOST system as presented. The elements available in Mini MOST are adequate to cover all those work measurement situations in which Mini MOST is the suitable technique.

5

The Maxi MOST System

In many long-cycle, nonrepetitive, nonidentical assembly, machining or mainte-nance operations, the use of the Basic MOST sequence models will likely pro-duce a method description with unnecessary detail. For certain long-cycle operations, the variation in the actual method from cycle to cycle is so great that the relatively precise methods description of Basic MOST is not required and can be misleading. A more general description of the method is desirable to allow for the variations in the actual method used.

This phenomenon indicates that long-cycle jobs could have a higher level analysis system applied to them and still produce a meaningful and descriptive method description as well as an accurate analysis established in less time. To meet this need, the MOST Work Measurement System was expanded to include sequence models designed expressly for the measurement of long-cycle opera-tions. Such sequence models would produce accurate results, be fast to apply and easy to learn and understand, and provide a meaningful method description.

Although Maxi MOST was intended for and certainly can be used in a man-ual mode, the development of Maxi MOST focused from the beginning on features that would adapt the technique for computer application. The descrip-tion of Maxi MOST in this chapter therefore reflects this computer orientation. The same procedures, however, may very well be used in manual applications.

A. The Sequence Models

As with the Basic MOST sequence models, the Maxi MOST sequence models provide for the analysis of the movement of objects. It has been determined that only three sequence models are needed for the analysis of long-cycle, manual operations: one for the analysis of the movement of parts or objects, one for the analysis of the use of common hand tools or equipment, and one for the analysis of operating a machine. These sequence models are *Part Handling, Tool/ Equipment Use,* and *Machine Handling.* In addition, the Powered Crane Sequence allows the analysis of the movement of object(s) with the aid of an overhead bridge crane, and the Truck Sequence allows the analysis of the movement of object(s) with the aid of a wheeled truck. The five Maxi MOST Sequence models, including parameter descriptions, are shown in Figure 5.1.

Sequence Model Description

Compared with Basic MOST, the Maxi MOST sequence models have unique definitions and applications even though the same parameter letters and keywords are used in both versions.

Part Handling

Part Handling is used for the analysis of any type of movement of one or more parts or objects to a general or specific location.

Examples: Move bracket from tote pan to truck frame. Bring two tools from tool box and five parts from rack to workbench for assembly.

The Part Handling Sequence Model is therefore used for such situations as:

- Get and place part(s) by hand with total walking distance and total amount of body motions analyzed.

ACTIVITY	SEQUENCE MODEL	SUB-ACTIVITY
PART HANDLING	**A B P**	A - ACTION WALKING DISTANCE B - BODY MOTION
TOOL USE	**A B T**	P - GET AND PLACE PARTS T - TOOL USE
MACHINE HANDLING	**A B M**	M - OPERATE MACHINE OR FIXED EQUIPMENT
POWERED CRANE TRANSPORT	**A T K T P T A**	A - ACTION WALKING DISTANCE T - TRANSPORT K - HOOKUP AND UNHOOK P - PLACE OBJECT
WHEELED TRUCK TRANSPORT	**A S T L T L T A**	A - ACTION WALKING DISTANCE S - START AND STOP T - TRANSPORT L - LOAD OR UNLOAD

Figure 5.1   Maxi MOST sequence models. Multiplier = 100.

- Push or pull objects over a distance.
- Get several parts at different locations, and place those parts at another location.
- Exchange a workpiece in a machine with analysis of walking and body motions.
- Position a hand tie-wrap around cables.
- Handle fasteners and tools when no fasten or tool use is involved, (only placement occurs).
- Place an object, with additional hand moves to secure the object, such as push buttons for starting machine; close fixture holders; open and close cabinet doors.

Tool/Equipment Use

The Tool Use Sequence Model is applied to the analysis of the use of common hand tools or equipment or the use of the fingers or hand as a tool.
Examples: Tighten bolt with wrench. Drive 10 nails with hammer.
The Tool Use Sequence Model is used for the analysis of such activities as:

- Get, use, and aside or return a tool with total walking distance and total amount of body motions analyzed.
- Get, make ready, use, and aside a tool.
- Get, place, and fasten fasteners by hand.
- Loosen and place or aside fasteners by hand.

Examples: Fasten bolts or nuts with or without washers. Place bolt, and turn nut on bolt with or without previous placing of washers. Fasten threaded fasteners with final adjusting by hand. Turn wire nut on wire ends. Attach fasteners by hand turning or striking. Use hand or power tool and return it. Make ready hand or power tool (such as change socket), and then use tool. Use glue tubes, sticks, oil cans, spray cans, etc. Use hand as a tool for striking, pushing, turning, or cranking objects. Place tool with simultaneous placement of fastener.

Machine Handling

Machine Handling is used for analysis of the manual operations associated with manipulating the controls of machines. The Machine Handling Sequence Model is used for the analysis for such situations as

- Set controls on a machine or fixed equipment with total walking distance and total amount of body motions analyzed.
- Secure the workpiece for machining.
- Set feed and/or RPM (revolutions per minute).
- Activate controls.

Transport with Powered Crane

Transport with Crane is used for the analysis of the movement of objects with the aid of a powered bridge crane. The Crane Sequence Model describes such activities as

- Walk to the crane.
- Start and transport empty crane to the location to hook up the object.
- Hook up object to crane.
- Transport object to the location for placement.
- Place object with necessary manipulations of the crane.
- Unhook and transport crane to another location.
- Return by walking.

Transport with Wheeled Truck

Transport with Wheeled Truck is used for the analysis of the movement of objects with the aid of a wheeled truck, either human or motor powered. The Truck Sequence Model describes such activities as

- Walk to the truck.
- All activities necessary to start and park truck.
- Move the truck empty to a location to load the truck.
- Load object(s) mechanically.
- Move the truck loaded to a location to unload the truck.
- Unload the truck mechanically.
- Move the empty truck to another location.
- Return by walking.

Parameter Definitions

As with the Basic MOST sequence models, the parameters making up the Maxi MOST sequence models have unique definitions that determine their use when creating Maxi MOST analyses. The following are definitions for all the parameters found in the Maxi MOST sequence models.

Description of Manual Handling Parameters

A Action Distance

Action Distance covers all horizontal movement of the hands and body during a move from one location to another that occurs within the sequence. "Action walking distance" also covers the walking to or from the location of transportation equipment (crane or truck, e.g.).

B   Body Motion

Body Motion covers all vertical body motions or overcoming obstruction(s) or impairment(s) to body movement occurring within the sequence, such as

- Bend and Arise.
- Sit and stand.
- Walk through doors.
- Climb or crawl on or off platform.
- Climb ladders.

P   Part Handling

Part Handling covers gain control and placement of object(s) to a defined location that can be "final" or from which further handling of the part(s) can be made.

T   Tool Use

Tool Use covers getting, using, and asiding tool(s) or hand-operated equipment, including tool preparation (e.g., socket change or use of counter tool). Tool Use also provides for the analysis of manually controlled process time (i.e., power wrench).

M   Machine Handling

Machine Handling covers grasping and operating machine controls or fixed machine equipment, such as

- Buttons and switches
- Cranks and wheels
- Slides

Description of the Equipment Use Parameters

T   Transportation

Transportation covers transport truck or crane (loaded or unloaded) mainly horizontally to the location where the loading or unloading will take place. Vertical moves are normally performed as part of load or unload and place object(s).

S   Start and Park

Start and Park covers the time to start and park a truck.

K   Hook and Unhook

Hook and Unhook covers the time to connect and disconnect object(s) to a crane. Included are the necessary crane moves for tightening or setting the lifting devices. Handling the lifting devices (such as bringing them from another area) are not included, only the time to hook and unhook the object(s) to the crane.

P Place with Crane

Place with crane covers the activity to place the object using a crane. The necessary vertical distance to lower the object is included.

L Load or Unload Truck

Load and Unload Truck covers the activity to mechanically load or unload an object using a truck. If the truck is unloaded or loaded manually, use the Part Handling data card.

Indexing the Sequence Models

As with the Basic MOST sequence models, to properly index each parameter a full understanding of individual parameter definitions and data card keywords is required. It is through understanding the definition and scope of subactivities represented by each keyword that the proper index value is assigned. Once selected, the correct index value (0, 1, 3, 6, 10, 16, etc.) is assigned as a subscript to the appropriate parameter, for example; A_6. When the entire sequence model has been indexed, the time in TMU (Time Measurement Units) is calculated by adding the index values for each sequence model, applying a frequency if appropriate, and multiplying the total by 100. The total time for each sequence model is presented in a time unit equal to $^1/_{1000}$ of an hour (millihour, mh). Or, by simply adding the index values and applying a frequency if appropriate, the time for each sequence model is directly presented in millihours (mh) or $^1/_{1000}$ of an hour. These time units can be easily converted to seconds, minutes, or hours according to

  1 hour = 1000 mh

  1 minute = 17 mh

  1 second = 0.3 mh

It must be remembered that measured times produced with MOST Systems including Maxi MOST represent a performance level of 100%. They represent the performance of an "average" trained worker, working under adequate supervision, and under "average" work conditions at a "normal" pace. The computation of the total time value for an activity produces a "normal time" without allowances. Usually the allowances as a percentage of "normal" time are added as a final step in establishing a "standard time".

Maxi MOST involves the application of larger blocks of time than Basic MOST. The result of using larger blocks of time is that many more combinations of activities can be described. Consideration of these combinations has led to broadening the scope of Maxi MOST parameters. The data cards for Maxi MOST, therefore, contain a far greater number of entries than the cards for Basic MOST.

However, there are still a great number of work activities that were not analyzed and placed on the data cards. Because of this, we anticipate the need for additional special elements important to the Maxi MOST user. The development of special elements is described in Section G of this chapter.

Workplace Layout

Prior to applying sequence models for analyzing manual work using Maxi MOST, a work area layout must be made including work area data, such as

- Workplace names
- Tools and their locations
- Objects and their locations
- Equipment and its location
- The operator(s) and their starting location(s)
- Body motions always associated with particular workplaces
- The distance in steps between workplaces

Figure 5.2 is an example of a computer printout of a simple workplace including a sketch and data.

The Maxi MOST Calculation Sheet

The Maxi MOST calculation sheet (see Fig. 5.3) is divided into two parts: the header data and space for the method description with sequences and index values. The header data are of particular interest because they provide the scope of and set limits for the Maxi MOST analysis.

The Header

Contained in the header of a Maxi MOST calculation sheet is information about the suboperation or operation with the purpose of an explicit and consistent identification of the data unit.

Area: Describes application area covered by the Work Management Manual (see Chap. 7).

Operation: The task or job for which a standard is needed, the final or intermediate product requiring labor time or work content data.

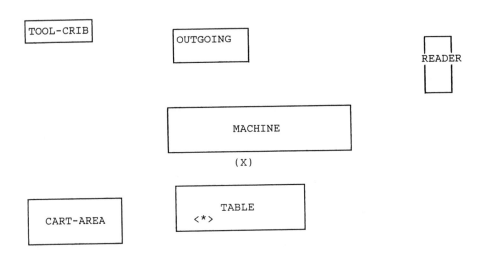

Figure 5.2 *(above and facing page)* Computer printout of a work area for Maxi MOST.

```
       Name                     Location             Body/Frag/PT
    ------------              ------------          -------------
WORKPLACES:
 MACHINE
 TABLE
 READER
 OUTGOING
 TOOL-CRIB
 CART-AREA


OPERATORS:
 OP1                         MACHINE                      B


CARRIERS:
 TOOL-BOX                    TABLE


TOOLS:
 HAMMER                      MACHINE
 AIRHOSE                     MACHINE
 SPANNER-WRENCH              MACHINE
 ALLEN-WRENCHES              TABLE
 MICROMETER                  TABLE
 FILE                        TABLE
 CALIPER                     TABLE
 RIGHT-ANGLE                 TABLE
 FEELER-GAUGE                TABLE


OBJECTS:
 BRUSH                       MACHINE
 RAGS                        TABLE
 CUTTER                      TOOL-CRIB
 IN-CART                     CART-AREA
 OUT-CART                    CART-AREA


EQUIPMENT:
 BUTTON                      MACHINE
 WHEEL                       MACHINE
```

```
       From                       To                  Steps
    ------------              ------------          ---------

 MACHINE                     TABLE                     2
 MACHINE                     READER                    32
 MACHINE                     OUTGOING                  94
 MACHINE                     TOOL-CRIB                 147
 MACHINE                     CART-AREA                 10
 TABLE                       READER                    30
 TABLE                       OUTGOING                  92
 TABLE                       TOOL-CRIB                 145
 TABLE                       CART-AREA                 8
 READER                      OUTGOING                  80
 READER                      TOOL-CRIB                 140
 READER                      CART-AREA                 38
 OUTGOING                    TOOL-CRIB                 100
 OUTGOING                    CART-AREA                 84
 TOOL-CRIB                   CART-AREA                 133
```

No.	Method Description	Sequence	Fr	mh

Maxi MOST® SYSTEMS CALCULATION   100X

Area *Packing*

Operation *Pack Item on pallet*

Title *Secure item to pallet with tape and wire*

Code

Date *4/7/81* Sign *KW* Page *1/1*

Hrs. (mh) min TMU *92*

Conditions   Crew *1/1*   Per *Pallet*

No.	Method Description	Sequence	Fr	mh
	OPERATOR TO BEGIN: OP-1 BEGINS AT: Pallet-1			
1	Place roll of green tape from tool box-1 with 16 steps	$A_3 B_1 P_1$	1	5
2	Apply 3 feet stripe of green tape to secure workpieces to pallet with bend	$A_0 B_1 T_6$	6	42
3	Place roll of green tape to tool box with 16 steps and bend	$A_3 B_1 P_1$	1	5
4	Move roll of wire from rack in shop with 12 steps and wire cutter	$A_3 B_0 P_1$	1	4
5	Uncoil wire for cutting	$A_0 B_0 P_1$	6	6
6	Cut wire with wire cutters	$A_0 B_0 T_1$	6	6
7	Manipulate and tie down 6 wires to pallet with bend	$A_0 B_1 P_3$	6	24

©HBMCo T118-81

PART HANDLING A B P	TOOL EQUIPMENT USE A B T	MACHINE HANDLING A B M	CRANE TRANSPORT A T K T P T A	TRUCK TRANSPORT A S T L T L T A	Total mh 92

Figure 5.3 Maxi MOST calculation: Packing.

Title: The name for the analyzed suboperation describing the content of the method performed.

Conditions: Additional information concerning the proper application, such as size of part or the identification of specific tools.

Code: Ten-digit filing code of the suboperation as described in Chapter 7 to be used for simple manual filing and retrieval of data units in a "data bank."

Date, signature: Calculation date and identity of the analyst.

Page: Page number and total number of pages for the suboperation. For example, $3/4$ indicating page three of four.

Time value: Time value of the calculated suboperation added and converted to the unit (millihours, minutes, or hours) used for the standards calculation (worksheet units). Note that millihours (mh) should be rounded and shown without decimals. The unit used should be circled.

Per: The production unit for which the time and title are applied. It is important to maintain consistent and countable units in preparation for the application of frequencies to these units when calculating standards or combining suboperations.

Crew: The number of operators required for the operation. For example, a $2/1$ indicates a crew of two operators for the operation. On the other hand, when one operator runs a group of machines, a 1 to the left of the slash mark and the number of machines to the right of the slash mark are entered (e.g., $1/3$ indicates that one operator is serving three pieces of equipment).

The Body of the Calculation Sheet

The proper procedure is to assign one method description step for each sequence model and vice versa. The sequence model (parameters) are written next to the text and indexed and a frequency applied if appropriate. Because of limited space in the sequence model column, the equipment handling sequences (crane or truck) must be written on two lines. All method descriptions, sequence models, and frequencies should be completed even when some activities are internal to others. They will be canceled out in the same manner as in Basic MOST. The method description should cite to which activities the limited activities are internal. After all method steps have been written and indexed, the index values are totaled and the frequencies applied as appropriate. The resulting time is in millihours (mh). For a time value in TMU, multiply the total index value by 100 and the result will be presented in TMU. If necessary, round the values to one decimal place following the application of a frequency. All sequence model totals should then be added, with the total of these index values placed at the bottom of the calculation sheet. This value should be rounded off to even mh or TMU.

Method Steps and Sequence Models

The system was designed to adequately and accurately analyze the movement of parts, objects, or tools. Normally, the operator moves a distance to Get the part(s), object(s), or tool(s) and moves a distance to Place the part(s) or object(s) or Use the tool(s). For proper application of the Maxi MOST sequence models, consider the complete activity, which includes both the Get and Place of one or more parts or objects independent of the number of locations visited to get the parts or objects. The same principle applies for the Tool Use or Equipment Sequence Model.

Example: An operator walks to a parts bin, gets a flange, moves to a pallet to get a bracket and then carries both back to a workbench where they are laid down. Use one sequence model (A B P) and one method description step: Move flange and bracket to workbench. Identify each complete and logical activity as a method step and thereafter assign the appropriate sequence model and index values. Any breakup of "logical activities" should be avoided.

Method Description Language

The clarity of the method description language is extremely important. The accuracy of the analysis depends on the language rather than the index values themselves which do not provide all the essential information necessary. When the language of the method description is clear and consistently applied, the method is more clearly understood.

First, to make the language clear, keywords and standardized sentence formats should be used. A *keyword* is a unique word assigned to each variant of a parameter that helps identify the specific activity being analyzed. The keyword is the identifying verb heading each column on the data card. The keyword combined with the application details provides complete documentation of the index selection considerations.

Second, the movements of operators, parts, tools, and so on, should be clearly tracked. This helps in selecting appropriate sequence models and index values, making the method description even more understandable and consistent.

Design of the Method Description

Each method description should refer to specific objects, such as parts, tools, and equipment, and to a work area with defined workplaces and locations. The procedure to create a method description is as follows:

1. Choose the object(s) to be moved or used.
2. Name the activity concerning the object(s) (select the keyword).
3. State the magnitude of the activity and/or tool use.
4. State the tool or equipment used.

5. State the location *from* which the object(s) are moved (if undefined in work area).
6. State the location *to* which the object(s) are moved.

The Method Description Format

To provide consistency among applicators and the inherent accuracy that results from following a structured and thoughtful approach, the following sentence formats should be used when constructing a method description.

Part Handling

OPERATOR(S) / ACTIVITY / MAGNITUDE / MOVABLE ITEM / FROM LOCATION / ACTION DISTANCE # STEPS or # FEET STRAIGHT / TO LOCATION / PUSH/PULL/SLIDE DISTANCE # FEET / BODY MOTION RETURN TO LOCATION or HOLD / ADJUSTMENT / F, PF, and/or SIMO

Example: MOVE 4 BRACKETS FROM BIN 22 STEPS TO TRUCK FRAME WITH 2 BENDS.

Tool/Equipment Use

OPERATOR(S) / ACTIVITY / MAGNITUDE / MOTION, DIMENSION, or FASTENER DIAMETER and/or LENGTH / ITEM(S) / AT LOCATION / USING TOOL/HAND/FINGER / AT LOCATION / TOOL DISPOSITION / RETURN TO LOCATION / ACTION DISTANCE / BODY MOTION / PF, F, and/or SIMO

Examples: DISASSEMBLE-LONG 2 BOLTS ¹/₂ INCH DIAMETER 3 INCHES LONG USING WRENCH AND ASIDE.

Machine Handling

OPERATOR(S) / ACTIVITY / MAGNITUDE / DEVICE(S) / AT LOCATION TO LOCATION / RETURN TO LOCATION / ACTION DISTANCE / BODY MOTION / PF, F, and/or SIMO

Example: INSTALL 5 JACKSCREWS TO WORKPIECE AT MACHINE 20 STEPS AWAY.

Crane Transport

OPERATOR(S) / ACTIVITY / ACTION DISTANCE / MOVABLE ITEM / FROM WORKPLACE / ACTION DISTANCE / USING / CRANE / HOOK AND UNHOOK / TO WORKPLACE / ACTION DISTANCE / PLACE ITEM / RETURN CRANE / RETURN TO WORKPLACE / ACTION DISTANCE / PF, F, and/or SIMO

Example: TRANSPORT PART USING CRANE WITH HOOK + SLING TO BENCH, PLACE + MANEUVER PART AND RETURN CRANE AND RETURN TO WORKBENCH.

Truck Transport

OPERATOR(S) / ACTIVITY / ACTION DISTANCE / START / MOVABLE
ITEM / FROM WORKPLACE / ACTION DISTANCE / LOAD / USING / TRUCK
TO WORKPLACE / ACTION DISTANCE / UNLOAD / RETURN TRUCK DISTANCE
DISTANCE / RETURN TO WORKPLACE / ACTION DISTANCE / PF, F, and/or
SIMO

Example: TRANSPORT PART FROM WORKPLACE-1 USING FORK-TRUCK TO RACK
AND RETURN TRUCK AND RETURN TO WORKBENCH.

SEQUENCE MODEL / VARIABLE	PART HANDLING	TOOL/EQUIPMENT USE; MACHINE HANDLING	POWERED CRANE; WHEELED TRUCK
OPERATOR(S)	●	●	●
ACTIVITY (KEYWORD)	●	●	●
MAGNITUDE	●	●	
OBJECT(S)	●	●	●
SIZE		●	
"FROM" LOCATION	●		●
TOOL EQUIPMENT SIZE		●	
TOOL USE		●	
TOOL/EQUIPMENT SIZE		●	●
"AND"		●	
ASIDE OR RETURN		●	
TOOL/EQUIPMENT		●	
"TO" LOCATION	●	●	●
WITH ADJUSTMENT(S)	●		
TOTAL STEPS	●	●	
BODY MOTIONS	●	●	
EQUIPMENT RETURN			●
OPERATOR RETURN			●

Figure 5.4 Method description format.

Note: Action Distances in the CRANE and TRUCK TRANSPORT sequence models may be entered as indicated or "automatically" transferred from the work area data by the computer with an override option.

The sequence structure for the different Maxi MOST sequence models has primarily been developed for the input of data to the computerized Maxi MOST Analysis module. By using the same format for manual analysis, an equal degree of consistency and uniformity is achieved. The established method description format is therefore recommended to be applied for all analysis work using Maxi MOST. The significant variables for each sequence model are shown in Figure 5.4.

Analysis Examples

Two examples of complete analyses using the Maxi MOST sequence models described above are displayed in Figures 5.5 and 5.6.

B. Part Handling Sequence Model

The Part Handling Sequence Model consists of just three parameters A B P, which are defined here.

Action Walking Distance (A)

The Action Distance parameter (A) is used for the analysis of the horizontal movement of an operator with or without a load from one work area to another or from one workplace to another. Action Distance includes the horizontal movement of the trunk of the body caused by the taking of steps. Steps can be taken forward, to the side, or to turn the body around.

Operator Movement

Operator movement in Maxi MOST is described in a single Action Distance (A) parameter in each of the sequences. This is different from the Basic MOST sequence models in which a separate Action Distance precedes each action (e.g., Get, Place, and Tool Use) of the sequence model. Stated simply, the Basic MOST Action Distance allows time for a one-way action but the Maxi MOST Action Distance allows time for a complete round trip. (For examples of operator movement, see Fig. 5.7.)

Types of Walking

The Action Distance (A) parameter of the Maxi MOST sequence models is indexed by the type of walking that occurs. Walking is broken down into two categories; *segmented* and *straight*.

m⟩	**Maxi MOST® SYSTEMS CALCULATION**	100X	Code			

	Area	Cab Station 129				

Maxi MOST® SYSTEMS CALCULATION   100X   Code | | | | | | | |

	Area	Cab Station 129	Date 4/10/80	Sign BN	Page 1/1
	Operation	Assemble Support Brackets			

Title	Install RS Rear Cab Latch Assy to Cab	Hrs. mh (min) TMU 4.44

Conditions		Crew 1/1	Per RCL Cab

No.	Method Description	Sequence	Fr	mh
	OPERATOR TO BEGIN: Operator 1 BEGINS AT: Stand			
1	Loosen 5 cage nuts using prybar at cab — 6 steps	$A_1B_oT_3$		4
2	Grind out 1 hole PK-1 sec using Pwee grinder-10 steps-bend	$A_3B_1T_3$		7
3	Place air hose to impact and move impact to cab-fixture	$A_oB_oP_3$		3
4	Assemble 7 bolts and 7 washers, move to cab-fixture-4 steps-bend	$A_1B_1P_3$		5
5	Apply Loctite on 7 bolts with squeeze bottle	$A_oB_oT_3$		3
6	Place cab latch Assy to cab underside-12 steps-bend	$A_3B_1P_1$		5
7	Hand start and run down 5 bolts to cab latch assy - 15 steps	$A_3B_oT_{32}$		35
8	Hand start 2 bolts and nuts to cab latch Assy	$A_oB_oT_3$		3
9	Tighten 7 bolts using impact wrench return impact wrench to stand-12 steps	$A_3B_oT_6$		9

PART HANDLING A B P	TOOL/EQUIPMENT USE A B T	MACHINE HANDLING A B M	CRANE TRANSPORT A T K T P T A	TRUCK TRANSPORT A S T L T L T A	Total mh 74

Figure 5.5 Maxi MOST calculation: Install latch assembly to cab.

Maxi MOST® SYSTEMS CALCULATION 100X						

Maxi MOST® SYSTEMS CALCULATION   100X

Area	*Fab Shop*
Operation	*Press Brake 423*

Code |　|　|　|　|　|　|　|　|

Date: 3-26-80   Sign: BN   Page: 1/1

Title	Load and unload 1100 LB Plate with Crane	(Hrs.) 0.026 mh min TMU

Conditions	Hooks hanging from Crane 2-operators	Crew 2/1	Per Plate

No.	Method Description	Sequence	Fr	mh
	OPERATOR TO BEGIN: OP-1 BEGINS AT: IN-PILE			
	OP-2 IN-PILE			
1	OP-1 Lift up Plate edges at in-pile using prybar - Pt 2 sec.-4 steps F-4	$A_1 B_o T_1$	4	8
2	OP-2 Place 4 plate hooks to plate -SIMO	$(A_o B_o P_3)$		—
3	OP-2 Transport plate using crane to press. lower and place 5 in. and adjust crane	$A_1 T_1 K_o$ $T_3 P_1 T_1 A_o$		7
4	OP-1 Remove 2 plate-hooks from plate	$A_o B_o P_1$		1
5	OP-1 Position plate to press and align against steps, start machine	$A_o B_o P_3$		3
6	OP-1 + OP-2 situate plate to cut-pile (SIMO use of prybar) in front of machine	$A_o B_o P_3$		3
7	OP-2 Transport crane to in-pile	$A_o T_1 K_o$ $T_3 P_o T_o A_o$		4

PART HANDLING A B P	TOOL/EQUIPMENT USE A B T	MACHINE HANDLING A B M	CRANE TRANSPORT A T K T P T A	TRUCK TRANSPORT A S T L T L T A	Total mh 26

HBMCo T118-81

Figure 5.6 Maxi MOST calculation: load and unload plate with crane.

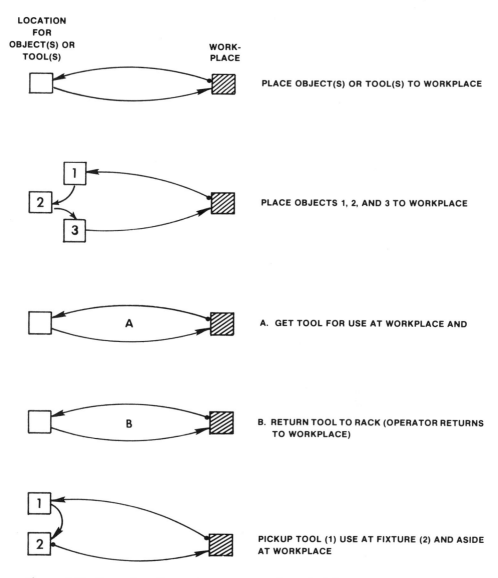

LOCATION FOR OBJECT(S) OR TOOL(S)

WORK-PLACE

PLACE OBJECT(S) OR TOOL(S) TO WORKPLACE

PLACE OBJECTS 1, 2, AND 3 TO WORKPLACE

A. GET TOOL FOR USE AT WORKPLACE AND

B. RETURN TOOL TO RACK (OPERATOR RETURNS TO WORKPLACE)

PICKUP TOOL (1) USE AT FIXTURE (2) AND ASIDE AT WORKPLACE

Figure 5.7 Examples of operator movement (round trip).

Segmented Walking

Segmented walking values should be used when the Action Distance for an operator occurs within a defined work area, when walking is obstructed, when a heavy load is carried, or any time the operator's steps must be reduced in length $\leq 2^{1}/_{2}$ feet (75 cm) per step, such as when a trip includes multiple stops and changes of direction.

The *work area* is that area in which the worker is primarily engaged, for example, "assembly line station #24." A work area most typically is composed of many "workplaces," for example, a workbench, the truck chassis, or a tub containing parts.

The Action Distance index values for segmented walking are determined according to the number of steps taken. *Step* refers to the number of times the foot hits the floor.

Examples: Walk through welding area, stepping over hoses and cables. Walk around end of workbench to pallet.

The time to take one or two steps is included in the Part Handling (P), Tool Use (T), and Machine Handling (M) parameters. This is recognized in the Action Distance (A) parameter by assigning an index value of zero to distances that require two steps or less. The analyst counts the total steps taken and selects the index value directly from the index card. The analyst does not adjust the observed number of steps for the two steps included in other parameters. All necessary adjustments have been made in constructing the data card (Fig. 5.8).

A segmented walking distance should always be determined by either counting actual number of steps taken or estimating the number of steps required.

Straight Walking

Straight Walking is used for longer distances when the operator is walking in a relatively straight path (walking at full stride). The distance should then be entered in feet or meters. The table covers the activity to walk empty or with a light load. For carrying a heavy load, use the value from the Segmented Walking Steps column.

Straight Walking normally occurs when walking between work areas, for example, when an operator walks from assembly line station #24 to the foreman's office. It should be noted that the values in the Straight Walking column of the data card are appropriate when the operator, either unloaded or with a light load only, walks with a normal stride.

You will notice that the Straight Walking Distance columns on the Action Distance card (Fig. 5.8) show an index value of 0 for distances up to 5 feet ($1^{1}/_{2}$ m). This is because the Part Handling, Tool Use, and Machine Handling parameters include time for up to two steps. The Action Distance card is used by looking up the total trip distance and allowing the corresponding index value.

Maxi MOST® System				A - ACTION DISTANCE
INDEX X 100	SEGMENTED WALKING	STRAIGHT WALKING		INDEX X 100
	STEPS	FEET	METERS	
0	2	6	2	0
1	9	24	7	1
3	23	60	18	3
6	42	120	36	6
10	70	190	60	10
16	108	300	90	16
24	153	420	130	24
32	203	550	170	32
42	264	720	220	42
54	333	920	280	54
67	408	1120	340	67
81	489	1350	410	81
96	578	1590	490	96
113	675	1860	570	113
131	784	2160	670	131
152	901	2480	770	152
173	1023	2820	870	173
196	1153	3170	980	196

Figure 5.8 Action Distance data card. Values are read "up to and including."

No adjustment to the measured distance is required as all necessary adjustments for the first two steps are included in the charts.

Examples: Walk 50 feet down a relatively clear aisle to the tool crib:

A_3 3 mh or 300 TMU or 10.8 seconds

Walk 40 feet to the foreman's office, get a job packet, and return (40 feet) to the workstation:

A_6 B_0 P_1 7 mh or 700 TMU or 25.2 seconds

An Action Distance Decision Model has been inserted as Figure 5.9 to facilitate the determination of action distance index values.

Body Motions (B)

Body Motion represents the vertical movement of the body or overcoming any obstruction or impairment to body movement. The Body Motion index values allows time for moving or positioning the body.

Special Body Motions

In addition to the body motions, such as bend and kneel, values for climbing a ladder and passing through openings have been developed and are included on the Body Motion data card. (See Fig. 5.10.) Note that walking up and down normally inclined stairs is an Action Distance subactivity, but climbing a ladder (Body Motion) always requires grasping the ladder, handrail, or rung for balance.

Body Motions Associated with Obstacles

Some of the Body Motions account for time to overcome an obstacle to the operator's progress during an Action Distance. These Body Motions deal with such activities as climbing on or off platforms or large items, climbing up or down ladders, and passing through doors or other openings. Additional activities associated with these Body Motions, such as opening or closing a door or hatch, taking hold of and placing the foot on a ladder, or turning toward or away from an obstruction that is climbed over, are included in the Body Motion index value. When determining the Action Distance, do not include the steps on or off an obstruction, the steps through a door or hatch, or turning to or away from an obstacle that is climbed as these steps are included in the Body Motion index value.

Keywords

The method description is greatly simplified by using keywords for certain representative Body Motions. It is important to read and understand the defini-

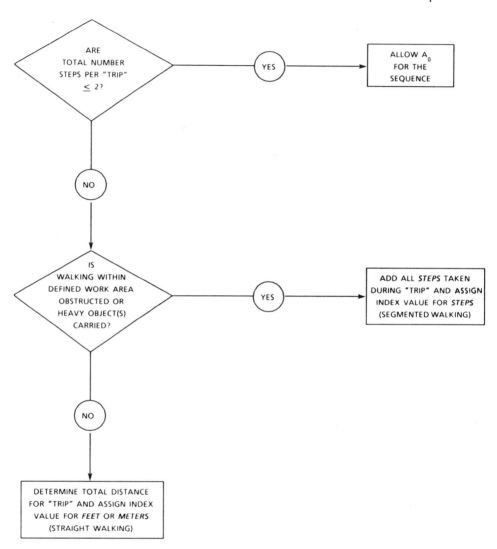

Figure 5.9 Action Distance Decision Model.

tions of each keyword so that a consistent and accurate application results. With frequent use, many Maxi MOST values will be learned by memorization and applied without consultation of the data card.

The following contains the Body Motion data card activities (Fig. 5.10) and lists the Body Motion keywords and their definitions.

Maxi MOST® System

B - BODY MOTIONS

INDEX X 100	ONE OR TWO WAY BODY MOTION	PASS THROUGH OPENINGS	COMBINATIONS OCCURRING IN SEQUENCE	LADDER		OBSTR-LADDER		INDEX X 100
				LIGHT LOAD	HEAVY LOAD	LIGHT LOAD	HEAVY LOAD	
				NUMBER OF RUNGS				
1	1 OR 2 BENDS KNEEL SIT STAND CLIMB	DOOR HATCH	BEND + SIT STAND + BEND					1
3	SIT + STAND CRAWL CREEP 2 KNEELS 2 CLIMBS 3 BENDS CLIMB - OBJECT ON FLOOR	2 DOORS 2 HATCHES OP - DOOR MANHOLE	SIT + BENDS STAND + BENDS SIT + STAND + BENDS CLIMB + BENDS DOOR + BENDS HATCH + BENDS HATCH + ON-FLOOR 2 CLIMBS + BENDS	10	3	5		3
6	FLAT - CRAWL 2 ON - FLOOR	2 MANHOLES 2 OP - DOORS OBSTR - MANHOLE	2 DOORS + BENDS 2 HATCHES + BENDS 2 HATCHES + ON - FLOOR	25	8	20	6	6
10		2 OBSTR - MANHOLES		45	17	40	14	10
16					29		26	16
24					42		40	24

Figure 5.10 Body Motions data card.

Category/keyword	Index	Definition
One-way body motions		
SIT	1	Sit down on stool or chair with or without adjusting the position of the stool or chair
STAND	1	Stand up from stool or chair with or without positioning the stool or chair
CLIMB	1	Climb on *or* off a platform approximately 3 feet high
CLIMB-OBJECT	3	Climb up *or* down three steps each 18 inches (45 cm) to 24 inches (60 cm) high, bend or position body carefully on object before working, or climb up taking two steps 18–24 inches (45–60 cm) each and climb on platform with knees into lying, sitting, or kneeling position on the object or climb off object the same way
Two-way body motions		
BEND	1	Bend, stoop, or kneel on one knee and arise; bend with hand below knees
KNEEL	1	Kneel on both knees and arise
SIT+STAND	3	Sit on stool/chair and arise or arise from stool/chair and sit on same or another
ON-FLOOR	3	Lie down on floor and arise into standing position
CRAWL	3	Kneel and crawl on hands and knees a distance ≤ 11 feet (3 m) and arise
CREEP	3	Lie down on wheeled creeper, pull in and out total distance ≤ 13 feet (4 m), and arise from creeper
FLAT-CRAWL	6	Lie down and crawl on stomach a distance ≤ 12 feet (3.5 m) and arise

Category/keyword	Index	Definition
Multiple body motions		
2 BENDS	1	Bend and arise twice
3 BENDS	3	Bend and arise three times
2 KNEELS	3	Kneel on both knees and arise twice
2 CLIMBS	3	Climb on *and* off platform
2 ON-FLOORS	6	Lay down on floor and arise (twice)
Pass through openings		
DOOR	1	Pass through hinged or swinging door by opening and closing; includes the time to take the three or four steps to go through the door
HATCH	1	Pass through a small, low opening requiring bending; the bottom of the opening may be raised, requiring an obstructed step to get through
OP-DOOR	3	Pass through mechanically operated door; wait for the door to open and close
MANHOLE	3	Pass through a vertical manhole at floor level or a horizontal manhole requiring a climb of three rungs to get up or down
OBSTR-MANHOLE	6	Pass through an extremely obstructed and tight vertical or horizontal manhole
Multiple pass through openings		
2 DOORS	3	Pass through two doors, opening and closing each
2 HATCHES	3	Pass through two hatches
2 MANHOLES	6	Pass through manhole twice
2 OP-DOORS	6	Pass through mechanically operated door; wait for the door to open and close twice
2 OBSTR-MANHOLES	10	Pass through extremely obstructed vertical or horizontal manhole twice

Category/keyword	Index	Definition
Combinations in sequence		
BEND + SIT	1	Bend and arise and sit on stool or chair at another location
STAND + BEND	1	Arise from stool chair and bend and arise at another location
SIT + BENDS	3	Bend and arise two to three times and sit on stool or chair at another location
STAND + BENDS	3	Arise from stool or chair and bend and arise two to three times at other locations
SIT + STAND + BENDS	3	Sit and arise from stool or chair and bend and arise two to three times at other locations
CLIMB + BENDS	3	Bend and arise two to three times and at another location climb on or off platform
2 CLIMB + BENDS	3	Bend and arise two to three times and at another location climb on and off platform
DOOR + BENDS	3	Bend and arise two to three times and pass through door
HATCH + BENDS	3	Bend and arise two to three times and pass through hatch
HATCH + ON-FLOOR	3	Pass through hatch and lie down on floor
2 DOORS + BENDS	6	Bend and arise two to three times and pass twice through door
2 HATCHES + BENDS	6	Bend and arise two to three times and pass twice through hatch
2 HATCHES + ON-FLOOR	6	Pass hatch twice and lie down on floor
Climb ladder		
LADDER # RUNGS		Climb up or down ladder more than two rungs without a load or with a light load

Category/keyword	Index	Definition
LADDER-HEAVY # RUNGS		Climb up or down ladder more than two rungs with heavy load (both feet rest on each rung)
OBSTR-LADDER # RUNGS		Climb up or down ladder more than two rungs with obstructed access at upper end (bend, kneel, or crawl under rail, e.g.) without or with light load
OBSTR-LADDER HVY # RUNGS		Climb up or down ladder more than two rungs with obstructed access at upper end, with heavy load, both feet rest on each rung
		Note: For climbing two steps or less (rungs), use the value for CLIMB under One-way body motions

Part Handling (P)

Definition of Parts

The first criterion for determining the index value to be assigned for the P parameter is the nature of the part(s) being handled. The terms used on the Part Handling data card (Fig. 5.11) to describe the nature of the part(s) are defined as follows:

Small or light: A small or light part may be held in the hand while working with another object in the same hand.

Medium: A part of medium weight and size cannot be held in the hand while working with another object in the same hand.

Heavy: A heavy part is recognized by the hesitation or pause exhibited by the operator when gaining control of the part (usually with both hands).

Large or bulky: A large or bulky object requires several regrasps gaining control of the object or intermediate moves when placing it.

Special: A special object is an object determined by the Maxi MOST analyst to have unique characteristics and is used frequently in workplaces being

Maxi MOST® System

GENERAL PART HANDLING

	HANDLE PART(S) ONLY							HANDLE PART(S) WITH ADJUSTMENT						
INDEX X 100	SMALL PART(S)	SMALL LIGHT PART(S) OR MEDIUM SIZE AND WEIGHT		MEDIUM OR HEAVY WEIGHT	HEAVY, LARGE AND BULKY OR SPECIAL	HEAVY AND BULKY OR SPECIAL		SMALL PARTS	SMALL LIGHT PARTS OR MEDIUM SIZE AND WEIGHT		MEDIUM OR HEAVY WEIGHT	HEAVY, LARGE AND BULKY OR SPECIAL	HEAVY AND BULKY OR SPECIAL	
	GRASP OR HOLD + MOVE	COLLECT + MOVE	MOVE	PLACE	POSITION	SITUATE	MANIPULATE	GRASP OR HOLD + MOVE	COLLECT + MOVE	MOVE	PLACE	POSITION	SITUATE	MANIPULATE
	NUMBER OF ACTIONS		NUMBER OF OBJECTS					NUMBER OF ACTIONS		NUMBER OF OBJECTS				
1	2	2	3	2	1			2		1				
3		8	10	6	3	2	1		6	7	4	2	1	
6		17		6	4	2			15	16	10	5	3	2
10				10	7	4						10	7	3
16					12	6							11	6

Figure 5.11 Part Handling data card. Values are read "up to and including."

studied. Procedures for establishing index values for special objects are covered thoroughly in a subsequent section of this text.

Units of Measure

The unit of measure describes the items counted to determine the index value. There are only two units of measure for general Part Handling. Number of *Actions* is the unit of measure used for small, light objects when one action may result in the handling of a handful of objects. Small, light objects may also be handled one at a time. When only one object is handled at a time, the number of actions is equal to the number of objects. Number of *Objects* is the unit of measure used for objects that cannot be handled more than one at a time.

Part Handling Activity Keywords

The Part Handling Activity keywords are used to describe the activity being done. This provides a more consistent description of the method since all analysts use the same keywords. The keywords are shown on the data card. The

	P - PART HANDLING					
MOVE OBJECT(S) ON SURFACE				LINE HANDLING		
MOVE ONLY		MOVE AND ADJUST		HANDLE		
LIGHT WEIGHT CART, CONVEYOR TABLE	MEDIUM OR HEAVY WEIGHT RAILS, TABLE CONVEYOR	LIGHT WEIGHT CART, CONVEYOR TABLE	MEDIUM OR HEAVY WEIGHT RAILS, TABLE CONVEYOR	STRAIGHT	INTO HAND OR ON FLOOR	INDEX X 100
PUSH OR PULL	SLIDE	PUSH OR PULL	SLIDE	TUGS	COILS	
DISTANCE IN FEET (M)				NUMBER OF TUGS/COILS		
8 (2.5)	3 (1)			2	1	**1**
29 (9)	13 (4)	21 (6.5)	10 (3)	8	3	**3**
58 (17.5)	28 (8.5)	50 (15)	24 (7.5)	16	7	**6**
99 (30)	48 (14.5)	91 (28)	45 (14)	28	13	**10**
157 (48)	78 (24)	150 (46)	74 (22.5)	44	21	**16**

following list defines each keyword. The keywords are grouped according to the size and weight of the object(s) for which the keywords may be applied:

Activity Keywords for Small, Light Objects

GRASP: Gain control of single part or handful of parts and hold, no placement included. *Example:* GRASP A HANDFUL OF WASHERS FROM TOTE PAN:

A_0 B_0 P_1 **100 TMU**

HOLD+MOVE: Hold part or handful in hand and simultaneously set them aside. *Example:* HOLD+MOVE BRACKET TO WORKBENCH:

A_0 B_0 P_1 **100 TMU**

Activity Keywords for Small, Light Objects or Medium Size and Weight Objects

COLLECT+MOVE: Collect parts into other hand or container and aside the collection. The value is determined by the number of collecting actions.

Example: COLLECT + MOVE BOLTS TO PAN:

A_0 B_0 P_3 300 TMU

MOVE: Get *and* move part(s) or object(s) to a general location, values are determined per part or per handful moved. *Example:* MOVE BASE FROM TOTE PAN TO BENCH FOR ASSEMBLY:

A_0 B_0 P_1 100 TMU

PLACE: Get *and* place a part or object at a specific location where placement adjustments are observed, values determined per number of objects moved. *Example:* PLACE PART INTO FIXTURE:

A_0 B_0 P_1 100 TMU

Activity Keyword for Medium to Heavyweight Objects

POSITION: Get *and* position part or object at a specific location with adjustments and insertion brief visual check of the alignment if necessary. Value determined per number of objects. *Example:* POSITION CASTING ONTO MILLING FIXTURE.

A_0 B_0 P_1 100 TMU

Activity Keyword for Heavy, Large, or Bulky Objects

SITUATE: Get *and* place or position object with an additional sliding movement ≤ 12 inches (30 cm) when gaining control of and/or when placing the object. Included is a brief visual check for location. *Example:* SITUATE AXLE ON WHEEL:

A_0 B_0 P_3 300 TMU

Activity Keyword for Heavy and Large or Bulky Objects

MANIPULATE: Get *and* position object with additional sliding movement ≤ 12 inches (30 cm) when more than one point on the object is aligned. *Example:* MANIPULATE BUMPER ON TO MOUNTING BRACKETS:

A_0 B_0 P_3 300 TMU

Since the nature of the object influences the selection of the keyword, a chart (see Fig. 5.12) has been prepared. It shows the most common combinations of keywords and object types. Other selections may occur.

Part Handling with Adjustments

Handle Part(s) with Adjustments may be used when additional adjustments are required to prepare for, or as a result of, placing the part(s). These adjustments may be performed on the part(s) or on the surroundings of the part(s).

PART HANDLING KEYWORD	SMALL LIGHT PART(S)	MEDIUM WEIGHT AND SIZE PART(S) OR OBJECT(S)	HEAVY OR SPECIAL PART(S) OR OBJECT(S)	HEAVY LARGE BULKY PART(S) OR OBJECT(S)
GRASP HOLD + MOVE	• •			
COLLECT + MOVE MOVE PLACE	• • •	• • •		
POSITION SITUATE MANIPULATE		•	• •	• •

Figure 5.12 Part Handling keywords. Keyword selection is based on part type.

The Adjustment does not refer to adjustment in the initial placement of the part(s). Adjustment as used here refers to preliminary adjustments required to prepare for the placement and to supplemental adjustment made necessary subsequent to the placement.

Handle Parts with Adjustments is similar to Handle Part(s) in that the type of part(s) considered and the units of measure are the same. The only difference between the two categories is the added adjustment.

Adjustment Definitions

Adjustments may include adjustments to the object(s), adjustments to the surroundings, or a few seconds waiting for a process to occur.

Adjustments to the part(s) includes an additional sliding or second movement of the part(s). The adjustment may involve guiding or aligning the part(s) from one to three stops or marks.

Adjustments also provide time, up to 4 seconds, for inspecting the part(s). The inspection may occur before or after the placement.

Adjustments to the surroundings are those brief activities required for placing the part(s). These adjustments include opening or closing a clamp or fixture, pushing or pulling nearby object(s), alignment (up to three points) of a nearby object(s), an inspection of the surroundings lasting up to 4 seconds, or activating a button or lever when required for, or resulting from, placing object(s).

Waiting is also considered an adjustment when the waiting is associated with the placement of object(s). The waiting may occur prior to or after the placement.

Keyword for Adjustment(s)

The keyword ADJUSTMENT is recorded or specified at the end of the Part Handling method step to document or account for adjustment activities.

Move Object(s) on Surface

Moving an object over a surface is also shown on the Part Handling data card. These values apply to any sliding, pushing, or pulling of object(s) over a surface a distance greater than 12 inches (30 cm). The moving on a surface applies to sliding object(s) on a solid surface, pushing or pulling a wheeled table or stand across a flat surface or along rails, or sliding object(s) along a conveyor.

Move object applies to moving an object along a surface when adjustment(s) are not required.

Types of Parts for Moving on Surface

The part(s) considered in moving object(s) on a surface are divided into two categories based on the force required to move the part(s):

Light weight: A lightweight part can be pushed or pulled with one hand without noticeable hesitation to start the part in motion. Examples of lightweight parts are a small wheeled cart, a 20 pound (9 kg) part on a low friction surface, or object(s) on a conveyor.

Medium or heavy weight: A medium or heavyweight part is an object that requires two hands to slide on a surface or can be slid with one hand when the force required to start the sliding results in a noticeable hesitation prior to movement of the part. Examples of medium or heavy parts are a 50 pound (23 kg) part that is slid across a table or the floor, a heavy plate that is pushed along steel rails or a steel surface, or an extremely heavy plate pushed along a conveyor.

Unit of Measure

The unit of measure for moving object(s) on a surface is always the distance moved in feet (meters).

Keywords for Moving Objects

The keywords are applied according to the nature of the object(s) moved. Lightweight object(s) require the keywords PUSH or PULL, depending on which is more descriptive of the activity. Medium or heavyweight object(s) require the keyword SLIDE.

Move with Adjustment(s)

Move with Adjustment(s) applies to moving object(s) along a surface when additional adjustment(s) are required prior to completing the move or subsequent to the completion of the move. The adjustments referred to here are not those adjustments required for the initial alignment or location of the object(s). This time is included in the moving of the object(s). These adjustments refer to the activity that prepares the surroundings for the object, turns or relocates the part(s) after the original location is complete, or makes changes to the surroundings necessitated by moving the object(s).

Move with Adjustment(s) is quite similar to move (only) in that all the Move activity is included in Move with Adjustment(s). The only difference between these two cases is the added adjustment. The two categories deal with the same part classifications. The unit of measure, distance in feet, is the same. The keyword ADJUSTMENT is also used when Move with Adjustment(s) data are appropriate.

The adjustments provided for in Move with Adjustment(s) and Handle Part(s) with Adjustment(s) are identical. Adjustment includes and provides time for a number of brief activities, usually requiring 4 seconds or less, that are associated with the primary activity.

Line Handling

Line Handling includes the manual motions required for activities performed to handle lines, hoses, cables, or any long, flexible object. The actions considered are those peculiar to these objects. Lines are pulled from place to place, through openings, from reels, and into coils either in the operator's hand or on the floor. The index values include time to gain control of the line and manipulate the line for the purpose of relocating or coiling the line.

Types of Line Handling

There are two types of Line Handling, straight pulls or tugs and coil forming either in the hand or on the floor.

Straight Straight Line handling refers to handling the line with relatively straight strokes of the hand or hands. This involves very little control of the line after the tugging action that pulls a section of the line to a new location. This action may occur to *pull* a line through an opening, to *clear* a line from an area, to provide *slack* in a line at the operator location, or to *remove* a line from a reel when little or no arrangement of the line is required. The action may be performed with alternate actions of the hands, "hand over hand," or with simultaneous use of both hands.

Into Hand or on Floor Into Hand or on Floor describes a coiling activity. These index values are used when the operator coils or arranges the lines in a coillike arrangement in the hand or on the floor or other flat surface. The first part of the action is much like straight handling in that the line is generally pulled toward the operator. The significant difference is the added arranging of the line in the operator's hand or on the surface. When the coil is formed in the hand, time is included in this parameter for asiding the coiled line to a hook or to a surface.

Units of Measure

Line Handling values are based on the number of actions required for the activity. For straight-line handling, the number of tugs are counted and the index value determined from the count. When the line is *coiled,* the number of coils becomes the basis for selecting the index value as each action results in an added coil.

Keywords for Line Handling

The keywords for Line Handling are TUG and COIL. TUG refers to straight-line handling in which each pulling action or tug is counted as the basis for selection the index value. COIL is used as the keyword when, in addition to pulling a section of line, the operator arranges each section into a coil or loop.

Part Handling Sentence Structure

For consistent application, it is recommended that the following sentence structure be used for Part Handling. This provides a readily recognizable format for the method description.

OPERATOR / ACTIVITY / MAGNITUDE / MOVABLE ITEM / FROM LOCATION / ACTION DISTANCE # STEPS or FEET STRAIGHT / TO LOCATION / PUSH/PULL/SLIDE DISTANCE # FEET / BODY MOTION RETURN TO LOCATION or HOLD / ADJUSTMENTS / F, PF, and/or SIMO

The following are typical descriptions of Part Handling method steps:

1. PLACE OBJECT TO . . . AND START MACHINE WITH ADJUSTMENT
2. MOVE OBJECT TO . . . AND CLOSE FIXTURE WITH ADJUSTMENT
3. POSITION PART TO . . . AND PUSH PART WITH ADJUSTMENT
4. MOVE OBJECT TO . . .
5. PLACE OBJECT TO . . . AND ADJUST AGAINST STOP
6. POSITION OBJECT TO . . . ALIGN AGAINST STOP
7. SITUATE GLOVES TO HANDS ON AND OFF
8. MANIPULATE AND ATTACH 2 SLINGS TO OBJECT
9. PULL HOSE 10 PULLS AND RETURN TO . . .
10. COIL HOSE 5 COILS AND RETURN TO . . .
11. PLACE 5 BOLTS WITH 5 WASHERS . . .

Examples

WELDER FITTER HELPER MOVE LEVER-FULCRUM-ASSEMBLY TO
FINAL-TACK-TABLE

A_3 B_0 P_1 **400 TMU**

MOVE ROD-FULCRUM-ASSEMBLY TO IN-PROCESS-STAGING

A_1 B_0 P_1 **200 TMU**

PLACE 2 CLAMPS TO INITIAL-TACK-TABLE WITH ADJUSTMENT

A_0 B_0 P_3 **300 TMU**

PUSH TOOL-CART FROM WELD-AREA TO UNIT . . . AND RETURN

A_6 B_0 P_6 **1200 TMU**

SECURE 5 CLAMP-FIXTURES TO UNIT

A_0 B_0 P_6 **600 TMU**

MOVE HAMMER TO UNIT-LADDER 5 RUNGS

A_3 B_3 P_1 **700 TMU**

Frequency Extrapolation

Occasionally there will be situations in which the number of activities observed exceeds the number of activities shown on the data card. For the majority
of cases, the next higher index value applies.

If the number of activities is significantly higher, you can obtain an approxi-
mation of the index value by using a partial frequency: Divide the number of
activities into equal groups just small enough to appear on the data card, assign
the appropriate index, and then use the divisor as a partial frequency for the
parameter.

Example: You observe an operation in which a worker is pulling a cable
through an opening in a wall. The worker takes 45 pulls to accomplish the task.
Note that the maximum value provided is for 44 pulls. In this case you may use
the next higher index value, P_{24}.

If the work requires 60 pulls, divide 60 by 2 (the lowest partial frequency you
can use), giving you 30 pulls. On the data card 30 pulls fall in the range of ≤ 44
tugs, which has an index value of 16. Then follow P_{16} with a parameter frequency of 2: A_x B_x (P_{16}) (2).

If a more exact value is desired for later use, the index value can be established by setting up the equation $y = mx + c$ and solving for the m and c
values. The table can then be extrapolated (see also page 257).

Note: If the number of actions greatly exceeds the limits of the data card, a methods improvement is probably the best solution.

Part Handling Sequence Model Examples

PLACE JACK AND PIPE TO TEAR-DOWN AREA WITH ADJUSTMENT

A_0 B_0 P_1 **100 TMU**

POSITION JACKING STUD, WASHER, AND STRONG BACK ON TO EXTENSION-ARM WITH ADJUSTMENT AND 3 STEPS

A_1 B_0 P_6 **700 TMU**

POSITION 10 OBJECTS FROM RACK 55 STEPS TO MACHINE WITH BEND

A_{10} B_1 P_{10} **2100 TMU**

SITUATE VISE FROM PALLET 12 STEPS ON TO MACHINE TABLE

A_3 B_1 P_3 **700 TMU**

SLIDE BOX WITH 10 STEPS AT BENCH 40 FEET (13 m)

A_3 B_0 P_{10} **1300 TMU**

C. Tool Use Sequence Model

The Tool Use Sequence Model consists of three parameters A B T. Only the T parameter is defined here since A and B are identical to the Action Distance and Body Motion parameters in the Part Handling sequence.

The Tool Use parameter applies when a tool is used to perform work or when hands or fingers are used as tools. Use of eyes (think or read) and process times are also classified as tool use. To reduce the number of method steps in an analysis, certain additional activities are included within the Tool Use parameter, including

- Change socket on tool.
- Use counter or holding tool.
- Place fastener onto tool or onto object.

All Tool Use index values include the time to take one to two steps to get and aside the tool or object.

The Tool Use parameter is presented in the form of seven data cards. The first division of the Tool Use parameter is further divided into broad categories of similar activities, such as Install or Remove Standard Threaded Fasteners, Measure, and Clean Surface. These broad categories are then usually divided

Maxi MOST® System — ASSEMBLE OR DISASSEMBLE STANDARD THREADED FASTENER(S) COMPLETE — T-TOOL USE

NUMBER OF FASTENERS

INDEX X 100	SCREWDRIVER MACHINE SCREW ALL	SCREWDRIVER SHEET-METAL SCREW ALL	WRENCH 3/4" (20 mm)	WRENCH 1-1/2" (40 mm)	WRENCH >1-1/2" (>40 mm)	RATCHET 3/4" (20 mm)	RATCHET 1-1/2" (40 mm)	POWER TOOL 1/4" (6 mm)	POWER TOOL 1" (25 mm)	POWER TOOL >1" (>25 mm)	HAND START ONLY N/A	HAND RUN DOWN LOOSE 1/4" (6 mm)	HAND RUN DOWN LOOSE 1" (25 mm)	HAND RUN DOWN LOOSE 1-1/2" (40 mm)	HAND RUN DOWN LOOSE >1-1/2" (>40 mm)	HAND TIGHT 1/4" (6 mm)	INDEX X 100 / THREAD DIAMETER (UP TO)
1											2	1					1
3	1							1	1		4	2	1				3
6	2	1						2	2		6	3	2	1		1	6
10	3	2				1		4	3	1	10	5	4	2	1	2	10
16	4	3	1			2		6	6	3		8	6	3	2	3	16
24	6	5	2			3	1	9	8	4		10	8	4	3	5	24
32	8	6	3	1		4	2	12	11	6			11	5	4	7	32
42	10	9	4	2		6	3		11	9				7	6	9	42
54		11	6	3	1	8	4			12				8	7	11	54
67			7	4	2	9	5							10	9		67
81			9	5	3	11	6								12		81

Figure 5.13 Maxi MOST—Tool Use data card for standard threaded fasteners. Values are read "up to and including."

into more finite categories depending on the tool used or the action involved. Each of these categories is discussed in this chapter.

Standard Threaded Fasteners

There are two data cards for standard threaded fasteners such as nuts, bolts, and screws. A *Standard Threaded Fastener* may be defined as a fastener that, when secure, has been turned in a distance from one to two times its diameter.

The complete chart for assemble or disassemble Standard Threaded Fastener (Fig. 5.13) is used when a fastener is placed and started, whether or not it is fully run in or tightened. This data card is also used when a fastener, either tight or loose, is removed and laid aside. Therefore, even though the elements on this data card may include final tightening or initial loosening, it also applies when the threaded fastener is simply moved to the assembly and fastened or loosened and removed from the assembly.

The index values for assemble or disassemble Standard Threaded Fasteners—Complete include time for some brief associated additional activities:

- Assembling washers and opposing fasteners
- Changing sockets
- Handling counter or holding tools
- Adjusting wrenches

These activities are included on the basis of typical frequencies so that no adjustment is required for the presence or absence of these activities. The sub-activity index values may be applied without regard for these activities. It should be noted that the index values make no provision for connecting or disconnecting power tools, as well as the associated cord or hose handling, which must be analyzed separately using Part Handling values.

The index value for assemble or disassemble Standard Threaded Fastener—Complete is selected by the tool used, details concerning the type of fastener, how it is assembled or disassembled, and the number of fasteners. The tools and application details are as follows:

Tool	Application detail	Explanation
Screwdriver	Machine screw	Get screwdriver, get screw(s), place screw(s), run in and tighten, and aside screwdriver (all sizes). *Example:* ASSEMBLE SIX MACHINE SCREWS USING SCREWDRIVER AND ASIDE: A_0 B_0 T_{32} **3200 TMU**

Tool	Application detail	Explanation
	Sheet metal screw	Get screwdriver, get screw(s), place screw(s), run in and completely tighten, and aside screwdriver. *Example:* ASSEMBLE TWO SHEET METAL SCREWS USING SCREWDRIVER AND ASIDE:
		A_0 B_0 T_{10} **1000 TMU**
Wrench	$\leq {}^3/_4$ inch (20 mm) thread diameter $\leq 1{}^1/_2$ inch (40 mm) thread diameter $> 1{}^1/_2$ inch (40 mm) thread diameter	Get wrench, get fastener(s), start fastener(s), run in by hand, wrench tighten and aside wrench; select value by thread diameter. *Example:* ASSEMBLE FOUR BOLTS I INCH (25 MM) DIAMETER USING WRENCH AND ASIDE:
		A_0 B_0 T_{67} **6700 TMU**
Ratchet	$\leq {}^3/_4$ inch (20 mm) thread diameter $\leq 1{}^1/_2$ inch (40 mm) thread diameter	Get ratchet, change socket as required, get fastener(s), start, run in and tighten fastener(s) and aside wrench; select by thread diameter and number of fasteners. *Example:* ASSEMBLE EIGHT SPARK PLUGS ⅝ INCH (15 MM) DIAMETER USING RATCHET AND ASIDE:
		A_0 B_0 T_{54} **5400 TMU**
Power tool	$\leq {}^1/_4$ inch (6 mm) thread diameter ≤ 1 inch (25 mm) thread diameter	Get power tool, change socket as required, get fastener(s), start, run in, tighten fastener(s) and aside wrench. *Example:* ASSEMBLE FIVE LUG NUTS ⅜ INCH (10 MM) DIAMETER USING POWER TOOL ASIDE:
		A_0 B_0 T_{16} **1600 TMU**
Hand	Start only	Get fastener(s), place, start threads up to two revolutions of the fastener(s). *Example:* START NUT USING HAND:
		A_0 B_0 T_3 **300 TMU**

Tool	Application detail	Explanation
	Loose	Get fastener(s), place, start threads until resistance is encountered; the additional application detail of thread diameter must be considered for running down or removal of fastener(s) by hand. *Example:* ASSEMBLE NUT ⅜ INCH (10 MM) DIAMETER USING HAND: A_0 B_0 T_6 **600 TMU**
	Tighten ≤ ¼ inch (6 mm) diameter	Get fastener(s), place, start threads, run in, and tighten by hand. *Example:* ASSEMBLE TWO WING NUTS ¼ INCH (6 MM) DIAMETER TIGHT USING HAND: A_0 B_0 T_{10} **100 TMU**

Sentence Format

The Tool Use Sequence method step format is:

OPERATOR(S) / ACTIVITY / MAGNITUDE / MOTION, DIMENSION, or FASTENER DIAMETER and/or LENGTH / ITEM(S) / AT LOCATION / USING TOOL / HAND / FINGER / AT LOCATION / TOOL DISPOSITION / RETURN TO LOCATION / ACTION DISTANCE / BODY MOTION / PF, F, and/or SIMO

Adjust Standard Threaded Fastener

The Adjust Standard Threaded Fastener data card (Fig. 5.14) is used when a standard fastener, already in place, is tightened or loosened with up to 5 revolutions but not removed from an assembly. The Adjust Standard Threaded Fastener index values for assemble and disassemble include time for common related additional activities:

- Changing sockets
- Handling counter or holding tools
- Adjusting wrenches

Line and connector handling for power tools must be analyzed separately using the Part Handling data.

The index value for Adjust Standard Threaded Fastener is selected by the tool used, details concerning the type of fasteners, and the number of fasteners. The tools and application details are as follows:

Tool	Application detail	Explanation
Screwdriver	Applies to any screw	Get screwdriver, place on screw(s) on assembly, run in, tighten screw(s), and aside screwdriver. *Example:* ADJUST SCREW USING SCREWDRIVER AND ASIDE: A_0 B_0 T_3 **300 TMU**
Wrench	$\leq 3/4$ inch (20 mm) thread diameter $\leq 1^{1}/_2$ inch (40 mm) thread diameter $\leq 1^{1}/_2$ inch (40 mm) thread diameter	Get wrench, place on fastener, run in or out, and aside wrench; select by thread diameter. *Example:* ADJUST SIX BOLTS I INCH (25 MM) DIAMETER USING WRENCH AND ASIDE: A_0 B_0 T_{54} **5400 TMU**
Ratchet	$\leq 3/4$ inch (20 mm) thread diameter $\leq 1^{1}/_2$ inch (40 mm) thread diameter	Get ratchet, change socket as required, place on fastener, run in or out, and aside ratchet; select by thread diameter. *Example:* ADJUST EIGHT BOLTS $\frac{1}{2}$ INCH (10 MM) DIAMETER USING RATCHET AND ASIDE: A_0 B_0 T_{42} **4200 TMU**
Power tool	$\leq 1/4$ inch (6 mm) thread diameter ≤ 1 inch (25 mm) thread diameter ≤ 1 inch (25 mm) thread diameter	Get power tool, change socket as required, place on fastener, (run in or out and aside power tool); select by thread diameter. *Example:* ADJUST FIVE NUTS I INCH (25 MM) DIAMETER USING POWER TOOL AND ASIDE: A_0 B_0 T_6 **600 TMU**
Hand	$\leq 1/4$ inch (6mm) thread diameter	Get fastener (already started), run in or out. *Example:* ADJUST TWO NUTS $\frac{1}{4}$ INCH (6 MM) DIAMETER USING HAND: A_0 B_0 T_3 **300 TMU**

Maxi MOST®System		ADJUST STANDARD THREADED FASTENER(S)								T - TOOL USE
INDEX X 100	SCREWDRIVER	WRENCH			RATCHET		POWER TOOL			HAND	INDEX X 100
THREAD DIAMETER (UP TO)	ALL	3/4" (20 mm)	1-1/2" (40 mm)	> 1-1/2" (>40 mm)	3/4" (20 mm)	1-1/2" (40 mm)	1/4" (6 mm)	1" (25 mm)	>1" (>25 mm)	1/4" (6 mm)	THREAD DIAMETER (UP TO)
1							1	1			1
3	1						5	3	2	2	3
6	3	1			1	1	10	7	3	4	6
10	6	2	1		2		17	12	6	7	10
16	9	3		1	4	2			10	10	16
24	13	4	3		5	3					24
32		6	4	2	7	5					32
42		8	5		10	6					42
54		10	6	3		8					54
67			8	4		10					67
81			9								81

Figure 5.14 Maxi MOST—Tool Use data card for Adjust Standard Threaded Fasteners. Values are read "up to and including."

Long Threaded Fasteners

During the course of making an analysis, you may be faced with a situation in which a long threaded fastener is used. Basically, a long threaded fastener is one that is run in or out a considerably longer distance than a standard threaded fastener. For the purposes of these data cards, a standard fastener with up to 3/4 inch (20 mm) thread diameter may be run in as far as 1 inch (2.5 cm). A standard fastener with a thread diameter greater than 3/4 inch (20 mm) may be run in as far as 2 inches (5 cm). Therefore, any fastener run in or out a distance greater than those just mentioned is considered a *long threaded fastener*.

The data card (Fig. 5.15) for assemble or disassemble Long Threaded Fastener—Complete is used in a manner quite similar to that for assembling or disassembling standard fasteners. The application criteria are the tool, details about the fastener, and the number of fasteners. The length considered is not the total length of the fastener but the length run in for assembling or out for disassembling. The lengths for installation and removal of long threaded fasteners are up to and including 2 inches (5 cm) and up to and including 4 inches (10

Maxi MOST® System — ASSEMBLE OR DISASSEMBLE — LONG STANDARD THREADED FASTENER(S) COMPLETE — **T - TOOL USE**

Index X 100	SCREWDRIVER		WRENCH			RATCHET			POWER TOOL				Index X 100
LENGTH	2"	4"	2"	4"		2"	4"		2"		4"		LENGTH
THREAD DIAMETER	ALL	ALL	3/4" (20 mm)	3/4" (20 mm)	>3/4" (>20 mm)	3/4" (20 mm)	3/4" (20 mm)	>3/4" (>20 mm)	1/4" (6 mm)	3/4" (20 mm)	1/4" (6 mm)	3/4" (20 mm)	THREAD DIAMETER
6									1	1	1	1	**6**
10	1								2	3	-	2	**10**
16									4	5	3	3	**16**
24	2	1			1	1			6	7	4	5	**24**
32	3		1					1	8	10	6	7	**32**
42	4	2			2				11		7	9	**42**
54	5					2	1	2			10	12	**54**
67	7	3	2	1	3								**67**
81	8	4				3		3					**81**
96	10	5	3		4		2						**96**
113		6			5	4		4					**113**

Figure 5.15 Maxi MOST—Tool Use data card for Long Standard Threaded Fasteners. Values are read "up to and including."

cm). When a threaded fastener is run in or out more than 4 inches (10 cm), allow the installation or removal for a 4 inch (10 cm) length, and in a separate sequence, allow the additional length from the Adjust Long Threaded Fastener data card.

Adjust Long Threaded Fastener

The Adjust Long Threaded Fastener data card (Fig. 5.16) provides for the adjustment (tightening or loosening) of long threaded fasteners or long threaded devices. These index values apply when a long threaded fastener is tightened in place or loosened in place. Neither assembly nor removal of the fastener occurs in an activity analyzed using these values.

The index values for adjusting long threaded fasteners are chosen by the tool used, details about the fastener (length of adjustment and thread diameter), and the number of fasteners. The lengths shown are up to and including 2 inches (5 cm) and greater than 2 inches (5 cm), up to and including 4 inches (10 cm).

Maxi MOST®System	ADJUST LONG STANDARD THREADED FASTENER(S)														T-TOOL USE
Index X 100	SCREWDRIVER		WRENCH				RATCHET				POWER TOOL				Index X 100
LENGTH	2"	4"	2"		4"		2"		4"		2"		4"		LENGTH
THREAD DIAMETER (UP TO)	ALL	ALL	3/4" (20 mm)	>3/4" (>20 mm)	3/4" (20 mm)	>3/4" (>20 mm)	3/4" (20 mm)	1 1/2" (40 mm)	3/4" (20 mm)	1 1/2" (40 mm)	1/4" (6 mm)	>1/4" (>6 mm)	1/4" (6 mm)	>1/4" (>6 mm)	THREAD DIAMETER (UP TO)
3											1	2		1	3
6	1										3	4	1	2	6
10	2										5	7	3	4	10
16		1						1			8	12	4	7	16
24	3				1						12		7	10	24
32	5	2					1	2		1			9		32
42	6		1			1							12		42
54	8	3			2		2	3	1	2					54
67	10	4			3					4					67
81		5	2			1	3	5		3					81

Figure 5.16 Maxi MOST—Tool Use data card for Adjust Long Standard Threaded Fasteners. Values are read "up to and including."

When the adjustment length exceeds 4 inches (10 cm), divide the total adjustment by 4 inches (10 cm), round to the next highest whole number, and allow the 4 inch (10 cm) value with a frequency determined by the division and rounding. Some of the tools also require that thread diameter be considered in selecting the index value. The ranges allowed for thread diameter are selected as appropriate for the tool considered.

A special use of the adjustment chart is for the installation or removal of threaded fasteners when the fastener is run in or out a distance exceeding 4 inches (10 cm). When this occurs, use the assemble or disassemble Long Threaded Fastener—Complete (Fig. 5.15) to account for the first 4 inches (10 cm) of run in or run out. In a separate sequence, use Adjust Long Threaded Fastener (Fig. 5.16) to allow for the additional run in or run out distance.

Turn by Hand

The index values for Turn by Hand are located on a general Tool Use data card (Fig. 5.17) along with Push or Pull, Strike, and Apply Material with Tool. The index values for turning by hand are selected by the type and number of actions.

The index values include time for up to two steps to get the object(s) and time for manipulating the object(s).

Finger Turns

Index values from the Finger column are selected when an object is turned or manipulated by the fingers while the position of the hand does not change significantly. The index value is selected by the number of total actions. The time to reach back and obtain a new grip is included in the index value and should not be counted when applying the value.

Wrist Turns

Index values from the Wrist column are selected when the object is turned or manipulated by wrist actions. Wrist actions occur when the hand is turned by rotations about the forearm. The index value is selected by the number of total actions. The time to reach back and obtain a new grip is included in the time for each action and should not be counted as an action when selecting the index value.

Arm Turns

Arm turn index values apply when an object is manipulated by circular motions of the hand. Examples of arm turns are rolling a car window up or down, turning a crank to advance or retract a machine slide, and winding a string on a spool by hand. The index value for arm turns is selected by the number of revolutions.

Sentence Format

OPERATOR(S) / ACTIVITY / MAGNITUDE / MOTION, DIMENSION / ITEMS AT LOCATION / USING / TOOL / AT LOCATION / TOOL DISPOSITION RETURN TO / ACTION DISTANCE / BODY MOTION

Examples: TURN WHEEL 5 ARM-TURNS USING HANDS:

A_0 B_0 T_3 **300 TMU**

TURN KNOB 2 FINGER-TURNS USING FINGERS:

A_0 B_0 T_1 **100 TMU**

TURN OBJECT 6 WRIST-TURNS USING HAND:

A_0 B_0 T_3 **300 TMU**

Maxi MOST® System											GENERAL TOOLS I	
INDEX X 100	TURN BY HAND			SHOVE OR DRAW NO. OF ACTIONS HAND		PRY NO. OF ACTIONS	STRIKE — NUMBER OF BLOWS					
	NUMBER OF ACTIONS		REVS.				HAND		HAMMER		MALLET	SLEDGE
	FINGER-TURNS	WRIST-TURNS	ARM-TURNS	NORMAL	HEAVY	PRY-BAR	WRIST-STROKES	ARM-STROKES	WRIST-STROKES	ARM-STROKES	ARM-STROKES	ARM-STROKES
1	3	4	2	6	1	3	10	5	17	4	3	
3	26	15	16	19	7	16	31	15	59	16	11	4
6	58	31	36		16	34		30		32	22	10
10	102	53	63			60					37	18
16												29
24												43

Figure 5.17. Maxi MOST—Tool Use data card: General Tools I. Values are read "up to and including."

Shove or Draw

Shove or Draw index values apply when an object is manipulated along a controlled path, less than or equal to 5 inches (12.5 cm). Shove or Draw may apply to a single linear action, to reciprocal actions, or to a series of actions along a controlled path. The index value is selected by the number of actions. Sometimes shoving or drawing is accomplished with one hand but heavier shoving or drawing may require the use of both hands. Shove or Draw Tool Use index values apply for distances less than or equal to 12 inches (30 cm). Part Handling should be used for distances greater than 12 inches (30 cm).

Shove or Draw index values apply when the hand acts directly on the object. Hand Shove or Draw index values are classified as Normal or Heavy. Count each direction as a separate action when determining the index value.

Shove/Draw: Normal

Shove/Draw actions are those when little resistance is encountered in performing the actions. Little hesitation is noted at the beginning of the action, and little slowing due to resistance is observed during the action. When Shove/Draw actions apply, the resistance is light enough to be overcome with one hand.

		APPLY MATERIAL WITH TOOL						T-TOOL USE
SEAL-GUN	GREASE-GUN	SQUEEZE-BOTTLE	TUBE	FINGER, HAND, BRUSH, OR STICK	SQUIRT-CAN	AEROSOL CAN	TAPE-ROLL	INDEX X 100
PULLS	LEVER-ACTIONS	DROP	1" SPOT (25 mm)	1" SPOT (25 mm)	SQUIRT	SQ. FT. (0,1 m²)	FOOT OR STRIP	
		1						**1**
1	4	7		2	8		1	**3**
5	14	16	6	6	20	1	3	**6**
11	28		16	12		3	5	**10**
19	48					6	8	**16**
28	72					9	12	**24**

Shove Draw: Heavy

Shove/Draw Heavy actions are used when there is considerable resistance. The actions are characterized by a pause in starting the action due to a building up of muscular force to overcome resistance to the action. If a reciprocating action has resistance in one direction, apply the Shove/Draw Heavy index values for all the actions. Shove/Draw Heavy actions often require the use of both hands to overcome resistance.

Pry

Pry actions occur when a tool is pushed or pulled to exert a prying force on an object. Pry index values include time to get and aside the tool within two steps as well as to use the tool. The index value is selected by the number of active prying actions. Back strokes and resetting the tool are included in the time for the pry index values.

Strike

Strike index values are located on the general Tool Use card (Fig. 5.17) with Turn by Hand and Shove or Draw. *Strike* applies to blows delivered by the hand or with a tool. The index values are determined by the number of times the hand or tool impacts against the object. Do not count the backswing as this is included in the time per blow.

Hand

Hand index values apply to all striking done with the empty hand. The hand may be opened or closed into a fist. The muscles of the hand may be tensed and relaxed. The point of impact may be any part of the hand. The Hand striking index values, however, are divided into Wrist strokes and Arm strokes.

Wrist Strokes

Wrist Strokes are those blows pivoted primarily at the wrist with the arm held relatively stationary. Count the number of blows. Do not count the backstroke.

Arm Strokes

An Arm Stroke is performed primarily by motion of the arm pivoted at the elbow or the shoulder. Count the number of blows. Do not count the backstroke.

Hammer

Hammer blows are delivered with the aid of a hammer or any tool or object used in the manner of a hammer. The index values include time to get and aside the hammer. An Action Distance index value must be allowed if more than two steps are taken. Hammer striking, like hand striking, is divided into two groups, wrist and arm strokes, based on the method of striking. See the discussion of hand striking for the distinction between wrist strokes and arm strokes. Count the number of blows. Do not count the backstroke.

Mallet

Mallet index values apply when the object is struck with a large hammer or mallet. Count the number of blows. Do not count the backstroke.

Sledge

Sledge index values apply to blows delivered with a sledge of up to 10 pounds (4.5 kg) weight.

Examples: STRIKE PART THREE WRIST STROKES USING HAND:

A_0 B_0 T_1 **100 TMU**

STRIKE OBJECT TWO ARM STROKES USING HAND:

A_0 B_0 T_1 **100 TMU**

STRIKE OBJECT SIX WRIST STROKES USING HAMMER AND ASIDE.

A_0 B_0 T_1 **100 TMU**

STRIKE BRACE AND RETAINER IO ARM STROKES USING SLEDGE AND ASIDE:

A_0 B_0 T_6 **600 TMU**

Apply Material with Tool

The index values for Apply Material with Tool are located on the General Tool Use card (Fig. 5.17). These index values provide for the analysis of material application with a variety of commonly used tools. A column is shown for each tool. The application unit is shown for each tool. The tools are defined as follows:

Tool	Application detail	Explanation
Seal gun	Pull	Get gun, place onto surface, and apply sealing compound along a seam; the process time can be up to 2 seconds; place to next spot and aside gun are included; index values also include refilling gun with new canister when required. *Example:* APPLY SEALANT AROUND HEADLIGHT THREE PULLS USING SEAL GUN AND ASIDE: A_0 B_0 T_6 **600 TMU**
Grease gun	Lever action	Get gun, place onto fitting, and apply grease by pushing lever (per power stroke); place to next fitting and aside gun are included; also includes refilling gun with new canister when required. *Example:* APPLY GREASE ON FITTINGS SIX LEVER OPTIONS USING GREASE GUN AND ASIDE: A_0 B_0 T_6 **600 TMU**
Squeeze bottle	Drop	Pick up squeeze bottle, open and shut cap, apply drop on spot, and aside bottle; index value chosen by the number of drops or squeezes applied. *Example:* APPLY THREAD SEALANT ON STUD 4 DROPS USING SQUEEZE BOTTLE AND ASIDE: A_0 B_0 T_3 **300 TMU**

Tool	Application detail	Explanation
Tube	1 inch (2.5 cm) spot	Pick up grease or glue tube, open and shut cap, apply grease or glue on spot, and aside tube; index value is chosen by the number of spots (up to 1 inch, 2.5 cm, across) to which the material is applied; this is not appropriate for laying a bead of material. *Example:* APPLY GLUE ON GASKET FOUR 1 INCH (2.5 CM) SPOTS USING TUBE AND ASIDE: A_0 B_0 T_6 **600 TMU**
Brush, stick, hand, or finger	1 inch (2.5 cm) spot	Pick up brush or stick, clean it against the can, get grease or glue from can, and apply on surface or spot; aside tool and wipe hand if necessary; index value is chosen by the number of spots (up to 1 inch, 2.5 cm) to which the material is applied. *Example:* APPLY GREASE ON SHAFT THREE 1 INCH (2.5 CM) SPOTS USING STICK AND ASIDE: A_0 B_0 T_6 **600 TMU**
Squirt can	Squirt	Pick up can or bottle and squirt liquid on one spot by pulling trigger, pushing pump, or squeezing the bottle; index value is chosen by the number of squirts required to apply the proper amount of material. *Example:* APPLY WINDOW CLEANER ON REARVIEW MIRROR WITH SQUIRTCAN AND ASIDE: A_0 B_0 T_3 **300 TMU**
Aerosol can	Square foot	Get aerosol can, remove and replace cap, shake can initially and during spraying, aim, spray and aside can; index values applied per square foot (0.1 m^2) of application area. *Example:* SPRAY LAYOUT INK ON PLATE. A_0 B_0 T_6 **600 TMU**

Tool	Application detail	Explanation
Tape roll		Get tape roll, such as masking tape, open end, pull tape, and apply on surface (up to 12 inches, 30 cm) or wrap around object (three to six revolutions); tear off and aside; *note:* select index values per foot (0.3 m) or per strip, whichever is greater. *Example:* APPLY 10 INCH (25 CM) STRIP OF MASKING TAPE TO NAME PLATE PRIOR TO PAINTING OPERATION: A_0 B_0 T_3 **300 TMU**

Clean Surface

Clean Surface index values are located on the second General Tool Use chart (Fig. 5.18), which also shows Cut, Twist or Bend with Pliers, Write or Mark, Think, Deburr with File, Free Tool with Drift Pin, Tap or Thread by Hand, and Process Time. The surface cleaning may be done with an air hose, a brush, a cloth, or similar tools used in the same way as these tools. Clean Surface data include getting the tool, using the tool for cleaning, and asiding the tool. The index values for Clean Surface are determined by the method or tool employed and the area cleaned in square feet (m^2).

Air Clean

The Air Clean index values include time to get an air hose (within two steps), activate the air hose, direct the air over the surface for cleaning, and aside the air hose. The index value is selected by the area cleaned in square feet (m^2).

Brush Clean

Brush Clean index values include time to gain control of a brush (within two steps), move the brush to a surface, clean the surface by brushing, and aside the brush. The index value is determined by the area cleaned in square feet (m^2).

Wipe

The Wipe index values apply to cleaning by rubbing the surface with a cloth, sponge, or other suitable material. Time is included for getting the tool or material (within two steps), cleaning the surface by wiping, and asiding the tool or material. The index value is selected by the area cleaned in square feet (m^2).

Maxi MOST® System								
	CLEAN SURFACE			CUT OR SLICE					TWIST OR BEND WITH PLIERS
INDEX X 100	SQ. FT. (0,1 m²)			CUTS OR STROKES					
	AIR CLEAN	BRUSH CLEAN	WIPE	PLIERS					
				SOFT	MEDIUM	HARD	SCISSORS	KNIFE	LOOPS
1				2	1		3	1	1
3	4	3	2	6	4	2	16	7	4
6	11	9	8	12	8	5	35	16	8
10	23	16	15		14	9		27	15
16	39	27	25			15			
24	57	40	37						
32		53	51						
42									
54									

Figure 5.18 Maxi MOST—Tool Use data card: General Tools II. Values are read "up to and including."

Cut

The Cut index values are located on the General Tool Use chart (Fig. 5.18) with Clean Surface. The values apply for the removal or separation of material by a cutting action using pliers, knife, or scissors.

Pliers

The index values for Pliers allow time for cutting through wire using pliers. The index value is determined by the difficulty of cutting the wire and the number of pieces cut from the original section of wire. Count the plier cuts, that

GENERAL TOOLS II   T - TOOL USE

WRITE — MARKER — CHARACTER OR MARK — SIZE — 1" (25 mm)	3" (75 mm)	MARK — HAMMER & DIE — LETTER OR FIGURE	THINK — INSPECT — POINTS	READ — WORD OR VALUE	DEBURR WITH FILE — FEET	FREE TOOL WITH DRIFT PIN — NO. TOOLS	TAP OR THREAD BY HAND — NO. OCCURRENCES — DIAMETER — 5/16" (8 mm)	3/4" (20 mm)	WAIT OR PROCESS TIME — SEC.	MIN.	INDEX X 100
			2	4					3.5		1
9	5	1	7	13	1	2			11		3
23	13	4	13		2	6			22		6
41	24	7			3	10			36		10
	40	12			5	16	1		58	1	16
		17			8			1			24
		23			11					2	32
							2				42
							3	2		3	54

is, the number of times a section of wire is cut through and separated from the original length of wire.

Soft

Soft Plier Cut index values apply when cutting soft or light-gauge wire. Soft cuts may be made with one closure of the pliers when handled with one hand.

Medium

Medium Plier Cut index values are for intermediate sizes and hardness such that two closing actions are normally required when the pliers are handled with one hand.

Hard

Hard Plier Cut index values are for heavy or especially hard wire. Use these values when two cuts are required and both hands must be used to manipulate the pliers.

Knife

Cut with a Knife includes time to get a knife (within two steps), place the knife to cut, cut, place the knife for additional cuts when required, and aside the knife. The index value is determined by counting the number of cutting strokes. Count only the actual cutting strokes as the move back and additional placements are included in the time for the cutting stroke.

Scissors

Cut with scissors includes time to get the scissors (within two steps), place for cutting, cut, relocate scissors, and aside the scissors. The index value is selected by the number of cutting strokes. Opening the scissors and relocating the scissors when required are included in the time per cut and are not counted.

Twist or Bend with Pliers

Twist or Bend with Pliers includes time to get the pliers (within two steps), place the pliers to the wire, form a bend, loop or twist, place the pliers for additional forming when required, and aside the pliers. The index value is selected by the number of bends or loops.

Write or Mark

Write or Mark refers to recording information on a surface with a writing instrument or marking device. The index value is selected by the instrument used and the number of characters marked on the surface.

Write

Use for normal size writing or printing (to 1 inch, 2.5 cm, high). Get pen, remove and replace cap, write characters, check for correctness, and aside pen. The index value is chosen by the number of characters written.

Example: WRITE 4 CHARACTERS FOR QUANTITY ON JOB TICKET USING PEN AND ASIDE:

A_0 B_0 T_3 300 TMU

Write Large

Use for writing characters over 1 inch (2.5 cm) and up to 3 inches (7.5 cm) high. The values include get marker, remove and replace cap, mark characters, check for correctness, and aside marker. The index value is chosen by the number of characters marked.

Example: WRITE LARGE 10 CHARACTERS FOR PART NUMBER ON STEEL PLATE USING CHALK AND ASIDE:

A_0 B_0 T_6 **600 TMU**

Mark (Hammer and Die)

This includes get hammer, select and position die, strike with hammer, return die to die set and aside hammer when finished, and inspect completed job. Index values chosen by the number of characters stamped.

Example: MARK 6 DIGITS ON PLATE USING DIE AND ASIDE:

A_0 B_0 T_{10} **1000 TMU**

Think

Think index values include the time to observe a characteristic and make a simple decision based on that characteristic.

Inspect

Position body, focus and check object by looking at or touching the surface. The index value is determined by the number of points inspected.

Example: INSPECT 3 POINTS ON PARTS:

A_0 B_0 T_3 **300 TMU**

Read

Read scale, gauge value, or words. Index values are determined per number of values or words read.

Note: These index values do not include time to pick up and/or aside paper, which must be analyzed separately with the Part Handling Sequence.

Example: READ 1 VALUE ON WORK ORDER:

A_0 B_0 T_1 **100 TMU**

Deburr with File

Deburr with file index values are used to analyze hand filing to remove burrs from a part. Time is allowed for getting the file (within two steps), placing the file to the part, filing, active strokes and back strokes, and laying the file aside. The count is based on the number of edges or feet deburred, whichever is greater. For each edge 1 foot (0.3 m) or less in length count the edge, for each edge 1 foot (0.3 m) or longer count each foot (0.3 m) of length plus one for any remaining partial foot (0.3 m). For instance, a part required deburring on three edges; one 3 inches (7.5 cm) long, one 22 inches (56 cm) long, and one 37 inches (94 cm) long. Allow one foot (0.3 m) for the 3 inch (7.5 cm) edge, 2 feet (0.6 m) for the 22 inch (56 cm) edge, and 4 feet (1.2 m) for the 37 inch (94 cm) edge. (Count one for each foot (0.3 m) or part of a foot (0.3 m).) Find the index value for 7 feet (2.1 m) on the chart, and therefore allow a T_{24} index value.

Free Tool with Drift Pin

Free Tool with Drift Pin includes the time to get a drift pin and a hammer, place the drift pin onto the base of the tool, loosen the tool by tapping the drift pin with the hammer, and aside the drift pin and the hammer. No direct handling of the tool or manipulation of the machine is included in the index value. Select the index value by the number of tools freed.

Tap or Thread by Hand

The values for Tap or Thread by Hand apply to hand tapping using a solid tap affixed to a handle or to hand threading using a solid threading die affixed to a handle. These index values include time to get the tool, tap into or thread onto the part, back the tool clear of the part, and aside the tool. The length tapped or threaded is great enough to accept a standard threaded fastener plus an added distance for clearance. No time is provided in these index values for handling the part or for attaching the handle to the cutting tool. Use Apply index values for the necessary addition of oil while tapping.

The value for Tap or Thread by Hand is determined by the thread diameter and the number of places tapped or threaded.

To $^5/_{16}$ inch (8 mm) diameter   This column applies to tapping or threading when the thread diameter is $^5/_{16}$ inches (8 mm) or less. Select the index value by the number of places tapped or threaded.

To $^3/_4$ inch (20 mm) Diameter   This column applies to tapping or threading when the thread diameter exceeds $^5/_{16}$ inches (8 mm) but does not exceed $^3/_4$ inches (20 mm). Select the index value by the number of places tapped or threaded.

Process Time

Process Time is defined as the time that is process or machine controlled, not manually controlled. Index values are chosen by the number of seconds or minutes established as process time from the right-hand column of Figure 5.18.

Measure

The index values for Measure are located on the Measuring Tool Use chart (Fig. 5.19) that also shows Prepare for Measuring. Measure index values have been developed for the most common standard measuring devices found in manufacturing. The index value is determined by the tool used and the number of measurements taken. The values include time to properly align the part and the measuring device, adjust the tool when required, and determine the fit to the tool or reading. Time is allowed for handling either the tool or the part, but not both.

Flat Rule or Scale

The Flat Rule or Scale column provides time to use a machine graduated scale up to 18 inches (45 cm) in length or to use a printed or etched flat rule up to 4 feet (1.2 m) in length. This column also applies to the use of a protractor.

Tape Rule

Tape Rule index values apply to the use of concave tapes housed in a case suitable for carrying in the pocket or clipped to the belt. These devices vary from 6 feet (1.8 m) to 25 feet (7.6 m) in length. These values may also be applied to flat pocket tapes not more than 6 feet (1.8 m) in length. The index values should not be applied to the use of flat, hand wound, engineers' tapes regardless of length. The index values include time to get and aside the tape rule (within two steps).

Wood Rule

The Wood Rule data apply to measurements taken with a 6 or 8 foot (1.8–2.5 m) folding rule. The index values may also be applied to aluminum or steel folding rules provided the measurement is to the same accuracy as a wood rule.

Profile Gauge

Profile Gauge index values apply to the use of gauges, such as angle, radius, and screw-pitch gauges, that are used to compare the shape of the part to that of the gauge.

Vernier Calipers

The index value for measure with Vernier Calipers applies to measurements taken with Vernier Calipers. The index values apply to outside and inside measurements.

12 Inch (30 cm) Vernier

This column applies to measurements of no more than 12 inches (30 cm) using a vernier caliper. The index value is based on using the lighter calipers normally used for smaller dimensions and includes the operation of one locking device.

36 Inch (90 cm) Vernier

This column applies to measurement of more than 12 inches (30 cm) but not exceeding 36 inches (90 cm). The index value is based on the use of the larger, heavier vernier calipers associated with measuring the greater dimensions. Time is included for separately locating and correcting the location of each end of the calipers. Time is allowed for the operation of two locking devices.

Feeler Gauge

These index values apply to the use of a feeler gauge to measure the gap between two points or surfaces. Time is included to get the gauge, fan out and select the appropriate blade, insert the blade, make visual and tactile checks of the fit, and aside the gauge. The index value is selected by the number of gaps checked.

Micrometer

Micrometer index values apply to the use of outside, inside, and depth micrometers. The index values include time to get the micrometer, set it on the part, adjust the micrometer to the part dimension, lock the setting, pick up and read the micrometer, unlock the micrometer, and set it aside. These index values do not include preparation activities, such as getting the micrometer from the case, changing the anvil, or the initial coarse adjustments to approximate the size of the part. The index value is selected by the size of the dimension and the number of measurements taken.

4 Inch (10 cm) Micrometer

This column applies to the measurement of dimensions no greater than 4 inches (10 cm).

36 Inch (90 cm) Micrometer

This column applies to the measurement of dimensions exceeding 4 inches (10 cm) but not exceeding 36 inches (90 cm).

Ring Gauge

Ring Gauge index values apply to the comparison of an outside diameter of a part to a standard ring designed to match the required part diameter. The index values include time to get the ring gauge, fit the ring to the part, check the fit of the ring to the part, and remove and aside the part. Select the index value by the number of places checked.

Plug Gauge

Plug Gauge index values include time to get the gauge, fit the go end of the gauge into the opening in the part, turn the gauge, fit the no-go end of the gauge to the part, determine that the no-go end will not fit into the opening, and aside the gauge. The index value is determined by the size of the gauge and the number of holes checked.

1 Inch (25 mm) Plug Gauge

This column is used to analyze the use of plug gauges that have a diameter of 1 inch (25 mm) or less.

8 Inch (200 mm) Plug Gauge

This column is for analyzing the use of plug gauges with a diameter greater than 1 inch (25 mm) but not greater than 8 inches (200 mm).

Thread Gauge

The Thread Gauge index values apply to the use of threaded plug gauges and threaded ring gauges for the purpose of inspecting a threaded section, male or female, of a part. These index values should not be used for screw-pitch gauges as these are analyzed as profile gauges. The index values apply whether the gauge is moved to the part or the part to the gauge. The index value is selected by the diameter of the gauge and the number of threaded openings or threaded protrusions.

4 Inch (100 mm) Thread Gauge

This column is used to determine the index value for inspection with a threaded ring or threaded plug gauge having a diameter no larger than 4 inches (100 mm).

8 Inch (200 mm) Thread Gauge

The index values in this column apply to the use of threaded gauges greater than 4 inches (100 mm) but no greater than 8 inches (200 mm) in thread diameter.

Square

The Square index values describe the locating and adjusting of a square to check the relationship of two planes or to locate a line in one plane parallel to

Maxi MOST® Systems										
INDEX X 100	FLAT-RULE OR SCALE	TAPE-RULE	FOLDING WOOD-RULE	PROFILE GAUGE	VERNIER CALIPER		FEELER-GAUGE	MICRO-METER		RING-GAUGE
					12" (30 cm)	36" (90 cm)		4" (10 cm)	36" (90 cm)	
3	2	1		3	2		1			1
6	3	2	3	5	3	1	2	1	1	2
10	6	3	7	10	6	2	4	2		3
16	10	6	14	15	10	3	7	4	3	5
24		8	21		15	5	10	5	4	8
32						7		7	5	11
42						9			7	
54						12			9	
67									11	

Figure 5.19   Maxi MOST—Tool Use data card: Measuring Tools. Values indicating size of measuring tool as well as number of measurements are read "up to and including."

another plane. The index value is determined by the number of planes checked or lines determined.

Set to Measure

The Set to Measure index values are used to analyze the use of tools used for indirect measurement. These tools are set to a dimension on the part, the tool removed from the part, and then a second tool used to measure the setting.

The index values for Set to Measure include the time to get the tool, to locate the tool on the part, to set the tool to the dimension being measured, to remove the set tool, and to aside the tool when the measuring is complete. There is no time allowed for measuring the setting with a second tool. The measurement of the setting with a separate tool must be separately analyzed. Allow a separate sequence for the tool set on the part and a sequence for measuring the setting

MEASURING TOOLS											T - TOOL USE	
PLUG GAUGE		THREAD GAUGE		SQUARE	SET TO MEASURE			SNAP-GAUGE	DIAL INDI-CATOR	TAPER GAUGE	DEVICE	INDEX X 100
					TELE-SCOPE GAUGE	CALIPER		16" (400 mm)				
1" (25 mm)	8" (200 mm)	4" (100 mm)	8" (200 mm)			SPRING-JOINT	FIRM-JOINT					
2				2	1			2				**3**
3	1	1		4	2	1	1	5		1	Telescope Gauge Firm Joint Calipers 12" (30 cm) Vernier Calipers 36" (90 cm) Vernier Calipers	**6**
6		2		7	3	2		9			Combination Square Bevel Protractor 4" (10 cm)	**10**
10	3	4	1	11	5	4	2	14	1	2	4" (10 cm) Micrometer Spring Joint Caliper 36" (90 cm)	**16**
15	4	6	2		8	6	3			4	36" (90 cm) Micrometer	**24**
	5	8			10	8	5		2	5		**32**
	7	10	3			11	6			7		**42**
	9		4				8		3	8		**54**
			5				10		4	10		**67**

with a second tool. The index value is selected by the type of tool used and by the number of measurements required.

Telescope Gauge

A Telescope Gauge is a gauge inserted into an opening, expanded to fill the opening, the setting locked, and then the gauge removed from the opening for subsequent measurement. The index value is determined by the number of openings measured.

Spring Joint or Firm Joint

The index values for Spring Joint Calipers or Firm Joint Calipers include the time to get the calipers (within two steps), place the calipers on the part, adjust the calipers for size, and remove the calipers for measurement. The time for measuring the caliper setting is not included in the index value and must be allowed in a separate sequence.

Snap Gauge

Snap Gauges are fit on the part, or the part fit into the gauge, to compare the actual dimension of the part to the standard gauge dimension. The index value is determined by the number of times the gauge is fit over a part (or a part into a gauge). Step-type go-no-go snap gauges can determine maximum and minimum requirements in one fitting between the gauge and the part. However, when separate gauges are set to minimum and maximum tolerances, each gauge must be counted separately.

Dial Indicator

The index values for Dial Indicator use include the time to stop the machine, wipe the workpiece, position the dial indicator in place, set the dial to zero, turn the part, check the dial as required, clear the dial indicator from the part, and restart the machine.

Taper Gauge

The time for measuring with a Taper Gauge includes opening the bluing containers, getting the taper gauge, brushing bluing on the gauge, positioning the taper gauge to the part, and removing the gauge. Time is also included for inspecting the displacement of the bluing to determining the contact area between the gauge and the part, wiping the bluing from the gauge, and setting aside the gauge.

Prepare for Measuring

Some measuring devices require preparation before use. This preparation usually includes removal from a case and coarse adjustments to the approximate size of the dimension of the part. The preparation of some measuring tools will require changing fittings or parts of the tool for the general size range of the dimensions to be measured. The time required to adjust the tool subsequent to use and return it to its case is also included in the preparation time value when required. The Prepare for Measuring index value does not include any time for use of the measuring device. The index value for Prepare for Measuring is determined by the tool required.

In volume production work the measuring device need only be prepared during the setup for each order. However, in low-volume work, especially when greatly varied dimensions must be made with the same tool, Preparation for Measurement may be required each time the tool is used. The tools described in the Maxi MOST Prepare for Measuring data card (Fig. 5.19) are telescope gauge, firm joint calipers, combination square, combination bevel protractor, micrometer to 4 inches (10 cm), and micrometer to 36 inches (90 cm). All the routine activities necessary to prepare these tools for use and return them to their storage locations are covered in the index values.

D. Machine Handling Sequence Model

The *Machine Handling Sequence Model* consists of three parameters A, B, and M. The M parameter is defined below; the definitions for the A and B parameters can be found under the Part Handling Sequence.

The Machine Handling (M) parameter accounts for activities associated with the manipulation of machine controls, the changing of cutting tools, and the securing or releasing of a workpiece.

Method Step Format

The Machine Handling method step format is

OPERATOR(S) / ACTIVITY / MAGNITUDE / DEVICE(S) / AT LOCATION
RETURN TO LOCATION / ACTION DISTANCE / BODY MOTION / PF, F, SIMO

Data Cards

There are two data cards for the Machine Handling parameter. The first data card (Fig. 5.20) covers the manipulation of machine controls and the activities associated with the changing of cutting tools. The second data card (Fig. 5.21) covers the activities associated with securing or releasing a workpiece.

Operate Machine Controls

The data for Operate Machine Controls cover the manipulation of buttons, switches, knobs, levers, cranks, and handwheels. The data card values include time for walking to the control(s) with one or two steps, gaining control of the control(s), manipulating the control(s), and relinquishing control of the control(s).

Operate Button/Switch

Index values for operating a button or switch are typically based on the number of buttons or switches that are activated. The notable exceptions are palm buttons. When two palm buttons are simultaneously activated, these two

Maxi MOST® System — OPERATE MACHINE CONTROLS — M - MACHINE HANDLING

INDEX X 100	BUTTON OR SWITCH (NO. OF CONTROLS)	LEVER 1 OR 2 STAGES (NO. OF CONTROLS)	LEVER DIFFICULT 3 OR 4 STAGES	CRANK (NO. OF REVS.)	KNOB (NO. OF ACTIONS)	HAND WHEEL NORMAL	HAND WHEEL HEAVY	CHANGE TOOL (TYPE OF DEVICE)	INDEX X 100
1	4	2	1	2	4	3	1	Quick Change Post	1
3	12	7	3	16	17	11	4		3
6		13	6	36	34	23	9	Jacobs Chuck	6
10			10	53			16	Carbide Insert	10
16									16

Figure 5.20 Maxi MOST—Machine Handling data card: Operate Machine Controls. Values are read "up to and including."

Maxi MOST® System

SECURE OR RELEASE PARTS | **M - MACHINE HANDLING**

INDEX X 100	OPEN OR CLOSE	INSTALL OR REMOVE LATHE DOG	OPEN OR CLOSE VISE	ENGAGE OR DISENGAGE TAIL STOCK CENTER	INSTALL OR REMOVE JACK SCREW	INSTALL OR REMOVE C-CLAMP	TIGHTEN OR LOOSEN PART IN FIXTURE — WITH WRENCH	— BY HAND	— WITH CAM OR ECCENTRIC CLAMP	CLAMP OR UNCLAMP PART ON BED — CLAMP AND NUT REMAIN ON STUD RELIEVE STRAIN	— CLAMP AND NUT REMOVED FROM STUD	INDEX X 100
					NUMBER OF DEVICES					NUMBER OF CLAMPS		
1	Collet	Cam Type	Hand or Air Operated	Lever-Operated	1	1	1	1	2			1
3	3 - Jaw Chuck	Standard	Mallet	Crank-Operated	2	2	3	3	6	1		3
6	4 - Jaw Chuck				4	3	5	6	12	2	1	6
10	6 - Jaw Chuck				6	5	8	10		4	2	10
16					9	7	12			6	4	16
24					16	10				9	6	24
32										13	8	32
42											10	42

Figure 5.21 Maxi MOST—Machine Handling data card: Secure or Release Parts. Values are read "up to and including."

buttons should be counted as only one for the purpose of establishing the index value.

The parameter variants for button or switch cover any stationary (panel-mounted) or pendant button. Activation of the button or switch will be characterized by a single action of the finger or hand.

Operate Lever

Operate Lever includes the displacement of a lever in either one or two stages. Operate Lever index values are based on the number of levers manipulated.

Operate Difficult Lever

Operate Difficult Lever covers the displacement of a lever in either three or four stages. Operate Difficult Lever index values are based on the number of levers manipulated.

Operate Crank

These data for Operate Crank are identical to the TURN BY HAND ARM-STROKE data found on the Tool Use data card. Duplication on the Machine Handling data card is for convenience only.

Operate Knob

Operate Knob is used to analyze the rotation of a device using the fingers or the hand. Operate Knob index values are based on the total number of positive actions involved in turning knobs. This may involve one or more knobs.

Operate Wheel

Operate Wheel includes moving the circumference of a circular device with either wrist or arm actions. The movement is characterized by little or no resistance. Operate Wheel index values are based on the total number of positive actions. This may involve one or more wheels.

Operate Heavy Wheel

Operate Heavy Wheel includes moving the circumference of a circular device with either wrist or arm actions. The movement is characterized by resistance that requires the application of muscular force. Operate Heavy Wheel index values are based on the total number of positive actions. This may involve one or more wheels.

Change Tool

The Change Tool data cover a single tool change involving a Quick-Change-Post, a Jacobs-Chuck, or a Carbide-Insert. The data card index values cover walking to the tool holder with one or two steps, removing the existing tool, and installing the next tool.

Change Quick-Change-Post

The Quick-Change-Post index value covers removing the existing tool and installing the next tool.

Change Jacobs-Chuck

The Jacobs-Chuck index value covers obtaining the chuck key, loosening the chuck with the key, removing the key and loosening the chuck by hand, removing the tool, installing the next tool, tightening the chuck by hand, tightening the chuck with the key, and disposing of the key.

Change Carbide-Insert

The Carbide-Insert index value covers obtaining the screwdriver, loosening the retainer with the screwdriver, removing the retainer, removing the old insert, installing the new insert in the retainer, installing the retainer, and disposing of the screwdriver.

Secure or Release Part

The data for Secure or Release Part cover opening or closing a holding device and relieving or increasing clamp pressure (strain) on a workpiece. All values include the time for walking one or two steps to the holding device.

Secure/Release Collet

The index value for Secure/Release Collet cover opening or closing a collet by utilizing a lever, handwheel, or hydraulic switch.

Secure/Release 3-Jaw-Chuck

The index value for Secure/Release 3-Jaw-Chuck covers obtaining the wrench, placing the wrench on the chuck, tightening or loosening the chuck with the wrench, and disposing of·the wrench.

Secure/Release 4-Jaw-Chuck

The index value for Secure/Release 4-Jaw-Chuck covers obtaining the wrench, placing the wrench to the first jaw, tightening or loosening the jaw, revolving the chuck to the second jaw, placing the wrench to the jaw, tightening or loosening the jaw, and disposing of the wrench.

Secure/Release 6-Jaw-Chuck

The index value for Secure/Release 6-Jaw-Chuck covers obtaining the wrench, placing the wrench on the jaws, revolving the chuck to tighten or loosen the jaws, and disposing of the wrench.

Secure/Release Hand-Vise

The index value for Secure/Release Hand-Vise covers obtaining the vise handle, placing the vise handle in the vise, opening or closing the vise with the handle, and disposing of the handle.

Secure/Release Air-Vise

The index value for Secure/Release Air-Vise covers opening or closing a vise by activating a hydraulic device by hand or foot.

Secure/Release Mallet-Vise

The index value for Secure/Release Mallet-Vise covers opening or closing a vise by utilizing a mallet to initially loosen or finally tighten the vise. The vise handle may be in place or placed in the vise. The index value includes time for placing the handle in the vise, obtaining the mallet, striking the handle to loosen or tighten the vise, asiding the mallet, and opening or closing the vise by hand.

Secure/Release Wrench-Fixture

The index values for Secure/Release Wrench-Fixture cover using a wrench to loosen or tighten bolts on a fixture for the purpose of securing or releasing a workpiece. These data include the time for obtaining the wrench, placing the wrench on the bolt(s), loosening or tightening the bolt(s), asiding the wrench, and running the bolt(s) in or out by hand. Secure/Release Wrench-Fixture index values are based on the number of bolts that are run either in or out.

Secure/Release Hand-Fixture

The index values for Secure/Release Hand-Fixture cover using the hand to loosen or tighten thumb screws, handwheels, or star wheels on a fixture. The purpose is to secure or release a workpiece. Secure/Release Hand-Fixture index values are based on the number of thumb screws, handwheels, or star wheels that are run in or out.

Secure/Release Cam-Fixture/Clamp-Fixture

The index values for Secure/Release Cam-Fixture/Clamp-Fixture cover placing cams or clamps on a fixture to tighten it or removing cams or clamps from a fixture to loosen it. Secure/Release Cam-Fixture/Clamp-Fixture index values are based on the number of clamps or cams manipulated.

Secure/Release Remains-On

The index values for Secure/Release Remains-On cover loosening and sliding clamps or sliding and tightening clamps for the purpose of releasing or securing a workpiece on a bed. The index values include time for obtaining the wrench (within two steps), placing the wrench on the nut, loosening or tightening the nut on the stud. asiding the wrench, running the nut out by hand to obtain clearance or in to tighten, and pushing the clamp clear of the workpiece or locating the clamp on the workpiece. With these index values, the nut and the clamp remain on the stud. Secure/Release Remains-On index values are based on the number of clamps manipulated.

The following illustrates the relationship of the workpiece, clamp, stud, and nut:

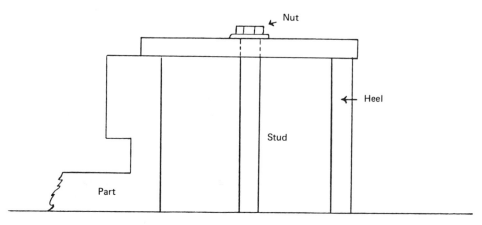

Secure/Release Removed-From

The index values for Secure/Release Removed-From cover loosening and removing clamps and nuts or placing and tightening clamps and nuts for the purpose of releasing or securing a workpiece on a bed. These index values include the time for obtaining the wrench, placing the wrench on the nut, loosening or tightening the nut on the stud, asiding the wrench, and removing the nut and clamp from the stud or placing the clamp and nut on the study and running down the nut. Secure/Release Removed-From index values are based on the number of clamps manipulated.

Secure/Release Relieve-Strain

The index values for Secure/Release Relieve-Strain cover loosening or tightening a nut for the purpose of relieving or increasing the clamp pressure (strain) on the workpiece, which rests on a bed. Secure/Release Relieve-Strain index values are based on the number of nuts manipulated.

Install or Remove Device

The index values for Install or Remove Device cover the installation or removal of lathe dogs, jack screws, or C-clamps used for the purpose of securing or stabilizing a workpiece. These index values include the time for walking to the device with one or two steps and installing or removing the device.

Install/Remove Cam-Type-Lathe-Dog

The index value for Install/Remove Cam-Type-Lathe-Dog covers obtaining the dog or moving the dog near the workpiece, opening the cam or removing the dog from the workpiece, and placing the dog on the workpiece or asiding the dog.

Install/Remove Standard-Lathe-Dog

The index value for Install/Remove Standard-Lathe-Dog covers obtaining the wrench, placing the wrench on the lathe dog bolt, loosening or tightening the bolt, asiding the wrench, and removing the dog from the workpiece or placing it on the workpiece.

Install/Remove Jack-Screw

The index values for Install/Remove Jack-Screw covers running the jack screw in or out by hand, setting the jack screw to the workpiece, locating the jack screw head, obtaining a wrench, placing the wrench on the jack screw, locking or unlocking the jack screw with the wrench, asiding the wrench, and asiding the jack screw. Install/Remove Jack-Screw index values are based on the number of jack screws manipulated.

Install/Remove C-Clamp

The index values for Install/Remove C-Clamp cover placing the C-clamp on the workpiece or removing it from the workpiece, tightening or loosening the C-clamp by hand, obtaining a wrench, placing the wrench on the C-clamp and tightening or loosening the C-clamp with the wrench, and asiding the wrench. Install/Remove C-clamp index values are based on the number of C-clamps manipulated.

Engage or Disengage Tail Stock Centers

The index values for Engage or Disengage Tail Stock Centers cover engaging or disengaging tail stock centers that are either spring-loaded, lever activated, or crank activated. The data card index values include the time for walking one or two steps to the activation device and engaging or disengaging the device.

Engage/Disengage Lever-Operated

The index value for Engage/Disengage Lever-Operated covers either engaging or disengaging the activation arm.

Engage/Disengage Crank-Operated

The index value for Engage/Disengage Crank-Operated covers cranking the center in or out, engaging and disengaging the center, adjusting the crank pressure, setting the lock lever, and tightening or releasing the lock lever.

Machine Handling Sequence Model Examples

PUSH 3 BUTTONS TO SET AND START MACHINE

A_0 B_0 M_1 **100 TMU**

MOVE LEVER 2 STAGES TO RETRACT TOOL

A_0 B_0 M_1 **100 TMU**

CRANK 10 REVOLUTIONS AND APPROACH TOOL TO WORKPIECE

A_0 B_0 M_3 **300 TMU**

CHANGE CARBIDE-INSERT ON MILLING CUTTER

A_0 B_0 M_{10} **1000 TMU**

SECURE PART IN 3-JAW CHUCK

A_0 B_0 M_3 **300 TMU**

SECURE 4 FIXTURE CLAMPS ON PART TO MACHINE TABLE

A_0 B_0 M_{10} **1000 TMU**

INSTALL 4 C-CLAMPS ON BED

A_0 B_0 M_{16} **1600 TMU**

E. The Powered Crane Sequence

The Powered Crane Sequence Model is appropriate for cranes that move the load laterally and longitudinally under power and that may resemble an overhead, pendant-operated bridge crane (Fig. 5.22).

The Powered Crane Sequence consists of the following activities:

1. The operator walks to the control panel (Action Distance).
2. The operator grasps the controls, elevates the crane hook, moves the crane so the hook reaches the position for coupling, and then releases the controls (Transport).
3. The object is fastened either directly with the crane hook or with a sling or chain, for example. The operator grasps the controls and elevates the crane hook to the correct position for hooking and then adjusts the controls so that the chain or other holding device is tight and secure (Hook-up, Unhook). The holding device is subsequently removed from the object.
4. The crane hook with the object is freed from its surroundings and elevated so the object can be moved. The object is then moved horizontally to the desired location (Transport).
5. The object is lowered and placed in the desired location (Placement).
6. The empty crane is moved aside (Transport).
7. The operator returns to the starting point after moving the crane aside (Action Distance).

The Powered Crane Sequence Model

These activities can be described by the following sequence model:

A   T   K   T   P   T   A

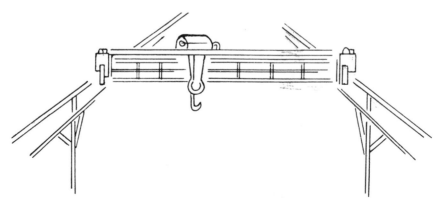

Figure 5.22 Overhead bridge crane.

where: A = Action distance
         T = Transport
         K = Hook up and Unhook
         P = Placement

If the local conditions call for a permanent bridge crane operator, only the K, T, and P parameters are needed for analysis purposes.

Powered Crane Data Card Backup Information

It is recognized that there are many manufacturers, models, capacities, and so on, of cranes available. As a result, the information presented on the Powered Crane data card, as determined by the backup data outlined below, should be treated as sample information. The *method must be verified* and the *process times must be validated* to fit a company's particular equipment.

The backup data below are provided as a key to the considerations that should be made when validating or developing appropriate index values for particular situations or cranes.

Basic Data for Powered Crane Parameter Values

The time values listed below were derived from a series of time studies.

1. Longitudinal traverse: low speed = 122 TMU/foot (400 TMU/m); high speed = 15.3 TMU/foot (50 TMU/m).
2. Vertical move: low speed = 30 TMU/inches (1200 TMU/m); high speed = 7.6 TMU/inches (300 TMU/m).
3. Lateral traverse = 152.5 TMU/foot (500 TMU/m).
4. Change direction using a control panel button: 40 TMU.
5. Lateral transportation frequency = 10%.

Parameter Definitions

A Action Distance

The Action Distance is the horizontal distance the operator walks to or from the bridge crane control panel.

T Transport

This parameter covers the movement of the crane with or without a load. The activities listed below were included in the T parameter provided on the data card (Fig. 5.23) and must be *verified* and *validated* to fit particular situations and/or cranes: The calculation times for an unloaded and a loaded crane is illustrated in Figure 5.24.

Maxi MOST® System	A T K T P T A			POWERED CRANE TRANSPORT	
INDEX X 100	A ACTION DISTANCE FEET (M)	T TRANSPORT FEET (M)	K HOOK UP AND UNHOOK HOLDING DEVICE	P PLACEMENT DIFFICULTY	INDEX X 100
1	24 (7)				1
3	61 (19)			Without or With Single Change of Direction	3
6	127 (39)		Single Hook or Electromagnet		6
10	220 (67)	2 (.5)			10
16	360 (110)	25 (8)		With Double Change of Direction	16
24	505 (154)	50 (16)	1 Hook Plus Slings or Chains	With Several Changes of Direction	24
32	673 (205)	80 (25)	2 Hooks Plus Slings or Chains		32

Figure 5.23   Maxi MOST—Powered Crane Transport data card. Values are read "up to and including."

UNLOADED	TMU	LOADED	TMU
GRASP CONTROL PANEL AND DEPRESS BUTTON	40	GRASP CONTROL PANEL AND DEPRESS BUTTON	40
RAISE 3.3 FT. (1M) (HIGH SPEED)	300	RAISE 1.5 FT. (0.5 M) (CREEP SPEED)	600
	-	RAISE 5 (1.5 M) (HIGH SPEED)	450
ACCELERATION AND RETARDATION	200	ACCELERATION AND RETARDATION	500
CHANGE DIRECTION	40	CHANGE DIRECTION	40
LONG, TRAVERSE (VARIABLE)	-	LONG TRAVERSE (VARIABLE)	-
CHANGE DIRECTION	40	CHANGE DIRECTION	40
LOWER 3.3 FT. (1M) (HIGH SPEED)	300		-
TOTAL	920	TOTAL	1670

Figure 5.24 Calculation times for an unloaded and a loaded crane.

Development of Transport (T) Constant   Since the T parameter is appropriate for both loaded and unloaded movement of the crane, the weighted T constant was developed to include

- Unloaded Move, to move the crane to the object or aside with a frequency of 60%:
- Loaded Move, to move the crane with the object, 40%:

$$920 \text{ TMU} \times 0.60 = 552 \text{ TMU}$$
$$1670 \text{ TMU} \times 0.40 = 668 \text{ TMU}$$

Constant total time = 1220 TMU

Note that the T constant includes the freeing of the object using creep speed and average vertical moves before or after the horizontal movement. Vertical moves made during the horizontal movement are internal.

The average horizontal speed is determined by weighting the longitudinal and lateral speeds according to work area observations (lateral speed frequency).

Only the high speed value is to be used in the calculation, as the low speed is included in the acceleration and deceleration times for the prevention of object swinging.

The weighted horizontal speed includes

- Lateral speed: 152.5 TMU/foot × 0.10 = 15.3 TMU/foot
- Longitudinal speed: 15.3 TMU/foot × 0.90 = 13.8 TMU/foot

$$\text{Horizontal speed} = 29.1 \text{ TMU/foot}$$
$$(8.9 \text{ TMU/meter})$$

The transport (T) time and the corresponding index values are based on the following formula:

$$t = 1220 + (29.1 \times n) \text{ or } t = 1220 + (8.9 \times n)$$

where: t = time in TMU
         1220 = move constant (TMU)
         29.1 = horizontal transportation speed in TMU/foot
          8.9 = horizontal transportation speed in
                TMU/meter
            n = number of feet (meters) moved

K   Hook-up and Unhook

This parameter includes the activities involved in both connecting and disconnecting the object from the crane. The parameter begins when the hook has been transported close to the hooking position and is completed when the holding device has been disconnected from the object. Adjustments of the crane for hooking and for tightening and securing the holding device are included. Hooking and Unhooking includes fastening chains, slings, or other holding devices to the crane hook or to the object.

Getting and moving aside chains or slings, for example, and fastening them to the object (or to the crane hook) initially are not covered by the K parameter. Such activities are analyzed using the Part Handling Sequence Model.

Hook-up and Unhook index values are chosen by the type of holding device used.

P   Placement

This parameter involves all actions necessary to lower the object with a combination of high speed and creep speed and to place the object in the desired location. Index values are based on the following data.

1. With or without single direction change:
   Lower 20 inches (50 cm) (high speed)   150
   Lower 2–3 inches (5–8 cm) (low speed)   75
   Change direction   40
   $^1/_2$ longitudinal traverse 4 inches (10 cm)   20
   $^1/_2$ lateral traverse 4 inches (10 cm)   25
                                                    Total   310 TMU
2. With double direction change:
   Lower 5 feet (1.5 m) (high speed)   450
   Lower 20 inches (50 cm) (low speed)   600
   4 × change direction   160
   Longitudinal traverse 20 inches (50 cm)   200
   Lateral traverse 20 inches (50 cm)   250
                                                    Total   1660 TMU
3. With several direction changes:
   Lower 6.6 feet (2 m) (high speed)   600
   Lower 20 inches (50 cm) (low speed)   600
   8 × change direction   320
   Longitudinal traverse 3.3 feet (1 m) (low speed)   400
   Lateral traverse 3.3 feet (1 m)   500
                                                    Total   2420 TMU

Figure 5.25 is presented to illustrate the sequence of events that occurs when an object is moved with a power traversed crane. *Note:* The data in Figure 5.23 should be treated as *sample data* and must be *validated* prior to their use.

Use of the Powered Crane Data Card

The data card (Fig. 5.23) is divided into four columns. Index values are selected by the distance involved (A and T), by the holding device used (K), or by the difficulty involved (P) in placing the object.

Sequence Model Indexing

A Action Distance

Choose the index value by the distance the operator walks to get to or move away from the crane.

T Transport

Choose the index value by the distance the crane is moved horizontally, either loaded or unloaded. All vertical distances are included in the (T) index values; separate vertical analyses are not necessary.

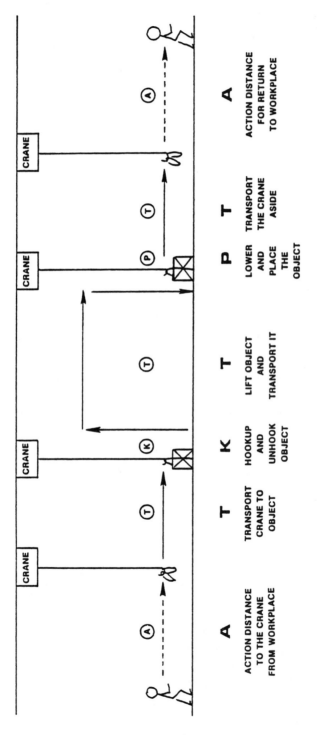

Figure 5.25 Illustration of Powered Crane Sequence Model.

K Hook-up and Unhook

Choose the proper index value by the holding device used.

P Placement

Choose the proper index value by the difficulty involved in lowering the object the last 2–3 inches (5–8 cm) and placing it in the desired location. Once the sequence model is indexed, the index numbers should be added and the total multiplied by 100 to convert to TMU.

Example: An operator walks 90 feet (27 m) to a powered crane control panel and transports the crane to a part 25 feet (7.5 m) away. The part is connected to the crane with one hook and a sling and transported 2 feet (0.6 m), where it is placed with a double change of direction. The operator then moves the crane 9 feet (3 m) out of the way and walks back to the part.

$$A_6 \quad T_{16} \quad K_{24} \quad T_{10} \quad P_{16} \quad T_{16} \quad A_1$$

$$(6 + 16 + 24 + 10 + 16 + 16 + 1) \times 100 = 8900 \text{ TMU}$$

F. The Wheeled Truck Sequence

The Wheeled Truck Sequence is primarily used for determining a time for the horizontal transportation of material from one location to another using a wheeled device. Equipment covered by this sequence falls within two general categories: trucks operated from a riding position and those moved by walking (Fig. 5.26).

Riding trucks: forklift truck, high stacker
Walking trucks: hand truck (two to four wheels), low-lift pallet truck, stacker

Transportation of material with trucks consists of the following activities:

1. The operator walks to the truck (Action Distance).
2. The operator takes a seat (if riding) and starts the truck (Start).
3. The truck is driven or transported to the material (Transport).
4. The material is picked up or loaded by the fork or lifting attachment (Load).
5. The material is transported to another location (Transport).
6. The material is unloaded (Unload).
7. The truck is driven to another area and parked (Transport).
8. The operator switches off the ignition and/or parks the truck.
9. The operator returns to the original (or another) location (Action Distance).

The Wheeled Truck Sequence Model

The above activities are described by the following sequence model:

A   S   T   L   T   L   T   A

RIDING TRUCKS

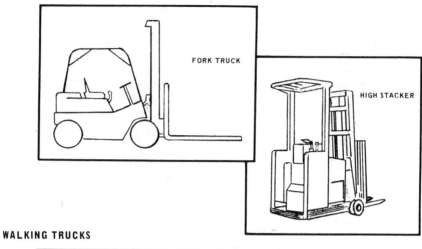

WALKING TRUCKS

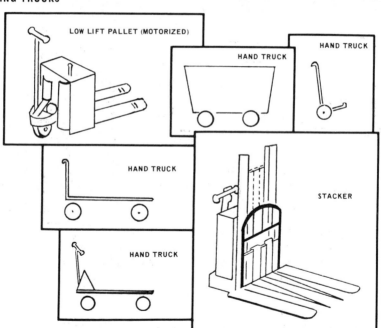

Figure 5.26 Types of riding and walking trucks.

where: A = Action distance
         S = Start *and* park
         T = Transport
         L = Load *or* unload

To more easily see the sequence of events that occurs in moving an object with a wheeled truck, follow the sequence model and the events as pictured in Figure 5.27.

Parameter Definitions

A   Action-Distance

This is the distance walked by the operator to or from the truck.

S   Start and Park

This value includes the actions to prepare the truck for moving plus the parking activity following the final transport. For the *riding truck* these activities include climbing in and out of the seat, starting and stopping the engine, and releasing and engaging the hand brake. For the *walking truck* these activities include taking hold of the handle, starting and stopping the power, if applicable, and tilting the body or handle.

T   Transport

This parameter applies to the movement of the truck with or without a load. The time values are based on a sample of typical trucks (riding and walking) operated under average conditions. Note that *all time values must be validated* for the trucks actually being used prior to any analysis work involving the Wheeled Truck Sequence Model.

L   Load or Unload

This involves either picking up the material at the original location or placing the material at the destination using the forks or other lifting attachments. If a hand truck is used, however, loading and unloading is analyzed with the Part Handling Sequence. If such is the case, the L parameters of the Wheeled Truck Sequence Model carry a zero index value.

Use of the Wheeled Truck Data Card

The data card (Fig. 5.28) is divided into four main sections, each representing a parameter as defined above. Index values are selected by the distance involved (A and T), by the type of truck used (S), or by the location of the object (L).

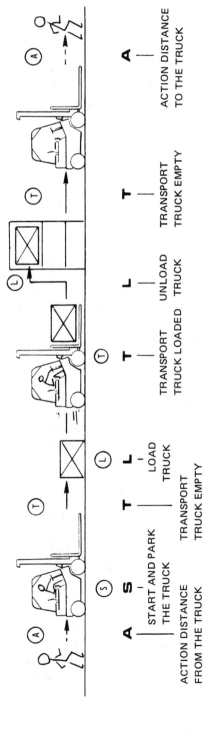

Figure 5.27 Illustration of Wheeled Truck Sequence Model.

Maxi MOST® Systems			A S T L T L T A					WHEELED TRUCK TRANSPORT	
	A	**S**	**T**					**L**	
			TRANSPORT WITH OR WITHOUT LOAD-FEET (M)						
INDEX X 100			RIDING		WALKING			LOAD OR UNLOAD	INDEX X 100
	ACTION DISTANCE FEET (m)	START AND PARK	FORK LIFT TRUCK	HIGH STACKER	STACKER	LOW LIFT PALLET TRUCK	HAND TRUCK		
1	24 (7)		27 (8)	21 (6)	11 (3)	14 (4)	24 (7)		**1**
3	61 (19)	Walking Truck	67 (20)	50 (15)	27 (8)	34 (10)	50 (15)	Floor - Simple	**3**
6	127 (39)	Riding Truck	132 (40)	100 (30)	50 (15)	67 (20)	100 (30)	Floor	**6**
10	220 (67)		198 (60)	165 (50)	83 (25)	100 (30)	165 (50)	Pallet Rack	**10**
16	360 (110)		329 (100)	247 (75)	116 (35)	165 (50)	264 (80)		**16**
24	505 (154)		460 (140)	362 (110)	182 (55)				**24**

Figure 5.28 Maxi MOST—Wheeled Truck data card. Values are read "up to and including."

Sequence Model Indexing

A Action Distance

Choose the index value by the distance the operator walks to get to or move away from the truck.

S Start *and* Park

Choose the index value by the type of truck used: S_3, walking truck; S_6, riding truck.

T Transport

First choose the correct column by the general truck type (riding or walking) and then the specific kind of truck (forklift, high stacker, stacker, low-lift pallet truck, or hand truck). Next, select the index value based on the distance (in feet or meters) that the truck is transported.

L Load *or* Unload

Choose the correct index value by the location of the object when mechanically loading or unloading: L_3, when loading or unloading an object either from or to the floor when no adjustments are required; L_6, when loading or unloading an object either from or to the floor with adjustments; L_{10}, when loading or unloading an object either from or to a pallet rack (above the floor).

Again, due to the vast number of manufacturers and seemingly infinite configuration of trucks, the data provided in Figure 5.28 should be treated as *sample information*. Before its use in establishing a labor standard, the *method must be verified* and the *process time must be validated* to a company's particular trucks and conditions. Once index values are selected from the data card, they are placed on the Wheeled Truck Sequence Model, added, and multiplied by 100 to convert to TMU.

Examples: An operator walks 120 feet (36 m) to a forklift truck, climbs into the seat, and starts the engine. It is driven 12 feet (4 m), where a pallet is picked up from the floor and then transported 75 feet (23 m) and placed in a pallet rack. The truck is then parked 30 feet (9 m) away, and the operator returns 60 feet (18 m) to the workplace.

TRANSPORT PART FROM WORKPLACE FLOOR TO RAISED PALLET-RACK USING HAND-WHEEL TRUCK AND RETURN TO WORKPLACE.

A_6 S_6 T_1 L_6 T_6 L_{10} T_3 A_3

$(6 + 6 + 1 + 6 + 6 + 10 + 3 + 3) \times 100 = 4100$ TMU

An operator walks six steps to a bench, picks up a heavy object, and places it on a low four-wheeled hand truck five steps away. After this, the operator takes the handle of the truck (four steps away) and transports the object 36 feet (11 m). The truck is parked, and the operator walks 150 feet (46 m) to another work area.

MOVE OBJECT TO FOUR-WHEELED HAND TRUCK.

A_3 B_1 P_1

$(3 + 1 + 1) \times 100 = 500$ TMU

TRANSPORT PART TO WORKPLACE USING HAND TRUCK AND RETURN TO WORK AREA.

A_1 S_3 T_0 L_0 T_3 L_0 T_0 A_{10}

$(1 + 3 + 3 + 10) \times 100 = \underline{1700}$ TMU

$\underline{2200}$ TMU

An operator walks 15 feet (5 m) to a low-lift pallet truck, starts it, and transports it 21 feet (6 m) to a pallet located on the floor. The pallet is loaded on the truck and then transported 100 feet (30 m) to a warehouse where it is then placed on the floor. The operator then transports the truck 89 feet (27 m), parks it, and walks 30 feet (9 m) to a workbench.

TRANSPORT PART WITH HOOK+SLING TO BENCH USING CRANE PLACE+MA-
NEUVER AND RETURN TO WORKBENCH.

$$A_1 \quad S_3 \quad T_3 \quad L_6 \quad T_{10} \quad L_6 \quad T_{10} \quad A_3$$

$$(1 + 3 + 3 + 6 + 10 + 6 + 10 + 3) \times 100 = 4200 \text{ TMU}$$

G. Application of the Maxi MOST System

Maxi MOST can be used in any area where the job is such that large amounts of methods variation occur from cycle to cycle—as a result of the cycle length, however, not as a result of poor methods engineering. Areas where Maxi MOST may be used include:

Heavy assembly
Welding
Heavy machining and fabrication
Long-cycle surface treating, such as blasting or coating
Maintenance
Setups

Developing New Elements

Because of the wide variations in the tools, conditions, and methods described with Maxi MOST, developing new elements (index values) is a common and necessary procedure. Knowledge of the element development technique is important. The following should be noted:

- The element backup may be in the form of a time formula.
- The backup analysis should preferably be made with Basic MOST Sequences.
- Keywords should be assigned to new values for (1) type of activity or object and (2) application details, such as the nature of the part or tool, the nature of the surroundings, and a measure of magnitude, such as number of items or occurrences, size, weight, or distances.
- An index card showing the keywords and a suitable number of variables should be designed.
- Document and preserve the backup supporting the new elements.

The majority of the Maxi MOST elements were calculated using the time formula

$$y = mx + c$$

where: y = time in TMU
        m = TMU per unit
        x = number of activities
        c = constant time

Constants and TMU per unit were developed for the activities shown on the data cards and index values selected. The formula shows a straight-line application. Data can also be developed for curved-line applications by following the same format but using different formulas.

Selecting the unit of measure and evaluating is sometimes the most difficult aspect of establishing a formula basis. Suppose we wish to develop index values for "fasten $5/32$ inch (4 mm) plate screw using a spiral screwdriver." Our analysis of the activities gives us the following component times:

Get and aside screwdriver   40 TMU
First and last strokes combined   68 TMU
Place screwdriver to screw   40 TMU
Time for screwdriver stroke
(other than first and last)   13 TMU

Assuming at least two strokes, we can add together the time for the first and last strokes (68 TMU) to the time for placing the screwdriver to the screw (40 TMU) to get a "per screw" value.

If we study the number of screwdriver strokes and develop a reliable average of $3^1/_2$ strokes per screw, we can determine that the strokes needed beyond the first and last are $1^1/_2$.

With these data, we can develop times for fastening any number of $5/32$ inch (4 mm) plate screws with a spiral screwdriver:

$$y = mx + c$$

where: y = total time to fasten X screws
        c = constant for getting and asiding screwdriver (40 TMU)
        m = per screw average time (128 TMU) ($1^1/_2$ strokes per
              screw × 13 TMU per stroke + 40 TMU per screwdriver
              placement + 68 TMU for first and last screw combined)
        x = number of screws to be fastened or loosened

$$y = 128X + 40$$

The maximum number of screws for each index value can then be determined by solving this formula for X, assigning the maximum interval limits to y, and rounding the X value solutions to the nearest whole number.

Taking values from the Index Value Table (Fig. A.3) the data table produced will look like that shown in Figure 5.29.

Index value	Maximum (y value) interval limit	X value	Number of screws (X rounded off)
1	170	1.016	1
3	420	2.969	2
6	770	5.703	5
10	1260	9.531	9
16	1960	15.000	15
24	2770	21.328	21
32	3660	28.281	28
42	4760	36.875	36

Figure 5.29 Index values for spiral screwdriver.

Data tables should only be extended to the practical limits of their application. Theoretically, this spiral screwdriver data table could be extended to cover 268 screws (index value 330), but the upper ranges of the table would rarely be used.

Multiple Operator Activities

It is not uncommon to find that many of the long-cycle assembly or machining activities studied will be multioperator operations. Analysis of such situations can be comfortably handled using the Maxi MOST calculation form.

First, it is imperative that for multioperator operations, the calculation sheet must contain the number of operators for the operation under analysis. For example, on the Maxi MOST calculation sheet under Conditions, specify $1/3$ inch (0.6 cm) steel plate, 4×6 feet (1.2×1.8 m) manning-2". Also, Maxi MOST analysts should locate each operator at the start of the analysis. *Example:* Op-1 (Operator 1) begins at workbench. Op-2 begins at outstock.

At the beginning of each method description step, name the operator performing the activity. *Example:* Op-1 push plate on conveyor.

The analysis of simultaneous motions with the right and left hand, as discussed in Section E of Chapter 3, can be applied to the analysis of simultaneous actions between multiple operators. Therefore, the techniques of "limiting out" certain parameters or entire sequence models by drawing a circle around the work performed internal to an equal or longer activity is appropriate for the analysis of multioperator operations. The same principles and techniques apply. In some more complex multioperator tasks, it may be advantageous to prepare a operator analysis chart based on a separate analysis for each operator.

Care must be taken when creating such analyses to keep the final application format (the worksheet or titlesheet) in mind. Select countable production units, and provide the final time in the desired format (total labor hours or total elapsed time). Indicate the unit of measure if the calculated total is elapsed time, and then extend the elapsed time on a worksheet by multiplying it by the number of operators for the operation to get total labor hours.

6

MOST for Clerical Operations

The emergence in the 1940s and 1950s of predetermined motion time systems, especially those that focus on the clerical area, provided management personnel with the tool to determine the time needed to perform certain tasks, with minimal disruption in the office. However, the analysis time consumed by the detailed systems of that time, and the considerable amount of documentation required, resulted in the hesitation to use such work measurement systems. Also, clerical operations contained wide variations in the methods used to perform them, as little methods engineering time focused on clerical operations. These factors led to a predominant use of the stopwatch over the predetermined motion time systems as the best way to tackle the clerical work measurement task.

There have been many improvements in work measurement techniques since the 1960s, with MOST in the forefront. MOST Clerical Systems, unlike other clerical predetermined motion systems, is quickly learned and implemented. Its methods sensitivity encouraged methods engineers. By applying the MOST Clerical Systems, the managerial staff acquires accurate data and the standards needed to produce personnel tables, performance charts, and other meaningful management documents.

MOST Clerical Systems is a variation of the Basic MOST Work Measurement System for industrial operations. Although it is applied using the same sequence model and analysis format as the general production version, there are additions to the General and Controlled Move data cards. A new Equipment Use data card has also been added specifically to handle clerical operations. MOST Clerical Systems provides the same advantages for clerical work measurement as the general production version provides for industrial applications and produces equivalent results.

MOST Clerical Systems is based on three activity sequence models. They are the General Move, Controlled Move, and Tool/Equipment Use (see Fig. 6.1). Using the definitions provided in a separate text, the analyst indexes these sequence models in the same manner as previously mentioned in Chapter 3.

General Move

The Clerical General Move data card is based on the same theory as the Basic MOST System as defined in Chapters 1 and 3. The sequence model deals with spatial displacement of an object under manual control, in which the object's path is not restricted. Because of the nature of the clerical operations, additional values were added to the General Move data card. For example, *Collect and Jog Paper* (G_6) includes the time needed for an operator to collect or gather several sheets of paper and jog them together, a common clerical activity. It is this type of activity that has been taken into consideration and provided for the General Move data card of the MOST Clerical Systems.

Example: An operator collects several sheets of paper and jogs them twice

ACTIVITY	SEQUENCE MODEL	SUB - ACTIVITIES	
GENERAL MOVE	**A B G A B P A**	A - ACTION DISTANCE B - BODY MOTION G - GAIN CONTROL P - PLACEMENT	
CONTROLLED MOVE	**A B G M X I A**	M - MOVE CONTROLLED X - PROCESS TIME I - ALIGNMENT	
EQUIPMENT USE	**A B G A B P A B P A**	H - LETTER/PAPER HANDLING T - THINK R - RECORD K - CALCULATE W - TYPE	
TOOL USE	**A B G A B P A B P A**	F - FASTEN L - LOOSEN C - CUT M - MEASURE	

Figure 6.1 Sequence models—MOST Clerical Systems.

and asides them to the "out" basket. The sequence model for analyzing this operation is as follows:

$$A_1 \quad B_0 \quad G_6 \quad A_1 \quad B_0 \quad P_1 \quad A_0$$

$$(1 + 6 + 1 + 1) \times 10 = 90 \text{ TMU}$$

Another example of a value added to the clerical General Move data card is *Gain Control with Intermediate Moves* (G_6). The value covers several moves or repositionings of the fingers or hands to gain complete control of the object.

Example: The clerk prepares an envelope for mailing by removing a label from an adhesive pad (with intermediate moves) and places it on the envelope (with intermediate moves). The following sequence model reflects this activity:

$$A_1 \quad B_0 \quad G_6 \quad A_1 \quad B_0 \quad P_6 \quad A_0$$

$$(1 + 6 + 1 + 6) \times 10 = 140 \text{ TMU}$$

Controlled Move

Like the General Move, the Clerical Controlled Move data card has been altered to include several additional values that provide for various clerical controlled move operations. The Controlled Move Sequence Model describes the manual displacement of an object over a "controlled" path. That is, the movement of an object is restricted in at least one direction by contact with or attachment to another object.

Many clerical examples of controlled moves occur when handling paper. Therefore, the Clerical Controlled Move data card provides additional information for these activities in the Move Controlled (M) parameter under the general heading of paper handling operations. This parameter applies to handling paper to change its shape, direction, or position (i.e., interleaf paper or unfold paper). For example, interleaf paper covers the action of lifting the sheet(s) of paper with one hand while reaching and grasping a divider sheet or carbon paper, for example, with the other hand and inserting it beneath the sheet that was lifted.

Example: An operator interleaves four sheets of blue divider among the first four sections of a report. The MOST analysis to interleaf all four sheets would be

$$A_1 \quad B_0 \quad G_1 \quad M_6 \quad X_0 \quad I_0 \quad A_0 \qquad 4$$

$$(1 + 1 + 6) \times 4 = 32 \times 10 = 320 \text{ TMU}$$

Equipment Use

The major difference between the Clerical and Basic MOST Work Measurement Systems is the addition of new elements covering equipment use. An additional data card is used to analyze common clerical activities including common pieces of office equipment. The Equipment Use Sequence Model shows the same format as the Tool Use Sequence Model and it is also mentally divided into five sections:

Get equipment	Place equipment	Use equipment	Aside equipment	Return
A B G	A B P		A B P	A

The open space or gap in the sequence model provides for the insertion of one of the following Equipment Use parameters:

H = letter/paper equipment handling
T = think/read
W = type
R = record
K = calculate

The Equipment Use data cards contain values for such clerical functions as stapling, sealing, stamping, typing, writing, and calculating. To apply the information appearing on these data cards, the user follows procedures similar to those outlined previously in Chapter 3. For example, the subactivity typewrite, which appears on the Equipment Use data card, refers to the use of fingers and hands performing multiple Control and General Moves to type words, sentences, letters, headings, etc., on a keyboard. The index value chosen from the data card is based primarily on the number of characters typed or the functions performed on the keyboard. So if, for example, a word processor operator inserts a sheet of paper into the platen in preparation for typing a letter, the appropriate value for this insertion would be a W_{24}. The sequence model for this insertion reads:

$$A_1 \quad B_0 \quad G_1 \quad A_1 \quad B_0 \quad P_1 \quad W_{24} \quad A_0 \quad B_0 \quad P_0 \quad A_0$$
$$(1 + 1 + 1 + 1 + 24) \times 10 = 280 \text{ TMU}$$

The same operator then types a 14-word letter with two carriage returns. The sequence model for typing the 14 words will read:

$$A_0 \quad B_0 \quad G_0 \quad A_1 \quad B_0 \quad P_1 \quad W_{42} \quad A_0 \quad B_0 \quad P_0 \quad A_0$$
$$(1 + 1 + 42) \times 10 = 440 \text{ TMU}$$

The two carriage returns would be analyzed

$$A_1 \quad B_0 \quad G_1 \quad M_1 \quad X_0 \quad I_0 \quad A_0 \quad \quad 2$$
$$(1 + 1 + 1) \times 2 = 6 \times 10 = 60 \text{ TMU}$$

Total time to perform the paper insertion plus typing the 14 words with the two carriage returns is equal to 780 TMU, which represents a 100% performance level and includes *no allowances*.

Tool Use

During a clerical operation there may be a need to use one of several common hand tools (e.g., knife, scissors, ruler, or brush). Values for the use of these tools are found on the Tool Use data card. Clerical Tool Use application procedures are identical to those stated in Chapter 3. Selection of the appropriate index value will be based on the tool used or, in some cases, the type and number of motions performed. For example, a secretary picks up a bottle of correction fluid and with six finger actions unscrews the cap and places the bottle on the desk. The analysis for that operation is:

$$A_1 \quad B_0 \quad G_1 \quad A_1 \quad B_0 \quad P_1 \quad L_{10} \quad A_1 \quad B_0 \quad P_1 \quad A_0$$
$$(1 + 1 + 1 + 1 + 10 + 1 + 1) \times 10 = 160 \text{ TMU}$$

Application of the MOST Clerical System

Often, in a clerical environment, the jobs performed by a person vary widely. Clerical work is very seldom "repetitive." For example, a secretary may type three letters, the first a 21-line ($1/2$-page) letter, the second a 40-line (full-page) letter, and the third a 64-line ($1\,1/2$-page) letter using a word processing system. Although this example reflects only one type of variation—length—other variations, such as margin size, tabular typing, and spacing, could be performed and could be numerous. MOST Clerical Systems is capable of handling these variations because of the high application level, ease of analysis, and sound statistical principles upon which MOST Work Measurement Systems are based. Because it is an easy system to use and understand, as well as method sensitive, MOST Clerical Systems provides the analyst with a tool for comparing the effects of various methods of performing clerical activities and, in fact, "engineers" workplaces and methods to allow the clerical worker to work more efficiently and more productively. Also available within the MOST Clerical Application Systems is the statistical framework that makes analysis of variable situations possible. The clerical analyst will find any or all of the approaches to the calculation of time standards (Chap. 7) appropriate. Proper application of these approaches produces consistent and well-documented standard times. The system also allows a choice of standard calculation formats based on the type and variability of the work being analyzed.

MOST Clerical Computer Systems

All the advantages of the manual system are incorporated and enhanced in the MOST Clerical Computer Systems. Generation of standard times can occur 20–40% faster than with the manual system. By using the MOST Clerical Computer System, the analyst can create MOST analyses, suboperation data, staffing data, document the workplace, calculate performance, and establish unit costs.

```
┌─────────────────────────────────────────────────────────────┐
│                    METHOD DESCRIPTION                        │
├─────────────────────────────────────────────────────────────┤
│  •  PLACE CHECK FROM DESK 6 TO TABLE 2                       │
│  •  HANDLE COVER ON XEROX-MACHINE  SIMO 1                    │
│  •  PUSH DIAL ON XEROX-MACHINE FOR THE NUMBER OF COPIES      │
│  •  PUSH BUTTON AT XEROX-MACHINE FOR PROCESS                 │
│  •  HANDLE COVER AT XEROX-MACHINE  SIMO 1, 2, 3             │
│  •  PICKUP CHECK                                             │
│  •  MOVE COPY FROM XEROX-MACHINE TO DESK 6 WITH SIT          │
└─────────────────────────────────────────────────────────────┘
```

Figure 6.2   Method description for copy checks.

Note: A glossary of terms and a more detailed description of the MOST Computer Systems appear in Chapter 8.

To develop a clerical data base using the computer, the analyst begins by inputting the work area data—describing the layout of the area, the distances between workplaces (in steps), the equipment being used, the objects being worked on, and any tools that are used. A layout sketch is produced along with detailed work area data information.

After the work area data have been entered, the analyst observes the operation and "speaks" the method description (Fig. 6.2) into a portable dictation device. A typist keys the method description into the computer. The computer then calculates the amount of time needed to perform the operation. Figure 6.3


```
     COPY   CHECK ON XEROX-MACHINE AT CASH AND MAIL ROOM
PER COPY                                        OFG: 4  04-Dec-78

 1 PLACE CHECK FROM DESK.6 TO TABLE-2
               A1   BO   G1   A10 BO   P3   AO       1.00    150.
 2 HANDLE COVER ON XEROX-MACHINE SIMO 1
              <A1>BO   G1   M6   XO   IO   AO       1.00     70.
 3 PUSH DIAL ON XEROX-MACHINE FOR THE NUMBER OF COPIES
               A1   BO   G1   M1   XO   IO   AO       1.00     30.
 4 PUSH BUTTON AT XEROX-MACHINE FOR PROCESS
               A1   BO   G1   M1   X10 IO   AO       1.00    130.
 5 HANDLE COVER AT XEROX-MACHINE SIMO 1 2 3
              <A1  BO   G1  >M6   XO   IO   AO       1.00     60.
 6 PICKUP CHECK
               A1   BO   G1   A1   BO   PO   AO       1.00     30.
 7 MOVE COPY FROM XEROX-MACHINE TO DESK.6 WITH SIT
               A1   BO   G1   A10 B10 P1   AO       1.00    230.

                                        TOTAL  TMU         700.
```

Figure 6.3   MOST analysis.

CLERICAL TITLE SHEET - CASH AND MAIL ROOM

ASSEMBLE/DISASSEMBLE
25   ASSEMBLE CHECKS ON NOTICE WITH STAPLER AT DESK.6

EXAMINE
8   RESEARCH PAYMENT ON MICROFICHE ON DESK

9   RESEARCH PAYMENT AT HOUSE CARD FILE IN FILE CABINET

10   SORT AND REVIEW PAYMENTS FOR RESEARCH ON MICROFICHE WITH VIEWER

11   CHECK ACCOUNT STATUS FOR ACCOUNT TRANSFER

15   INSPECT CARD FOR COMPLETENESS BEFORE PROCESSING

MOVE
3   RETURN PAYMENTS TO MAIL SECTION FOR PROCESSING

22   TRANSPORT MAIL

23   TRANSPORT CHECKS TO ENDORSER

OPERATE
2   OPEN ENVELOPE ON TABLE WITH AUTOMATIC LETTER OPENER

4   BUNDLE ENVELOPES FOR DISTRIBUTION WITH HANDS

6   SORT MAIL IN SLOTS WITH HANDS

16   BUNDLE FORMS

18   REMOVE FORMS FROM ENVELOPES

19   COPY NUMBERS ON FORM WITH PEN

20   COPY 5 NUMBERS ON FORM WITH PENCIL

21   COPY 11 DIGIT NUMBER ON FORM WITH PENCIL

24   COPY NUMBERS ON FORM WITH PEN

26   CALCULATE CHECKS AT DESK.6

27   COPY NUMBERS ON FORM WITH PEN

30   SEQUENCE CHECKS FOR XEROXING AT DESK

33   COPY CHECK ON XEROX MACHINE

PREPARE
1   PREPARE DUPLICATE BILL FOR PAYMENT ON CUSTOMER ACCOUNT

7   MAKE   READY   TO PREPARE DUPLICATE BILL FOR PAYMENTS RECEIVED WITH
     NO COUPONS

12   PREPARE WORK TABLE FOR PROCESSING MAIL

17   PREPARE DESK

28   MAKE READY NOTICES FOR STAPLING AT DESK.6

SURFACE TREAT
5   CLEAN UP AFTER SLITTING ENVELOPES

13   WIPE   OFF   VIEWER-SCREEN   SMUDGES   BEFORE   RESEARCHING   CUSTOMER
     ACCOUNT

14   CLEAN EXCESS GLUE FROM ENVELOPE BEFORE MAILING

Figure 6.4   Sample of clerical Title Sheet.

provides an illustration of a completed MOST analysis based on the work area data and the method description (Fig. 6.2).

The completed MOST calculation is then filed in the database simply by using the title of the MOST analysis (see Chap. 8 for a detailed description of the computerized data filing system). A search can then be made of the database. MOST calculations are organized into a list of all possible operations and suboperations that could occur for a cost center. This list (called a *title sheet;* Fig. 6.4) is the key to the standards setting process. From this title sheet the analyst can select the various operations that occur and set a standard for a particular job. The output, the *time standard,* is presented in three formats: the *standard calculation sheet* (Fig. 6.5), the *time calculation sheet,* and the *method instruction sheet* for the operator (Fig. 6.6). Any suboperation can be traced from its work area layout through a final time standard. In addition to establishing standards, the Clerical Computer System provides the analyst with performance reports and staffing requirements.

The *performance report* generation program calculates effectiveness, earned hours, coverage, and performance of an individual employee, section, or department. The user inputs the number of the standard, the actual quantity of work, the actual time it took to perform the work, and any delay or administrative time. The computer accesses the standard database for the appropriate operational description and the standard time. The program output is a summary of the performance of an employee or section; it contains performance figures, standard hours, nonstandard hours, earned hours, delays, and so on. A weekly report for each section is then stored for the generation of monthly, quarterly, and annual reports.

TYPE OF WORK	ELEMENTAL TIME	PERCENT ALLOWANCE	ALLOWANCE TIME	STANDARD TIME
EXTERNAL MANUAL	18910.	15.	2837.	19194.
INTERNAL	(0.)			
PROCESS TIME	0.	0.	0.	0.
STANDARD (TMU/CYCLE)	18910.		2837.	19194.
UNITS PER CYCLE	1			
STANDARD (HOURS/UNIT)				0.192
UNITS PER HOUR @ 100%				5.21

REASON FOR CHANGE -- CHANGE IN PROCEDURES

Figure 6.5 Standard calculation sheet.

STEP	METHOD INSTRUCTION		FREQ
1	OPEN ENVELOPE ON TABLE WITH AUTOMATIC LETTER OPE NER	(2)	1
2	SORT MAIL IN SLOTS WITH HANDS	(6)	1
3	TRANSPORT MAIL * MAIL TRANSPORT WITH CART	(29)	1
4	REMOVE FORMS FROM ENVELOPES	(18)	1
5	COPY NUMBERS ON FORM WITH PEN * OLD FORM 111	(27)	1
6	CALCULATE CHECKS	(26)	1
7	SEQUENCE CHECKS FOR XEROXING	(30)	1
8	COPY CHECK ON XEROX-MACHINE	(33)	1
9	TRANSPORT CHECKS	(23)	1

Figure 6.6   Method instruction sheet.

The *staffing requirement* program determines the staffing for a cost center. The analyst inputs such variables as the name of the cost center, the number of percentage factions or loaned employees, and the planned quantity of work. The program retrieves data pertaining to the cost center from such data files as time standards and performance reports. The output includes a summary of the standard hours, nonstandard hours, miscellaneous hours, and the projected staff level for the cost center. A third program, *unit costing,* becomes useful when, for instance, a document (unit) is processed in several different departments and the total cost is needed.

MOST Clerical Systems provides managers with a higher level, easily learned and understood clerical work measurement tool, along with a meaningful and statistically sound application system. With such tools, that ever-growing portion of our workforce can have realistic goals placed before it. Based on these goals, proper assignment of personnel can be accomplished and unit costs can be estimated. To improve productivity in clerical organizations is to improve profit. The ease of data analysis and manipulation using the computer has now made the measurement of clerical operations a manageable task.

7

Systematic Development of Engineered Labor Time Standards

Two Alternatives: Direct Measurement or Suboperation Data

MOST Work Measurement Systems unquestionably provides all the necessary features for an effective work measurement system either for the direct establishment of time standards for operations or for the development of suboperation data for parts of operations. As is indicated in previous chapters, MOST provides several capabilities superior to conventional techniques. In this chapter, MOST refers to any one of the three versions: Basic, Mini, and Maxi MOST. The development procedure for time standards is the same whichever MOST version is used for backup.

There are many situations in which the *direct approach* of calculating time standards with MOST is both the fastest and most economical. An assembly line with relatively short-cycle operations and few product variations is an almost perfect example of an area within which the time standards can be set without intermediate steps or data levels. On the other hand, and in the majority of cases, some type of "building blocks" must be developed prior to the final stage of calculating time standards. The reason for this complication is primarily economical and to a certain extent practical.

Since the calculation of final time standards is often quite an ongoing process, it is obviously important to minimize the costs for this activity. Therefore, the procedures must be quick and simple to apply. However, adequate accuracy in the allowed time values must be retained. Even though MOST has a combined accuracy and speed characteristic superior to any other known system, the speed of MOST is still far from sufficient to calculate every time standard economically on a direct basis.

It is therefore quite necessary to introduce one or more levels between the basic work measurement system (MOST) and the final time standard. Traditionally, units or elements developed on levels below final time have been designated "standard data." Standard data units could range from very short time values of a few TMU to elements several minutes long. All standard data elements were grouped and classified at various data levels. With MTM-1 as a basis, for example, it has been common to define three to five different data levels.

The buildup of standard data was always made following the "bottom-up" principle, meaning that the smallest elements were developed first, with subsequent combining of such elements into larger and larger standard data units. Logically and technically this approach was sound; economically and practically it was very costly and time consuming.

With the introduction and application of the MOST Work Measurement Technique this standard data development procedure has been completely reversed. With MOST one always starts at the operation level (equal to *final time standards*) and then continues from the "top down," if necessary, by breaking operations into suboperations. By doing so, only those data that are actually required to set the standards must be developed. Normally, each completed MOST calculation form represents one complete operation or suboperation. It is for this reason that the *activity title* assigned to the MOST calculation is so important—it identifies the data unit. It seldom happens when using MOST, but it is possible that more than one level below the operation level is needed. Such situations are frequent for data developments in such industries as shipbuilding and heavy engineering in which the value of a final time standard may exceed 100 hours. In such cases, two or three levels of data may be required.

The general rule (for other than direct analyses) is that all MOST calculations produced be defined as *suboperations*. All suboperations are classified as *suboperation data* and placed on a level immediately below the operation level. This is also true when "higher levels" of suboperations are common; these higher levels are called *combined suboperations*. Although the concept of "standard data" is applicable for MOST Systems, the traditional expression "standard data" is not used in association with MOST.

There is no need to develop elemental standard data units with MOST; each sequence model is an element in itself. Usually, one MOST analysis (suboperation) consists of 5–15 method steps, or sequence models, corresponding to an identical number of individual elements in terms of standard data. Certainly, variations from this average may occur, but only in rare cases does a MOST analysis consist of only one sequence model or reflect the analysis of one element.

The distribution of sequence models per MOST calculation is shown in Figure 7.1 for a sample of manufacturing industries. MOST is so fast in application that the development, filing, retrieval, and possible revision of small elements (standard data units) has proven to be an inefficient and cumbersome procedure to follow. Because of the minute detail of MTM-1, the standard data building block approach was the only possible solution in the application of that system.

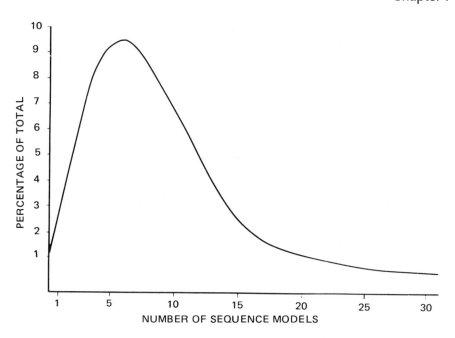

Figure 7.1   Distribution of the number of sequence models per MOST calculation.

This principle was also true for the higher level systems, such as MTM-2, MTM-3, GPD, and USD, but it no longer holds true when using the MOST Systems.

The direct approach with MOST is a quicker and simpler way to reach the final time standards. The key is the ease with which complete suboperations can be analyzed or existing ones updated to fit particular situations when using MOST.

Filing and Retrieval of Suboperation Data

It is obvious that the suboperation data units developed from MOST analyses must be organized in some way. For several reasons, it must be easy to retrieve one specific unit from a large quantity of suboperations. A unit may be needed and reviewed for the purpose of reference, method (and time standard) change, application in a different area, method evaluation, improvement, or comparison. Therefore, systematic filing of suboperation data units in a *data bank* using a uniform and simple coding system has become an integral part of an effective standard time system whether manual or computerized. For a manual application, each unit can be assigned a unique code or number consisting of, for instance, 10 digits. These digits, divided into three groups or categories, can give a brief description of the content of the suboperation.

- Activity (three digits)
- Object/component/equipment/tool (four digits)
- Method level (one digit)

The last two digits of the 10-digit code may be reserved for a sequential running number. Such a number is necessary to establish a unique code for each unit. To make the coding simple and practical, only 10 digits may be used. These digits are usually not enough to describe all the variations of a suboperation that may occur. On the other hand, a coding system with 20–25 digits is very cumbersome and impractical to use.

The following examples illustrate the application of a 10-digit code number for suboperation data units.

1. Set up and tear down a machine vise.
   Code: 103   03130   4   01

Activity: Set up and tear down	103
Object group: Holding devices	03
Object (within object group): Vise	10
Method level (infrequent activity)	4
Sequential running number	01

   (first analysis made having the indicated eight digits)

2. Assemble resistor on a PC board.
   Code: 101   5522   2   02

Activity: Assemble	101
Object group: Electronic components	55
Object: Resistor	22
Method level (frequent activity)	2
Sequential running number	02

   (Second analysis with this eight-digit code number)

3. Read instruction sheet for billing procedures (clerical activity).
   Code: 703   0011   3   05

Activity: Read	703
Object group: General	00
Object (within object group): Instruction sheet	11
Method level (infrequent activity)	4
Sequential running number	05

The suboperations can be filed according to *activity* and *object group* or *object*. Using this procedure there will be a cross register, and the search for a unit can be made with regard to either activity or object.

All MOST analyses (suboperation data units) are arranged sequentially in the data bank for easy retrieval. The search for data is a completely manual process even if the phrase *data bank* implies that a computer is involved. There are, however, many advantages to a computerized data base, as is indicated in Chapter 8. It must be emphasized, though, that a well-organized and well-maintained *manual* data bank can be an effective and practical instrument in the development and maintenance of time standards.

Approaches to the Calculation of Final Time Standards

The establishment of time standards, as indicated earlier, is quite often a continuous process, requiring a certain amount of labor to perform. Time standards must be set for the operation pertaining to new and changed products and components as well as to any change in the work conditions. Some companies may have to calculate and maintain hundreds of thousands of time standards, since (1) the total number of operations is very large; (2) product additions and variations are common; and (3) new facilities, equipment, and tools are constantly being added.

Depending on the quantity of new time standards and the effectiveness of the applied procedures for setting them, the required applicator capacity can be estimated. In order to keep the cost-benefit ratio for this function on an acceptable level, it is important that the procedures and data application formats for the establishment of time standards be properly developed and refined.

There are many ways of setting time standards, even if we limit ourselves to so-called *engineered* time standards. An engineered time standard is based on documented work conditions and a method specification, in addition to the time value. On the other hand, an *estimated* time standard consists of a time value only. No backup is usually available for an estimated time standard.

The most common data application formats for engineered time standards can be classified in three major groups:

1. *Standard time tables* indicating fixed time values and final time standards for the operations in an area.
2. *Work sheets* that normally contain all possible activities or suboperations within an area. The final time standard is calculated by "checking off" actual suboperations for a specific operation and adding together the time values for the suboperations. Frequently, process time and allowances must also be included (Fig. 7.2).
3. *Spread sheets* are made up of benchmark operations slotted into preset time groups. The time standard is established by comparing the work content of the actual operation with any one of the benchmarks on the spread sheet. The mean value of the time group into which the actual operation falls is the final time standard that will be allowed (Fig. 7.3).

WORK SHEET - EXAMPLE

Area	**ASSEMBLY**		Code	
			Date	75.04.12
Operation	OIL PUMP	PXA-4810	Sign.	A.A.

SUBOPERATIONS												Total MH	
												Set Up	Place
Preparation													
Simple	101	I	100	Normal		102	300	Complicated	103		600	100	
Transport to work place													
Elevate								104	I		77	77	
Crane								105			87		

		Pos. No.				Frequence			No	Fr	Mh		
Transport	To workplace	1			Elevate	1			201	1	77		77
					Crane				202		87		
Handling	Turn work piece	5			Crane	1			203	1	49		49
	Workpiece up/down	2			Crane	1			204	1	59		59
Assemble	Screw and/or nut				≤ 1/4"				205		10		
		3	4		> 1/4"	4	2		206	6	14		84
	Subassembly								207		42		
	Stud								208		12		
	Pin	6				2			209	2	8		16
	Locking wire								210		15		
	Locking pin / washer	4				2			211	2	12		24
	With turque				≤ 30 kpn				212		7		
Cut					> 30 kpn				213		14		
					≤ 10 holes Diam ≤ 5/8"				214		2		
Chamfer	Hole				> 10 holes Diam ≤ 5/8"				215		1		
					≤ 10 holes Diam > 5/8"				216		4		
					> 10 holes Diam > 5/8"				217		2		
									218				
	Radius								219		40		
									220				
					Diam. ≤ 8"				221		6		
Mark	Diameter				Diam. > 8" ≤ 16"				222		8		
					Diam. > 16"				223		10		
	With scriber								224		2		
									225				
								TOTAL				177	309
OPERATION TIME INCLUDE ALLOWANCES 10%												195	340

Figure 7.2 Sample work sheet. Setup time = 0.195 hour; run time = 0.340 hour.

Craft: **Automotive**		Code	1420.07
		Signature	VH
Task Area: **Electrical System**		Date	6/23
		Page	1/7

Group: **A**	**B**	**C**	**D**

Time

0	(0.10)	0.150	(0.20)	0.250	(0.40)	0.500	(0.70)	0.900

A	**B**	**C**	**D**
ENGINE TIMING SET W/LIGHT	BATTERY -R/R FORD CAB OVER OR EQUIV.	SWITCH -TOGGLE -R/R	BEARING -ALT. -R/R
1420.07- 07 .1350	1420.07- 44 .1960	1420.07- 48 .2785	1420.07- 71 .7813
SEAL BEAM (ONE)	BOLT -BATTERY CLAMP R/R (ONE) UNDER HOOD	TIMING & DWELL -CHECK DELCO -6 CYL. MOST EQUIPMENT	
1420.07- 10 .0808	1420.07- 45 .1791	1420.07- 56 .2982	
LIGHTS & INSTRUMENTS - CHECK	CHARGE BATTERY (FAST) HOOK UP & REMOVE	DIST. W/GOU. R/R ALL TRUCKS	
1420.07- 12 .0534	1420.07- 50 .1507	1420.07- 57 .3053	
POINTS -ADJUST. DELCO WINDOW TYPE	TAIL LITE ASSY. -R R ALL EQUIPMENT	S/PLUGS -R/R - MOST -6 CLY.	
1420.07- 13 .0811	1420.07- 51 .1574	1420.07- 58 .3253	
CLEARANCE LITE ASSY. R/R	POINTS & COND. -R R & ADJUST.	ELECTRIC PLUG -R R TRAILER CABLE ALL	
1420.07- 14 .0619	1420.07- 55 .2135	1420.07- 64 .3682	
CLEARANCE LITE ASSY. R/R USE LADDER	SWITCH -TURN SIGNAL - R/R UNIVERSAL TYPE	SWITCH -TURN SIGNAL - R/R FORD	
1420.07- 14A .0957	1420.07- 65 .1561	1420.07- 69 .3800	

Figure 7.3 Sample spread sheet.

Although *standard timetables* are used in situations in which the number of both final time standards and method variations is low, spread sheets, on the other hand, are applied when the total number of final time standards is large and the method variations are difficult to control, for instance in such areas as maintenance and warehousing.

A final time standard can thus be obtained directly from a timetable or a spread sheet by either a selection or a comparison. Establishing a final time standard from a work sheet is always a matter of selecting the relevant suboperations, assigning an order of sequence and applicable frequencies, and computing the time value. Specifications of the method, tooling, and process data are usually produced at the same time, mainly for instructional purposes. Both standard timetables and spread sheets are obviously very fast to apply once they have been properly developed. Therefore, the output rate of time standards is high, and a relatively limited applicator capacity will be needed.

Work sheets can be developed to any degree of detail desired. A detailed work sheet requires more time to use than a simple sheet. Therefore, it is important to pay attention to how work sheets are designed. The suboperations on the work sheet should be arranged and grouped so that it is easy for the applicator to locate them, as well as to make quick decisions about which suboperations to select.

By using a statistical approach in determining allowed deviations or tolerances for each suboperation, the number of suboperations listed on the work sheet can frequently be reduced by combining two or more suboperations. In the process of designing a work sheet, it is rather common that the total number of suboperations may be reduced by as much as two-thirds. Such a simplication of the work sheet minimizes the selection and decision time during the calculation procedure and makes the applicator more efficient, thus cutting the cost per standard.

There are additional benefits. It is, for example, quite possible to control the output accuracy of the time standards, as well as to improve the consistency of the output by applying a familiar statistical formula for standard deviation (for further explanations, see Appendix A).

Documentation of Work Conditions

It has been pointed out several times throughout this book that engineered time standards must be well documented with regard to *methods* and *work conditions*. This principle is as valid for MOST Systems as it is for any other predetermined motion time system. Without a proper documentation of actual backup data, the time standard can be considered neither engineered nor defendable should a dispute ever arise. It is also important that the documentation supporting a time standard reflect realistic and actual work conditions. Since work conditions change frequently, updating and maintenance of the time standards to match the prevailing conditions at any point in time become critical issues throughout the installation and application phase of the standards development process.

The documentation of work conditions is similar to taking a photograph of the shop or office where the work is performed. The work conditions we talk about here can be subdivided into the following categories:

- Facilities: machines, equipment, and tools
- Work flow, such as material flow, work area, and workplace layouts
- Technical and manual methods
- Standard practices

These and other work conditions are preferably described and documented for each work area in a manual with a standardized format. Such a manual is not only regarded as a reference for backup material for the time standards, but it also serves as a handbook for the supervisor or foreperson. All necessary information concerning the conditions within the supervisor's domain is readily available, with the objective to help the supervisor better perform his or her job of work management.

Properly developed, these manuals of work conditions or Work Management Manuals, can find many more applications. They can be used in training situations for industrial engineers, supervisors, and workers. They can be used as precedents for the development of new manuals in similar areas, and they can be used as reference material in the event of any disputes over time standards.

Systematic Development of Time Standards

The subject of systematic development of time standards is by itself large and complicated enough to fill a book. Only a few basic concepts and principles, together with the important features of the MOST Application Systems, have been outlined in this chapter. It has been necessary to exclude from this text most of the detailed procedures that make up a well-designed standard time system.

MOST Work Measurement Systems is like the powerful engine being built into an automobile or truck. The engine is needed to make the vehicle move and operate, but the steering, the wheels, and other components actually make the automobile or truck do what you expect it to do: transport people or material. Likewise, it is the components and features of a standard time system or, in this case MOST Application Systems, that really will help you get "the most out of MOST." MOST Application Systems is structured to produce engineered labor time standards with MOST Work Measurement Systems as the engine or drive train and the MOST Application Systems the chassis, steering, wheels, cab, etc., of the vehicle.

The systematic application procedures for MOST consist of a set of rules under which MOST should be applied, as well as a documentation package for improving the work management and thus the productivity of the industrial engineer and the company. In any case, such application procedures must be developed or acquired, provided they do not already exist in the company, to produce and maintain engineered labor time standards.

8

MOST Computer Systems

Throughout the past decade the use of the computer in industry has spread rapidly. Scores of computer terminals are located in companies to enhance the flow of information within or between various departments. In manufacturing engineering, the primary uses of computers have been for process and inventory control and for directing the flow of operational procedures to the factory floor.

Although these applications by manufacturing engineering departments have proven very useful, there are many other benefits yet to reap. The computer's speed, accuracy, and ability to sort and collate large amounts of data can be used to relieve the engineer of many routine tasks. With the advent of the mini-computer's on-line capabilities, the engineering department's access to the computer, so often a problem with large-scale company computers, is no longer a barrier. And microcomputers have further reduced these barriers.

MOST Computer Systems addresses one area of the industrial engineering realm—the establishment of labor time standards based on the MOST Systems described in this book. In the majority of companies today, most of the work involved in gathering data and preparing time standards is done manually by the industrial engineer. Yet many of these tasks can be performed more quickly and accurately by a computer, thus freeing the engineer to focus on more productive tasks. Although MOST as a manual system is consistent and fast, MOST Computer Systems offers even greater speed and uniformity of application.

A Totally Integrated System

Any properly functioning system is designed such that the various parts are interactive and form a unified whole. MOST Computer Systems is designed in this manner. Emphasis is placed on a "total system" to set and maintain complete labor time standards. The various system program components are linked together to accomplish five basic functions (see Fig. 8.1).

1. Development of data
2. Storage of data
3. Standard calculation
4. Storage of standards
5. Updating of data and standards

This linkage allows the engineer the opportunity to follow a unit of data (an operation or suboperation) through the system, all the way from the appropriate workplace layout to the time standard(s) of which it is a part. The system therefore provides a complete audit trail along with the proper documentation to produce an "engineered labor time standard." This design is the basis for the mass updating program that enables the industrial engineer to keep "all standards" current at the introduction of *any* change, that is, in workplace, method, or process. This feature provides an organization the opportunity to say, "Our standards are current and accurate!" no matter what or how extensive the change. To accomplish the five basic functions just listed, MOST Computer Systems is made up of a number of individual programs linked together and illustrated in Figure 8.1:

- MOST Calculation Program, which includes the work area generator, the methods analysis routine, the time calculation (MOST analysis) routine, editing routines for the workplace and method description, and printing routines
- Suboperation Database Program, which includes filing and retrieval routines for MOST analyses and the corresponding work areas: retrieval of suboperation data by multiple combinations of categories; preparation, filing, and retrieval of title sheets
- Time Standards Calculation Program, which includes selection and grouping of operations and/or suboperations from the title sheet; the standards calculation routine; preparation of the operator instruction sheet; the adding of allowances (personal, rest, and delay times); the entry of process times; the standard editing routines
- Time Standards Database Program, which includes the filing and retrieval of final time standards by multiple combination of categories; the linkage to the suboperation database
- Mass Updating Program, which includes updating and maintenance routines for both databases

Even though all these components are necessary for a total system for the development and maintenance of time standards, they are produced as modules. Therefore, some can be grouped together or used independently to fill particular

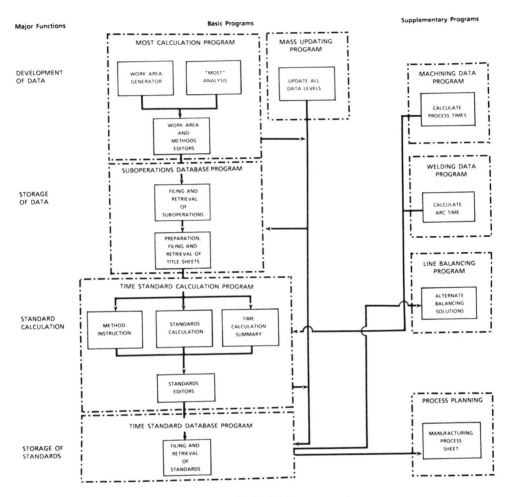

Figure 8.1 Program components of MOST Computer Systems.

requirements. For instance, the MOST Calculation Program and its subroutines can be run as a separate unit.

In addition to these program components, several supplementary programs interact with the basic programs and provide process times when applicable:

- Machining Data Program, which includes calculation of machine process times; the selection of machine feeds and speeds and the recommended tool grades
- Welding Data Program, which includes calculation of the arc time for automatic, semiautomatic, or manual welding operations

- Line Balancing Program, which generates alternate line-balancing solutions
- Process Planning, which generates the manufacturing process sheet
- Performance Reporting, calculating ratios for performance, productivity, coverage, utilization, etc.

And, for those situations that dictate the use of other analytical tools, a Multi-Man/Machine Analysis program is available.

A Few New Terms

Although it is based entirely on the MOST Work Measurement System and the MOST Application System (Chapter 7), the use of the computer has forced the development of a few new terms that appear throughout this chapter:

Term	Definition
CRT	Cathode ray tube, a video display terminal
Data	Any characters entered into the computer to be processed; data maintained in the computer on files is called stored data
Disk	A piece of equipment that magnetically records and stores data
Disk storage	Storage of data on a disk
Hardware	The tangible, physical aspects of a computer system; the equipment components that make up the computer system
Input	Information entered into the computer; the activity to enter data
Keyword	Special preprogrammed words, used in a method description, that are functional in the computer's development of sequence models
Minicomputer (or microcomputer)	A device capable of solving problems by accepting input data, processing that data, and producing output; a multicomponent computer, noted for quick response time; generally smaller and less expensive than large mainframe computers
On-line	The status of a communication link between a remote terminal (CRT) and the computer; that is, when on-line, direct communication can be accomplished

Term	Definition
Operator instruction sheet	Provides a listing of the method instructions for performing an operation
Output	Data, which are usually formatted, obtained from a computer
Program	Computer software that acts on input and produces output; a set of instructions
Software	A set of written instructions for processing data and/or solving problems
Standards calculation sheet	A summary listing of all manual, process, and allowance times for a particular operation
Terminal	Hardware with which a user supplies input to and receives output from the computer
Time calculation summary	A listing of the times for individual suboperations with appropriate frequencies; a summary of the mathematical standard time calculation
Time sharing	The computer's ability to interact with many users running many programs during the same time span
Title sheet	A listing of the titles of MOST calculations used to set standards

Development of Data

The Work Area Generator and MOST Calculation Program

The first step in calculating any engineered labor time standard is the documentation of the workplace. Many so-called engineered labor time standards are established without proper workplace documentation. In those cases when a question regarding a standard time arises, insufficient information concerning the work area leads to a situation in which the industrial engineer cannot defend a calculated time. When broken down to the basic input elements, any calculated time reflects only two factors, the *work area* and the *method* performed. MOST Computer Systems is based on these two inputs. Therefore, MOST Computer Systems provides complete documentation of the work area, including a sketch (see Fig. 8.2), and a comprehensive, logical, and easily understood method description.

```
                    ┌─────────────────────────────────┐
                    │                                 │
                    │          WORKBENCH              │
                    │                                 │
                    └─────────────────────────────────┘

                              (X)
              ┌─────────────────────────────┐
              │   FINISHED-PARTS-SHELF      │
              └─────────────────────────────┘
```

Name	Location	Body/Frag/PT

WORKPLACES:
WORKBENCH
FINISHED-PARTS-SHELF

OPERATORS:

Name	Location	Body/Frag/PT
OP1	WORKBENCH	B

TOOLS:

Name	Location
NUT-DRIVER	WORKBENCH
SCREWDRIVER	WORKBENCH
PLIERS	WORKBENCH
WRENCH	WORKBENCH
OFFSET-SCREWDRIVER	WORKBENCH
SCOTCH-BRITE-PAD	WORKBENCH
BRUSH	WORKBENCH
Q-TIPS	WORKBENCH
SCISSORS	WORKBENCH

OBJECTS:

Name	Location
FL-WASHERS	WORKBENCH
LK-NUTS	WORKBENCH
SHIM	WORKBENCH
GROMMET	WORKBENCH
CONNECTOR	WORKBENCH
FACE-PLATE	WORKBENCH
FILTER	WORKBENCH
TERM-STUDS	WORKBENCH
TERM-LUGS	WORKBENCH
LK-WASHERS	WORKBENCH
BUMPERS	WORKBENCH
LOCTITE	WORKBENCH
NON-METALIC-WASHER	WORKBENCH
STRAP	WORKBENCH
STANDOFFS	WORKBENCH
SEQUENCE-SHEETS	WORKBENCH
ADHESIVE-ACTIVATOR	WORKBENCH
SPEED-BONDER-CEMENT	WORKBENCH
CONNECTOR-PLATE	WORKBENCH
SCREW	WORKBENCH
PLASTIC-BAG	WORKBENCH
CHASSIS	WORKBENCH
HARDWARE	WORKBENCH
NUT	WORKBENCH
PLATE	WORKBENCH
BACK-PANEL	WORKBENCH
MOTHER-PLATE	FINISHED-PARTS-SHELF
INTERFACE-XTMR	FINISHED-PARTS-SHELF

From	To	Steps
WORKBENCH	FINISHED-PARTS-SHELF	10

Figure 8.2 Workplace data example: Mechanical Assembly Workbench.

The Workplace

To perform a MOST analysis using the computer, an industrial engineer gathers the work area information and "speaks" that information into a small tape recorder or dictating device. The tape is handed to a typist, who keys the information into a cathode ray tube (CRT) terminal. The work area is now complete, and a printout of the work area and the work area data can be easily obtained. Figure 8.2 is an illustration of such a printout for a typical multispindle vertical drill. Important work area information input to the computer includes: workplace names and tools and their locations; objects and their locations; equipment and its location, (along with a process time, if appropriate;) operator(s) and their starting location(s); body motions always associated with particular workplaces and the distance (in steps) between workplaces.

The Method

After describing the work area, the industrial engineer improves and specifies the method to perform the particular operation or suboperation. The method is spoken into the tape recorder in a plain-language sentence format. Figure 8.3 is an illustration of a method description for an assembly operation. Each method step begins with a "keyword" that designates to the computer the sequence model to use, as well as the values for the Gain Control (G) and Place (P) parameters. For example, the keyword Place means General Move, G_1, P_3. The word Move means General Move, G_1, P_1. These words, as well as the entire format for the method description, totally conform to familiar English sentence structure and industrial engineering terminology and are therefore very easy to learn. Given these keywords and the previously entered distances, body motions, and locations (A and B values), the computer can handily calculate an engineered time standard.

The taped method description is transcribed on a terminal by the typist. The computer then calculates the operation or suboperation time (Fig. 8.4). The

76. ASSEMBLE STANDOFF ON DEMODULATOR GROUND CHASSIS AT MECHANICAL ASSEMBLY
        WORKBENCH
     PER 1 OFG: 4 13-FEB-85
     OP1 BEGINS AT WORKBENCH

     1 MOVE LK-WASHER TO SCREW
     2 MOVE FL-WASHER TO SCREW
     3 PLACE SCREW TO CHASSIS
     4 FASTEN STANDOFF 2 WRIST-TURNS USING FINGERS
     5 PLACE WRENCH TO STANDOFF
     6 FASTEN SCREW 10 WRIST-TURNS USING SCREWDRIVER AND ASIDE

Figure 8.3 Method description example: Assemble standoff on demodulator ground chassis.

76. ASSEMBLE STANDOFF ON DEMODULATOR GROUND CHASSIS AT MECHANICAL ASSEMBLY
         WORKBENCH
     PER 1 OFG: 4 13-FEB-85
     OP1 BEGINS AT WORKBENCH

     1 MOVE LK-WASHER TO SCREW
                        A1   B0   G1   A1   B0   P1   A0   1.00   40.
     2 MOVE FL-WASHER TO SCREW
                        A1   B0   G1   A1   B0   P1   A0   1.00   40.
     3 PLACE SCREW TO CHASSIS
                        A1   B0   G1   A1   B0   P3   A0   1.00   60.
     4 FASTEN STANDOFF 2 WRIST-TURNS USING FINGERS
         A1   B0   G1   A1   B0   P1   F6   A0   B0   P0   A0   1.00   100.
     5 PLACE WRENCH TO STANDOFF
                        A1   B0   G1   A1   B0   P3   A0   1.00   60.
     6 FASTEN SCREW 10 WRIST-TURNS USING SCREWDRIVER AND ASIDE
         A1   B0   G1   A1   B0   P3   F24 A1   B0   P1   A0   1.00   320.

                                                    TOTAL TMU   620.

Figure 8.4 MOST analysis method description input example: Assemble
standoff on demodulator ground chassis.

industrial engineer's main function in the work measurement process becomes
one of establishing and inputting a proper work area layout and an efficient and
workable method. Once these basics have been established, the computer takes
over the task of calculating times. This frees the industrial engineer for more
productive tasks. An illustration of the entire basic data entry process appears as
Figure 8.5.

One of the major advantages of the computer system is the consistency offered by the keyword approach to method descriptions. Calculation errors and
errors from selecting wrong values from the charts are totally eradicated. Also,
by focusing upon the work area and method, the industrial engineer is directly
performing the tasks with the most influence on the productivity of the production function—the very reason for the industrial engineering department's
existence.

A key element of maintaining any data system is the ability to edit data both
during the input phase and immediately after the calculation has been made, or
at any time later. MOST Computer Systems is an on-line system: all input errors
are immediately diagnosed and can be corrected instantly. Once the data have
been processed, however, the MOST Computer Systems editors provide a useful
tool to simulate or make changes in the work area layout and/or methods. In the
work area, for example, locations, distances, and body motions may be
changed, workplaces and items added, and fixed process times adjusted. In the
method descriptions, steps may be inserted, deleted, or completely changed.
The system then reprocesses the data, based on the changes, and a new suboperation is immediately available. The editors are easy both to learn and to apply.
Both the "new" and the "old" analyses are stored in a holding area on disk

Development of Data

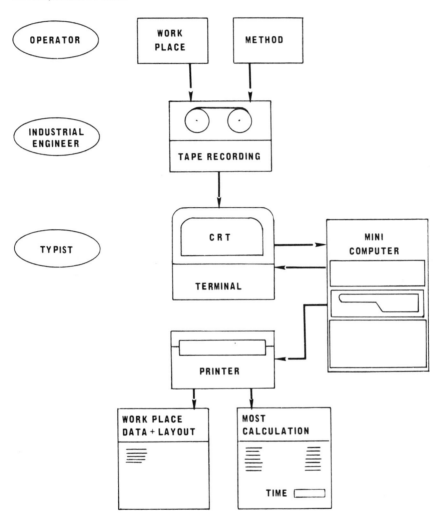

Figure 8.5   MOST Computer Systems Basic data entry.

until the engineer decides which data to transfer to the database. The editors function for both permanently and temporarily stored data. The benefits of the editing feature are as follows:

1. Simulation of changes in either work area or method is an easier task, as all calculations are made automatically. The engineer becomes the interpreter of the results rather than actually performing the new calculations.

2. Transfer of suboperation data from one area in a plant to another or between plants is readily accomplished by simply editing the workplace or methods to meet the conditions of the new application.
3. The engineer can establish prototype workplace layouts and methods and use the editors for adding details. This procedure shortens engineering time spent on analyzing similar situations.
4. Changes are easy to implement, and the impacts of change are instantly apparent.

Storage of Data

Suboperation Database Program—Filing and Retrieval of Suboperation Data

One of the critical components of documenting basic data for use in establishing time standards is the ability to retrieve it at will under any system, manual or computer. Data retrieval is dependent upon the way the data are coded. A prime advantage of a computerized filing and retrieval system is the computer's ability to manipulate and sort vast amounts of data. In manual systems, coding fields are usually kept to a minimum (Chap. 7) and multiple sorts of the data are nearly impossible to attain because of the difficulties encountered in trying to manipulate large amounts of data by hand. These physical constraints simply do not exist for a computer. In fact, a computer can sort words as quickly as it can sort numbers! These characteristics initiated the development of a unique data filing and retrieval system tailored to the needs of the industrial engineering department.

Using MOST Computer Systems, all suboperation data units are filed by a plain-language sentence containing the activity, object, product or equipment, tool, work area origin, size or capacity of the workplace, and work area number. Appropriate prepositions placed between these categories formulate a "title" for the MOST suboperation unit. Consequently suboperations can be retrieved by a search on predetermined title sheet category words. Suboperation titles organized in the proper sequence for an operation will form the operator instructions. The input expressed here as a suboperation title is also used later for other purposes within the system.

After approval of the selected categories by a data coordinator, the suboperation is filed in the database by each of the selected categories. Retrieval is accomplished by selection of one or any combination of the categories. For example, the data unit described by the title and categories shown in Figure 8.6 may be retrieved by any combination of categories described in Figure 8.7

Once the desired suboperation has been located, there is a choice of formats available to examine the data, for example:

MAJOR FILING CATEGORIES

• ACTIVITY	ASSEMBLE
• OBJECT(S) / COMPONENT(S) in / on / for	STAND OFF on
• EQUIPMENT / PRODUCT with	DEMODULATOR GROUND CHASSIS with
• TOOL(S) from / to / at	SCREWDRIVER at
• LOCATION	MECHANICAL ASSEMBLY WORKBENCH

SUPPLEMENTARY DATA

• PER unit	PER part
• OCCURRENCE FREQUENCY GROUP	OFG 2
• DATE	12 / 7 / 87
• SPECIAL USER CATEGORY(IES)	(APPLICATOR, PLANT, ETC.)
• CONDITIONS	(RESTRICTIONS, SPECIAL APPLICATIONS, ETC.)

Figure 8.6 Filing program categories for suboperation data units.

Title, applicator instructions, method description, sequence models, and TMU
   total
Title, applicator instructions, and method description
Title, applicator instructions, and TMU total
Work area layout and data

If the engineer locates an analysis that can be used in another operation, plant,
or location, the data can be edited and tailored to exactly fit the new situation.
   There are numerous advantages with the suboperation filing and retrieval
routines available in the MOST Computer Systems:

1. Data units are literally at the industrial engineer's fingertips—no more lost
   files or data without codes.
2. Work area layouts can be retrieved with every analysis.
3. The flexibility of the search technique allows many combinations of data to
   be retrieved at one time.
4. Use of the database and editor combination provides the ability to prefabri-
   cate an analysis for an entirely new part or operation.
5. Linkages between all types of data units and between the suboperation data

SEARCH CATEGORY	FILING WORD(S)	RETRIEVED SUB - OPERATION(S)
ACTIVITY:	ASSEMBLE	ALL "ASSEMBLE" OPERATIONS IN THE DATABASE INCLUDING THE DESIRED ANALYSIS
ACTIVITY: PRODUCT/EQUIPMENT:	ASSEMBLE DEMODULATOR GROUND CHASSIS	THE "ASSEMBLY" OF ALL COMPONENTS ON "DEMODULATOR GROUND CHASSIS" FOR ALL MACHINES
ACTIVITY: PRODUCT/EQUIPMENT: WORK AREA ORIGIN:	ASSEMBLE DEMODULATOR GROUND CHASSIS MECHANICAL ASSEMBLY WORKBENCH	THE "ASSEMBLY" OF ALL COMPONENTS ON "DEMODULATOR GROUND CHASSIS" AT "MECHANICAL ASSEMBLY WORKBENCH"
ACTIVITY: OBJECT: PRODUCT/EQUIPMENT: TOOL: WORK AREA ORIGIN:	ASSEMBLE STANDOFF DEMODULATOR GROUND CHASSIS SCREWDRIVER MECHANICAL ASSEMBLY WORKBENCH	ONLY "ASSEMBLE" "STANDOFF" ON "DEMODULATOR GROUND CHASSIS" AT "MECHANICAL ASSEMBLY WORKBENCH"
WORK AREA ORIGIN:	MECHANICAL ASSEMBLY WORKBENCH	ALL SUBOPERATIONS FOR "MECHANICAL ASSEMBLY WORKBENCH". THIS SEARCH TECHNIQUE IS UTILIZED FOR DETERMINING TOTAL COVERAGE AT A WORK AREA AND FOR RETRIEVING ITEMS FOR PLACEMENT ON A TITLE SHEET

Figure 8.7 Options for retrieval of suboperations.

and standards databases are an integral part of the system, allowing instant update and cross-checking. A suboperation can always be tracked to a final time standard.

6. Uniformity, the key to a good filing system, is demanded and, in fact, enforced.
7. The consistent filing system creates uniformity among departments and plants, allowing easier retrieval of data.
8. Plants within the same company can share data and even the same database at the same time.

```
86. TITLESHEET

        ELECTROMECHANICAL ASSEMBLY AREA




        Assemble/Disassemble
        -------------------
74.   INSTALL CONNECTOR IN DEMODULATOR GROUND CHASSIS

75.   ASSEMBLE AND MOUNT FILTERS ON MODULATORS GROUND CHASSIS

76.   ASSEMBLE STANDOFF ON DEMODULATOR GROUND CHASSIS

77.   ASSEMBLE GROUND LUG ON DEMODULATOR GROUND CHASSIS

78.   ASSEMBLE BUMPER ON DEMODULATOR GROUND CHASSIS

79.   INSTALL GROMMET IN DEMODULATOR GROUND CHASSIS

79.   INSTALL GROMMET IN DEMODULATOR GROUND CHASSIS

80.   ASSEMBLE BACK PANEL ON DEMODULATOR GROUND CHASSIS

81.   ASSEMBLE BACK PANEL ON DEMODULATOR GROUND CHASSIS

83.   INSTALL CABLE IN DEMODULATOR GROUND CHASSIS


        Join
        ----
84.   SOLDER (SPLICE) WIRES ON CABLE WITH SOLDER SLEEVE
      2 WIRES TO ONE

85.   GLUE MOUNT STRAP ON DEMODULATOR GROUND CHASSIS
```

Figure 8.8 Title sheet example: Electromechanical assembly area.

Creating a Title Sheet or Work Sheet

After analyzing the range of situations concerned with one operation or with varying operations involving one type of machine, the analyst will want to arrange the operations or suboperations into a format that can be used for the actual setting of time standards. Such formats are commonly referred to as worksheets. The computer performs all mathematical calculations from either a title sheet (listing suboperation titles) or a worksheet (simplified title sheet). The title sheet merely lists and groups by title all the suboperations of a particular operation. The title sheet is created by searching the database to identify all suboperations and then simply creating a list of those that are appropriate. Figure 8.8 is an example of a title sheet for the manual insertion machine. The completed title sheet is itself filed in the database under the category "work area origin."

Standard Calculation: The Time Standards Calculation Program

The final objective of MOST Computer Systems is to arrive at a complete time standard. This is accomplished by searching the database for the correct title sheet and selecting the appropriate suboperations from the title sheet, specifying their correct sequence, applying the appropriate frequencies, and indicating whether the suboperation is internal or external to another suboperation or process. The Time Standards program then produces three pieces of output:

1. Method instruction sheet for the operator (Fig. 8.9)
2. Standard calculation sheet (Fig. 8.10)
3. Time calculation sheet (Fig. 8.11)

With careful analysis of Figures 8.2, 8.4, and 8.8 through 8.11, you can follow the suboperation "Assemble standoff on demodulator ground chassis" through its work area layout (Fig. 8.2) to the final time standard (Fig. 8.10).

Up to this point, the discussion has centered upon the calculation of manual times. As seen in Chapter 3 on the Controlled Move Sequence Model, short and relatively fixed process times are usually included directly in the MOST analysis itself under the X (process time) parameter. Longer and variable process times must frequently be calculated separately. Several supplementary programs included in MOST Computer Systems can be utilized in process time calculation, depending upon company needs: the Machining Data program, the Welding Data program, and special calculations and storage of frequently occurring process times for nonmachining types of operations (e.g., foundry or clerical). Appropriate allowance factors are applied to the manual and process times. The result is the final time standard.

```
                    H. B. MAYNARD & CO., INC.
                    METHOD INSTRUCTION SHEET

                    (Locater #      2)


Part No.   357D517          Part Name   DEMOD-GRND-CHASSIS
           --------------               ------------------------
Oper No.   010              Dept  W4           Work Center  WY
           ---              ---                             ----
Oper Desc. MECHANICAL-ASSY OF DEMOD-GND-CHASSIS       I.E.  SYS
           -------------------------------------              ---
Material                    Issue No.  1      Date   7-Feb-86
           --------------             --             ---------

Step  Method Instruction                                    Freq
----  ------------------------------------------------      -----
  1  INSTALL  CONNECTOR IN DEMODULATOR GROUND CHASSIS (    74)     1
     * J1 CONNECTOR
  2  INSTALL  CONNECTOR IN DEMODULATOR GROUND CHASSIS (    74)     1
     * J2 CONNECTOR
  3  ASSEMBLE  AND MOUNT FILTERS ON MODULATORS GROUND (    75)     4
     CHASSIS
     * FL-1-2-3-4
  4  ASSEMBLE  STANDOFF ON DEMODULATOR GROUND CHASSIS (    76)     2
  5  ASSEMBLE  GROUND LUG ON DEMODULATOR GROUND       (    77)     2
     CHASSIS
     * E1-E2
  6  ASSEMBLE  BACK PANEL ON DEMODULATOR GROUND       (    80)     1
     CHASSIS
     * 16 -20 SCREWS
  7  ASSEMBLE  BACK PANEL ON DEMODULATOR GROUND       (    81)     1
     CHASSIS
  8  ASSEMBLE  BUMPER ON DEMODULATOR GROUND CHASSIS   (    78)     4
  9  GLUE MOUNT  STRAP ON DEMODULATOR GROUND CHASSIS  (    85)     8
 10  INSTALL  GROMMET IN DEMODULATOR GROUND CHASSIS   (    79)     1


          TOTAL HRS - MANUAL                     1.13298
          TOTAL HRS - PROCESS                    0.00000
          STANDARD HOURS PER PIECE               1.1330
          PIECES PER HOUR @ 100%                 0.883
```

Figure 8.9   Method instruction sheet.

Storage of Standards: Time Standards Database Program

Just as a suboperation is filed in a database by many categories, so is a completed time standard. The final time standard, along with the method instruction sheet and the standard calculation sheet, is filed in the standards database using the categories that appear in its heading (see Fig. 8.10) or any other categories so desired (see Fig. 8.11). Therefore, the standard can be retrieved by any one or any combination of the following (customized) filing categories:

```
                     H. B. MAYNARD & CO., INC.
                        STANDARD RATE SHEET

                       (Locater #      2)


Part No.   357D517          Part Name  DEMOD-GRND-CHASSIS
           ---------------             ------------------------
Oper No.   010              Dept  W4            Work Center  WY
           ---                    ---                        ----
Oper Desc. MECHANICAL-ASSY OF DEMOD-GND-CHASSIS        I.E.  SYS
           -------------------------------------              ---
Material                    Issue No.   1       Date    7-Feb-86
           ---------------             --               --------


Type of              Elemental   Allowance    Allowance   Standard
  Work                  Time      Percent        Time       Time
------------------   ---------   ---------    ---------   ---------

EXTERNAL MANUAL        0.98520      15.0         0.14778    1.13298

ASSIGNED INTERNAL   (  0.00000)    (15.0)     (  0.00000) ( 0.00000)

PROCESS TIME           0.00000      15.0         0.00000    0.00000

STANDARD(HRS/CYCLE)    0.98520                   0.14778    1.13298

PIECES PER CYCLE            1

STANDARD (HRS PER PIECE)                                    1.13298

     (PIECES PER HOUR @ 100%)                                 0.883
```

Figure 8.10 Standard calculation sheet.

- ● **PRODUCT / SUBASSEMBLY / PART NUMBER**
- ● **PRODUCT / SUBASSEMBLY / PART NAME**
- ● **COMPONENT CLASSIFICATION NUMBER**

- ● **PLANT NUMBER**
- ● **DEPARTMENT NUMBER**
- ● **COST CENTER NUMBER**
- ● **WORK CENTER NUMBER**

- ● **BILL OF MATERIAL NUMBER**
- ● **ROUTE SHEET NUMBER**
- ● **OPERATION NUMBER**

- ● **OPERATION NAME**

Figure 8.11 Typical filing categories for time standards.

Part number
Operation number
Operation description
Part name
Cost center
Machine center
Component classification number
Plant
Applicator
Date
Any other specific categories desired

The filing and retrieval of final time standards occur in exactly the same manner as for suboperation data. That is, a search can be conducted by one or any combination of categories. When a time standard is filed, links to the title sheet and its components are established. If the standard is a new issue, comparisons can be made with previous issues and decision rules for changes in incentive payments can be established according to a company's contract. Additionally, all operations under one number may be grouped on a route sheet with all information fed to other production systems. Figure 8.12 illustrates the complete data flow in the standards-setting process.

Mass Update of Standards

As seen from the description of MOST Computer Systems, the database programs provide a complete linkage between workplaces, suboperation data, title sheets, and final time standards. These vital links provide the basis for an automatic update of time standards based upon changes in any of the basic data elements: workplace, method, or title sheet.

Too often in the industrial engineering application of standards, updating poses a problem because of difficulties in finding all standards affected by a change. Even if they can be found, a massive clerical task usually accompanies all changes. Because of these difficulties, "small" changes in the workplace or method go unrecorded. The cumulative effect of this procedure, however, leads to inaccurate time standards, sometimes resulting in a badly deteriorated incentive plan or a product costing completely off target.

The Mass Update program solves these problems. The "where used" operation allows the user to query the database for all occurrences of standards dependent upon a basic data element that should be changed. This location feature results in a listing of all standards that would be affected by the change. The user then has an opportunity to edit the list for removal of standards that should not be changed.

The computer can then assume the clerical function of actually updating all the standards automatically, based on the changes in basic data supplied by the

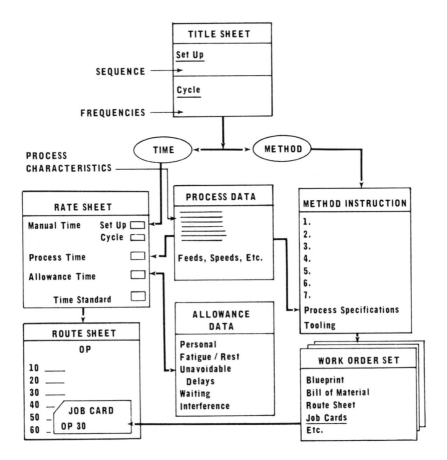

Figure 8.12 Standards calculation data flow.

appropriate personnel. Since mass changes to the active standards will occur, this must be a privileged feature, available only to the specified individual(s).

Probably the most exciting is the simulation of possible changes in methods or layouts as a response to the question "what if?" This simulation feature will open new doors for the industrial engineer in striving for improvement.

Once a substitution is made or suggested for a specified title sheet, the "where used" list is obtained, and the Mass Update command can then be issued to change the standards. Depending upon contract provisions, appropriate decision rules can be established, i.e., ±3% or ±5% rule. Thus, new standards will be issued only if the change(s) exceed the established limit.

In essence, the Mass Update function is a valuable addition to the editing features in MOST Computer Systems. If a change affects only one or two standards, the editing feature should be used. But when several standards are affected by proposed or mandated changes, the automatic facility of Mass Update is a necessary feature for keeping time standards current and accurate. The resources required for standards maintenance can be reduced by as much as 80–90% compared with a manual system.

Supplementary Programs

The Machining Data Program

The primary purpose of the speeds and feeds program is to calculate process time for such machine operations as drilling, milling, turning, gear cutting, and grinding.

The program determines the ideal speeds and feeds by using values recommended in the *Machining Data Handbook* (Metcut Research Associates, Inc., 1974). The user also has the choice of providing other source data, if desired.

In selecting speeds and feeds, consideration is given to material used, tool, machine specifications, dimensions of raw and finished workpiece, and so on.

Since the ideal speeds and feeds may not be available because of machine limitations, the program allows the user to select alternative speeds and feeds. This can be done automatically because the users' individual machine specifications have been included in the data file.

Output of the program is the speed in rpm, feed, recommended tool grade for the material being machined, the process time and allowances inherent in the machining operation, such as lead-on and overrun, and power utilization.

For turning and milling operations, the program also calculates the number of cuts. All speeds and feeds are based on a tool life of 1 hour. Figure 8.13 is an example of output for an operation including drill, face, cut-off and chamfer.

The Welding Program

The welding program calculates the process time (arc time) for arc-welding operations using either rod or wire electrodes. The calculations are based on filed geometric joint descriptions, electrode characteristics, and methods (i.e., electrodes, amperage, and wire speed). The output is an arc time and summary report. The joint and method identifications are given by the user, along with the weld length. These three items, plus the number of passes (from the method description), are shown in the arc time report heading line. The electrode identification, voltage, amperage for rod electrode, and wire speed for wire electrode are shown (from the method description), along with the calculated travel speed, frequency of electrode change and arc time. The travel speed is the rate at which the rod or wire should move along the weld; the electrode change frequency is applied as a frequency to the MOST calculation for the manual operation performed when changing such an electrode.

```
                    H. B. MAYNARD & CO., INC.
                    MACHINING PROCESS SHEET

                      (Locater #    16)
```

Part Number   898765   Part Name PULL ROLL
                   ---------------   -----------------------------
Operation Number   010   Machine Number 110312   Material 1020
                   -------   ----------   ---------------
Activity Sequence DRILL,FACE,CUTOFF,CHAMFER

Machine Type   TL   Date 13-Jan-87   I.E. DMO
                   -----------------------   ---------   ---

```
                                                TC      FREQ.     TMU
                                                --      -----     ---
```

1. DRILL .875 1.25 DEEP

	ACTUAL SFM	SET RPM	# CUTS	(Feed)	SET --IPR--	ACTUAL --IPM--			
Recommended:	90	392			0.01400	5.49			
Selected:	69	300	1		0.01200	3.66	140.	1.00	716.

2. FIN-BORE .875 TO 1 IN. DIA. 1.25 LONG USING .75 BORING-BAR ON TURRET

	ACTUAL SFM	SET RPM	# CUTS	(Feed)	SET --IPR--	ACTUAL --IPM--			
Recommended:	475	1814			0.00700	12.70			
Selected:	367	1400	1		0.00600	8.43	121.	1.00	272.

3. FIN-FACE 2.5 TO 1 .1 DEEP ON CARRIAGE

	ACTUAL SFM	SET RPM	# CUTS	(Feed)	SET --IPR--	ACTUAL --IPM--			
Recommended:	625	955			0.00700	6.69			
Selected:	526	800	1		0.00600	4.83	109.	1.00	302.

4. CHAMFER 1 .063 DEEP

	ACTUAL SFM	SET RPM	# CUTS	(Feed)	SET --IPR--	ACTUAL --IPM--			
Recommended:	90	343			0.01400	4.80			
Selected:	79	300	1		0.01200	3.66	3486.	1.00	29.

5. CUT-OFF 2.5 TO 1 USING .062 WIDE-TOOL ON CROSS-SLIDE

	ACTUAL SFM	SET RPM	# CUTS	(Feed)	SET --IPR--	ACTUAL --IPM--			
Recommended:	360	550			0.00450	2.47			
Selected:	265	400	1		0.00400	1.62	35.	1.00	933.

```
                                                TOTAL TMU      2252.
```

Figure 8.13 Machining Data program: Example of output.

The Line-Balancing Program

The line-balancing program is designed to solve the program of assigning work elements to assembly line stations to minimize the balance delay.

The program interacts with the user in assigning elements to a station and within a station to an operator. It is flexible in moving elements from one station to another. The elements can be either suboperations from the data base (electronically transferred) or estimated time elements. The program produces a balance report, operator instructions, and a utilization report per operator and station. The program automatically establishes standards based on the line balance and files these standards in the time standards data base. In addition to balancing assembly lines, the program can balance production cells with multi-man–machine operations.

Process Planning

MOST Computer Systems Process Planning is a key ingredient for successful computer-integrated manufacturing. MOST Work Measurement System complements the Process Planning with accurate, method-oriented, and consistent standards.

The process plan may be retrieved starting from a part family to a group family. In addition, the Process Planning module includes a company tailored filing and retrieval system with attributes specific to user needs.

Process plans may be created with estimated standards and revised with the standard generated using the MOST Work Measurement System. Existing process plans may be retrieved based on company-tailored attributes for the same or similar parts, allowing the process planner to make changes if needed. All standards for the new parts are automatically generated in the computer system. Thus, the traceability of the standards is always maintained.

Therefore, the top-down approach of starting from the process plan and setting standards helps to increase productivity and process standardization and improve better cost estimating and shop floor control. Figure 8.14 illustrates a process plan with a customized header for the electronic assembly operations required to build a PC board controller. Both "setup" and "run" standards are included.

The System

MOST Computer Systems is available on an IBM/PC, IBM/PC compatibles, MicroVAX, VAX, and IBM mainframe computers with IMS DB/DC.

The programs run completely on-line in a time-shared environment. CRT's are hardwired directly to the computer or can be connected by dedicated telephone lines. Printers are used to obtain hard copies of the data displayed on the

```
                    H.B. MAYNARD AND COMPANY

                         ROUTE SHEET

                    (Locater  #      10)
```

Part No. HJ1234   Drawing Rev. 345   Shop Order No. 1234
        ---------------   ----   ----------
Part Name   CONTROLLER PC BOARD

Raw Material Class 1   Finish Part Shape   RECTANGLE
                   --------   ----------
Part Family PC BOARD   Group Family CCA   Key Operation CONFORMAL
            ----------   ----------   ----------
Weight Class 1   Lot Size 12   Applicator DMO
            --------   ------   ---
     Type of Router P   Router Issue   1   Date 17-Sep-87
                   --   ---   ---------

OP #	LOC #	WORK CNTR	C D	OPERATION INSTRUCTION	TIME SETUP	RUN
020-P0	23	6624	M	STAMPING	0.08	0.02
030-P0	25	6624	M	STAKING	0.01	0.03
040-P0	27	6624	M	COMPONENT PREP	0.17	0.03
050-P0	26	6624	M	MAN-U-SERT	0.08	0.35
060-P0	133	6624	M	LOG POINT	0.17	0.06
070-P0	92	6624	M	WAVE SOLDER	0.18	0.02
080-P0	38	6624	M	POST ASSEMBLY	0.09	0.12
085-P0	42	6624	M	TOUCHUP PRE-INSPECT	0.03	0.10
090-P0	46	6624	M	MASKING	0.15	0.08
100-P0	50	4445	M	CONFORMAL COATING	1.37	0.01
110-P0	52	4653	M	UNMASKING	0.04	0.04

Figure 8.14   Process planning example: Electronic Assembly.

CRT. Finally, a word-processing system is available. Its function is to assist the engineer with the task of developing Work Management Manuals (Chap. 7). The word processing system can store a database of Work Management Manuals that can be quickly retrieved and edited, eliminating the time-consuming and costly function of rewriting and retyping manuals. The result is complete standards development and documentation under the guidance and control of the computer for accurate and consistently applied time standards.

Summary

As MOST Computer Systems is based on the MOST Work Measurement System and the MOST Applications System, it shares their features, such as consistency of application and documentation, a high degree of accuracy, uniformity among applicators, complete traceability of all backup data, and ease in learning and application. In addition to these features, MOST Computer Systems has some advantages of its own:

- It eliminates routine work, nearly all paperwork, and the use of a stopwatch.
- It is faster to use than the manual MOST System with increased consistency.

- It provides total integration of data from individual workplaces and work methods to operation time standards, process plans and cost estimates for parts, components and products.
- Supplementary programs provide accurate process times tailored to company machines and welding processes.
- Through the editing process, changes in workshop conditions are easily implemented and documented and the standards automatically adjusted and updated.
- The editors provide an opportunity for detailed methods analysis through simulation.
- The filing and retrieval system opens a host of possibilities for data organization, sharing data among plants or areas of a single plant, mass updating, and formulating of prototype work areas, suboperation data, and final time standards.
- It provides operator method instruction and route sheets as by-products of the time standard calculation process.
- The time standards can be easily linked into larger host computers for use by payroll, production control, forecasting, scheduling, costing, and other programs.

In essence, MOST Computer Systems is designed to assist the industrial engineer to become more productive on the job, with more time for concentration on new methods to increase manufacturing productivity. Because it is simple to learn and apply and can be easily related to the manual process, MOST Computer Systems can readily gain acceptance by union officials and workers, as well as management.

Simplicity, accessibility, consistency, and speed are the major features that make MOST Computer Systems an excellent tool for the industrial engineer, to increase self-productivity and make an important contribution to both departmental and company profitability.

9

In Summary

The MOST Systems family (see also Chap. 2), as presented in this text, provides the industrial engineer the tools with which to measure, document, and control manufacturing methods and costs. This family of techniques and systems is based on the strong support of its original member, the Basic MOST Work Measurement System. To satisfy some special work measurement needs, Mini MOST and Maxi MOST have become members of the MOST family during the 1980s.

Realizing that a higher level of work measurement techniques requires a higher level of application procedures, the MOST Application Systems were developed with specific guidelines for the major industries of general manufacturing, textiles, shipbuilding, clerical operations, and others. MOST Computer Systems incorporates the necessary functions, and as a result, it documents and guides the work measurement process from the establishment of the workplace through the development of the final time standard with an extension to process planning and cost estimating.

The MOST Systems family has grown significantly into a comprehensive system since its introduction in the mid 1970s. It can be applied manually or by the assistance of modern computer technology. The future will very likely bring further sophistication, refinement, and development in the direction of computer-integrated manufacturing (CIM). Calculations, decisions, and simulations made by a computer will become automated and faster as a part of the accelerated process of computer program integration.

Significant Concepts

In review, it may be worthwhile to restate a few of the significant concepts upon which the MOST Systems are built and applied.

302

The Sequence Model

With the sequence model rests the fundamental concept on which MOST originally was built. Because of the development of the sequence model, the analyst's focus is shifted from the operator's body movements to the *movement of objects*. This provides a larger data unit with which to work, resulting in a clearer and more understandable method description. Because of the sequence model, the analyst is forced to consider all the subactivities possible to move an object. The result is more analyst consistency and less application error.

Because of the sequence model, the lowest level of meaningful data should now appear as the complete movement of the object, not, for example, only the movement of the hand to reach for an object. It is from this higher basic level that work is analyzed and "suboperation data units" produced.

Suboperation Data

With MOST, it is both impractical and highly inefficient to break work (operations) into data units any smaller than a complete and logical segment of work, an "activity." In other words, there is no need to develop data units smaller than a logical sequence of method steps as analyzed on a MOST calculation form whether Basic, Mini, or Maxi MOST is used. Data units the size of a complete MOST calculation can be more easily understood and more efficiently filed and retrieved than smaller data elements. More importantly, they can be revised and/ or updated on one (high) level on the MOST calculation form, not through a series of standard data building block levels. Using MOST, the analyst should look at the entire operation (start at the top) and if necessary break down that operation into logical activities or suboperations. This *top-down approach* to data development is completely counter to previous standard data building block approaches, in which standard data units are *built up* from basic elements through a series of levels. The high-level suboperation data unit is the level at which analyses are edited and/or updated, producing times specific to particular operations with little additional analyst time or effort required.

The Statistical Foundation

The MOST Work Measurement System is based on the fundamental statistical standard deviation concept. It is through the application of "engineered deviations" that the system gains not only its speed, easy application, and accuracy but also an outstanding consistency. The four versions of the MOST Work Measurement System (Basic, Mini, Maxi, and Clerical) as described in this book were designed to produce a predetermined level of accuracy. Other systems were developed and subsequently their accuracy was determined. The statistically based deviations on which MOST is built provide accurate and consistent results throughout its application. With MOST, the deviations—the index ranges that the index numbers represent—are "engineered deviations", they do not occur haphazardly across the work measurement spectrum. Therefore, industrial engineers always know the system accuracy and the confidence level with which they are working. A statistical procedure based on occurrence frequency groupings (OFG) will help the system user determine the allowed tolerances for any suboperation data unit with inherent method variations. The practical implication of this principle is that the work sheet for calculations of standards can be simplified to match pre-established accuracy requirements. A simple work sheet reduces the application cost.

Appendix A provides detailed information regarding the statistical foundation of MOST and the development of the index numbers. Reading it will give you an appreciation of the system design, an understanding of the support that underlies the MOST Systems, and confidence in MOST analyses. The OFG concept is based on the same statistical principles as were used to design MOST and is included in a separate text describing MOST Application Systems.

MOST is a Method-Based System

As with all work measurement techniques, the time values that result from performing an analysis should always be based on a specific and well-engineered method. The primary job of the analyst, then, is to properly determine the representative method of an operation or suboperation. The second step, the analysis, is then easy to do when using either version of MOST Systems. From an engineering point of view, any deviation between the calculated time and the "actual time" lies between the "engineered method" and the method actually performed by the operator. The problem then is not in engineering but in education. If the operator is not following the engineered method, the question must be asked, "Was the operator properly trained, instructed, and informed?" If not, why even bother to "engineer" the job? Therefore, utilize the method description section of the Basic MOST calculation form to instruct the operators to use the engineered method. The Mini MOST form provides a more detailed description: the Maxi MOST form allows a less detailed method instruction.

The Keyword Principle

In the process of developing the computerized version of MOST, the use of *keywords* seemed to be a logical approach to solve the data input problem. The keyword concept provides an appealing practice for the computer user and for the manual MOST user as well.

Properly defined keywords combined with a pre-established and coherent sentence structure brought clarity and consistency to the method descriptions. The discipline that was added through well-defined keywords to both the computerized and manual MOST systems has increased the quality and uniformity in the description in a remarkable way. With the keywords a *common language* was built into the system, which can be used and understood by everyone involved in the development and application of work measurement data.

Communication—"Closing the Gap"

How do you close the gap between the industrial engineer and the supervisor, foreperson, and worker in the shop? Use the *method sensitivity* of MOST to do away with nonproductive efforts. Use the *method description* section of the MOST calculation form to instruct and train the operators. As just mentioned, the keyword concept simplifies and makes these descriptions easier to understand and use. Use the communicative powers of this "easy to learn and understand" system to inform workers and their supervisors of the method and actual calculation if required. MOST now provides the communication link (a common and easily understood keyword language) that heretofore has been lacking in work measurement systems and through which the worker and the engineer can exchange information about the work they both are associated with. The result will be the early alleviation of problems or potential problems at the analysis and installation level where they actually occur. Having achieved a desired level of understanding between those directly involved, the organization can function smoothly, allowing common productivity and profit goals to be realized.

appendix A

Theory

With existing predetermined motion time systems (PMTS), such as MTM, an "exact" method description must be recorded; that is, *basic motions* must be expressed in terms of distinct types, distances, weights, and other such variables. The result is a very detailed description of a method, but probably not the exact method actually performed in the majority of cases. Variations are inherent in any operation. The operator may follow a different motion pattern because of a lack of instructions or the variable nature of the operation; for example, reach and move distances may not be the same throughout an operation as the detailed description implies. The analyst must predict what methods will be used or describe what is perceived as an average or representative method for the operation. When distances are averaged, for example, in reaching into a bin with parts at different distances from the operator, the expected accuracy of the detailed system is not achieved. Why describe a detailed method from a table of "exact" values, when in actuality the operator will follow a method that varies from one occurrence to the next? There are, of course, situations in which this detailed approach is indeed appropriate, as for highly repetitive, short-cycle operations performed at workplaces designed to minimize any such variations. In terms of cost, however, this exacting method analysis required by existing PMTS work measurement techniques often seems unnecessary and impractical. In fact, there is even some question about the "exactness" of these systems given the presence of this inherent variability in work methods.

In the design of MOST, it was recognized that these variations or deviations could be easily compensated for by using basic statistical principles. Most importantly, by using these same procedures, it was also found that it was possible to greatly simplify the work measurement itself while retaining a high level of

307

accuracy. In other words, this inherent variation in work methods has actually been used to advantage in developing a more simplified work measurement technique, with resulting accuracy surprisingly close to such systems as basic MTM.

Accuracy of a Predetermined Motion Time System

Can a work measurement technique produce a time that is exact? The answer to this question is *no,* because

• Work is performed by humans and is, therefore, *variable* from one human to another—no two individuals accomplish exactly the same amount of work over a specified amount of time.
• Time standards (the results of work measurement) represent average times. They reflect the time of an *average* worker, of *average* skill, working at an *average* or normal pace, under *average* conditions.

Therefore, since no work measurement technique is exact, all have as either part of their original system design or as a result of their original design, a *balancing time.* The calculation of a balancing time is based on the statistical principle that the variance of a sum of independent variates equals the sum of the individual variances. Simply put, balancing time is the time needed for the system's desired level of accuracy to be attained. In other words, a certain minimum amount of work must be analyzed with the system before the accuracy of the analysis can be guaranteed to a specific level of confidence.

The statistical phenomenon that occurs during the balancing time is called the *balancing effect.* The balancing effect is what causes the desired level of accuracy of a system to be attained. In other words, the balancing time is *when* the system's accuracy is attained, and the balancing effect is *how* it is attained. The balancing effect results from the combination of individual deviations for a smaller total deviation. Deviation can be defined as the difference between the "true" time it takes for a task and the time the work measurement technique "allows." As independent (non-repetitive) elements are combined, their total percentage deviation becomes less than the individual percentage deviations. This is because these deviations balance each other because some are above the true time and others below. In the final result, the total relative accuracy is better than the accuracy for the individual measurements.

Since the "true" time to perform a job is indeterminant, the widely accepted accuracy of time values determined by MTM analyses served as a point of reference in the design of MOST. Later the same accuracy of MOST time values was calculated by applying conventional statistical formulas for standard deviation.

However, unlike MTM, whose balancing time is the result of its system design, the balancing time of Basic MOST was determined prior to its system design. To better understand how MOST produces accurate results, a look at the system design is necessary.

Basic MOST System Design

When Basic MOST was originally conceived, the decision was made that a balancing time of approximately 2 minutes would be desirable. It was reasoned that substantial simplicity in system design and application could be achieved with only a moderate reduction in accuracy. The system was therefore constructed to have a consistent balancing time of approximately 2 minutes (3300 TMU) as the target value for the original calculation.

The *theoretical balancing time* for Basic MOST was determined by Dr. William D. Brinckloe of the University of Pittsburgh to be 3235 TMU.* In the next section of this chapter, which covers the actual system construction, all calculations and index ranges are based on a balancing time of 3235 TMU. Therefore, the accuracy of Basic MOST is based on a balancing time of 3235 TMU, or approximately 2 minutes. This means that measurements totaling 3235 TMU or more are accurate to within ±5% of a true time value with a confidence level of 95%. This does not mean, however, that Basic MOST cannot be used to measure shorter activities. As will be shown in this appendix, the accuracy in the *final* result (standards) is the deciding factor. In other words, the minimum condition of 3235 TMU applies only to the standard and not to the individual element.

MOST Interval Groupings

Predetermined motion time systems, such as MTM, are constructed by determining the time duration of conveniently selected basic motions. In contrast, Basic MOST starts with the construction of time intervals based on a *stated balancing time* (3235 TMU) and thereafter determines which motion patterns fall within each time interval. The Basic MOST System, therefore, provides a consistent balancing time for any combination of elements.

Influential in the construction of the Basic MOST System time intervals was the establishment of the following objectives:

1. The mean value for each time interval will be a whole number and also a multiple of 10.
2. The time intervals will cover a continuous time scale with neither gaps nor excessive overlaps.

---

*The theoretical system accuracy of MTM-1, MTM-2, and MOST is discussed in *Comparative Precision of MTM-1, MTM-2 and MOST*, University Research Institute, June 1975.

The MOST time intervals were then calculated from the statistical formula for allowed deviation:

$$a = \pm r_{T_B} \sqrt{T_B \times t}$$

where: a = allowed deviation from interval mean in $\pm$TMU
  $\pm r_{T_B}$ = accuracy of $\pm 5\%$ for balancing time (± 0.05)
    T_B = established balancing time of 3235 TMU
    t = interval mean in TMU (a whole number and also a multiple of 10)

Figure A.1 is the result of using this formula with appropriate values.

The formula assumes a conventional normal distribution. If a uniform distribution is assumed, the formula then becomes:

$$a = \pm r_{T_B} \sqrt{T_B \times t} \times 0.878$$

The differences in Figure A.1 from using this second formula are quite minor and do not affect the construction of the MOST index number table (Fig. A.3) or the location of the boundaries between index numbers.

By placing the values from Figure A.1 on a linear scale and drawing half-circles, which represent the calculated allowed deviation range of each time interval, the graphical representation shown in Figure A.2, is produced for the first five intervals or index groups. Note that since the interval means were adjusted to be divisible by 10, the application of Basic MOST is simplified by eliminating zeros, thus creating a series of index numbers (circled) statistically representing each time interval.

The diagram shows that adjacent half-circles overlap slightly. The overlaps have median values of 17, 42, 77, 126, and 196 TMU. These are the upper limits of the first five Basic MOST index ranges. The calculation procedure was continued to determine the values shown in Figure A.3.

It is within these statistically calculated index ranges that the variation inherent in the majority of working situations is absorbed.

Basic MOST® TIME VALUES, TMU	DEVIATION, TMU	INTERVAL- LOWER LIMIT, TMU	INTERVAL- UPPER LIMIT, TMU
10	9	1	19
30	16	14	46
60	22	38	82
100	28	72	128
160	36	124	196

Figure A.1 Allowed deviations for Basic MOST time values.

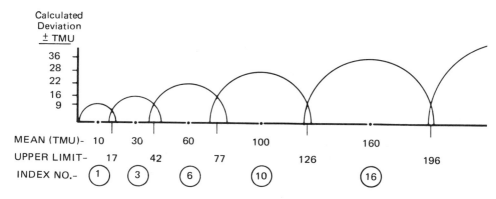

Figure A.2 Development of MOST time values.

INDEX VALUE	INTERVAL MEAN, TMU	INTERVAL LIMITS, TMU
0	0	0
1	10	1 - 17
3	30	18 - 42
6	60	43 - 77
10	100	78 - 126
16	160	127 - 196
24	240	197 - 277
32	320	278 - 366
42	420	367 - 476
54	540	477 - 601
67	670	602 - 736
81	810	737 - 881
96	960	882 - 1041
113	1130	1042 - 1216
131	1310	1217 - 1411
152	1520	1412 - 1621
173	1730	1622 - 1841
196	1960	1842 - 2076
220	2200	2077 - 2321
245	2450	2322 - 2571
270	2700	2572 - 2846
300	3000	2847 - 3146
330	3300	3147 - 3446

Figure A.3 MOST Index values with interval limits.

Backup Data

The Basic MOST time intervals described in the previous section serve as the basis for all parameter index values. Motion patterns are analyzed with MTM-1 or MTM-2 and assigned index numbers corresponding to the time interval into which the detailed analysis falls. The most frequently occurring of these motion patterns are listed on data cards under appropriate sequence model parameters and comprise the variants for the various sequence model subactivities defined in earlier chapters.

Each of these motion patterns (variants), with its corresponding index number, is referred to as a "parameter index value." For example, MTM analyses for "gaining control of an object requiring disengage" fall within the time interval 18–42 TMU. From Figure A.3, this translates to index number 3. Therefore, Gain Control with Disengage is represented in the sequence model by the parameter index value G_3. For every value on the Basic MOST data cards, corresponding MTM-1 or MTM-2 analyses are cataloged in a backup data manual.

Applicator Deviations

The total accuracy of any work measurement technique is dependent on both the system deviation and the applicator deviation. Although system deviation can be determined statistically, the deviations present, because of applicator error, must be determined empirically. Applicator deviations vary with individuals, depending largely on the amount of training and experience possessed by each analyst.

One of the basic assumptions concerning the accuracy of a work measurement system is that a fine breakdown of motion variables contributes to the reduction of system deviation. This is no doubt true, but there is at the same time a greater tendency for the applicator, through inexperience, misjudgment, or carelessness, to make errors in the selection of the correct time value. As a result, the systems taken to be the most precise (i.e., those with the finest subdivisions of motions) are the most susceptible to applicator error.

Applicator deviations can be influenced by the way in which motions are classified within the system. With existing PMTS systems, as many as four variables must be considered when selecting time values. For example, MTM-1 time values for Reach are classified by distance, case, and type; and time values for Move by distance, case, type, and weight. Obviously, the more variables that must be considered by the analyst, the more likely the possibility for applicator error. Index values in Basic MOST were designed to contain but one variable. To select the proper index value for Action Distance, only the distance is considered.

Perhaps the most frequent type of applicator error is that of carelessly omitting a motion from a motion pattern or erroneously including a motion that does not occur. This problem is virtually eliminated in MOST with the aid of the preprinted sequence models. During the analysis procedure, the applicator's attention is focused on each sequence model parameter as the calculation sheet is filled out.

Surprisingly, very little research has been done on evaluating applicator deviations in the various work measurement systems available today. This is unfortunate, since applicator error probably influences the total accuracy as much as or more than the system error. However, there is analytic evidence that indicates that the total accuracy of MOST is influenced to a lesser degree by applicator deviations than are existing predetermined motion time systems. It is thought that the loss in system accuracy (the larger balancing time of Basic MOST) could be compensated for by a reduction in applicator error, thus pulling the more detailed system and the more economical system together into an area of comparable total accuracy.

Accuracy of Work Measurement and Time Standards

Having reviewed the theory and construction of the Basic MOST Work Measurement technique, let us now look at this same theory extended to a higher level, that of analyzing operations or suboperations to establish a time standard.

A condition is said to be "accurate" when it conforms exactly to an accepted standard; that is, the condition falls within acceptable tolerance limits. Accuracy, then, is a relative concept, relative to an accepted standard. To a carpenter, accuracy is usually expressed in inches or eighths of an inch, but to the machinist may be expressed in thousandths of an inch. The physicist deals with even smaller tolerances. What about the work analyst? What is the "accepted standard" for work measurement accuracy? Should operation times be accurate within thousandths of a second, or would plus or minus 1 day be acceptable?

Obviously, both these conditions are inappropriate. In one case, the measurement would be extremely difficult to obtain, and in the other, the results would probably be meaningless. The fact is that accuracy requirements have very little to do with work measurement. The main consideration is of an economic nature. If it costs thousands of dollars to develop time standards for an operation that seldom occurs, we will be satisfied with a rough estimate or even a guess. On the other hand, if substantial economic benefits can be realized from a detailed analysis providing more "exact" times, these studies may well be worth the cost. So the question of work measurement accuracy must first be answered in terms of the cost involved to achieve a certain level of accuracy.

Theoretically, the accuracy of any work measurement system can be defined as the deviation or percentage difference between the "analyzed time" and the "true time." As stated earlier, the "true time," of course, is unknown. However, in this context, a practically established MOST value will be compared to a theoretically designated "true time value." Therefore, in terms of both the total standard and individual analysis deviation, the accuracy (in percent) of MOST can be defined as follows.

Unit Relative Deviation

$$r_t = \frac{MOST - true}{true} \times 100 = \frac{a}{t} \times 100$$

where: a = deviation from the actual unit time in TMU
         t = actual unit time in TMU

Total Relative Deviation

$$r_T = \frac{MOST - true}{true} \times 100 = \frac{A}{T} \times 100$$

where: A = deviation from the total true time in TMU
         T = total true time in TMU

The accuracy of a work measurement system is influenced by four factors, which, when assembled as a formula, explain the total relative deviation theory:

1. The *level of accuracy desired* in the final result depends on the planned use of the time standard, such as incentive payment calculations (individual or group), machine loading, and product costing.
2. The *time period* over which the desired level of accuracy must be attained. Do we want these time standards to achieve the desired level of accuracy on a 1-day basis, or will accuracy based on the 40-hour week be sufficient? This period is referred to as the calculation period, leveling period, or balancing time. *Note:* We are now discussing the balancing time for time standards calculation, *not* the balancing time of the work measurement technique used to determine the standard times.
3. The *degree of repetitiveness* of the suboperation being measured, that is, how many times does the suboperation occur during the calculation period?
4. The *duration of the suboperation* being measured.

These four factors are mathematically represented by the following statistical formula used to calculate "allowed deviation." The following formula is a derivation of the expression for standard deviation as discussed in detail below:

$$r^2t = \text{constant}$$

Each formula-variable definition is followed by a number referencing it to one of the four factors mentioned above.

$$r_t = \pm\, r_T \sqrt{\frac{T}{nt}}$$

where: r_i = measured suboperation's allowed deviation, percent
         r_T = total allowed deviation percent (1)
         T = total time, i.e., the calculation period or balancing time (2)
         n = suboperation's occurrence frequency over the calculation
               period (3)
         t = the suboperation's measured time (4)

Formula Derivation

Before we continue with examples of how to use the above formula, its derivation will be presented, starting with the terms:

Terms: (This discussion uses decimal fractions, not percentages.)

t = unit measured time of one sub-operation or work unit (in TMU), using
     a recognized work measurement system such as MOST

a = unit absolute deviation of the measured time for one suboperation
     from the true or actual time in TMU

r = unit relative deviation of the measured time for one suboperation from
     the true time, as a proportion of the analyzed time

n = occurrence frequency of the sub-operation (number of times it occurs)
     over the Calculation Period, defined as the total required time period
     of a series of suboperations that will just achieve the required accuracy

T = total measured time of a sufficient number of independent
     suboperations so that the statistical rounding effect of the unit
     measurement errors will just achieve a combined relative error for the
     series of suboperations of 0.05 (that is, $\pm 5\%$ of T), with a 95%
     statistical confidence (that is, the balancing time for the calculation
     period)

A = total absolute deviation of the measured total time from the true or
     actual total time in TMU

R = the required relative deviation of the measured total time from the total
     true time, based on the balancing time convention, i.e., 0.05, or $\pm 5\%$

N = number of repetitions of independent suboperations identical in
     duration and accuracy to the suboperation in question that would have
     to occur in order that the total relative deviation meet the balancing
     time convention of 0.05 at 95% confidence.

Relationships: In developing the required formula, we make use of the fact that
the variance of a sum of independent suboperations is equal to the sum of the
individual suboperation variances (σ):

$$\sigma_{TOT}^2 = \sum_{i=1}^{n} \sigma_i^2 = n\, \sigma_i^2$$

By the accuracy convention of motion-time measurement systems used by practitioners (that is, a relative error standard of not over $\pm 5\%$ to a 95% confidence), we have the following relationships for an acceptable system:

$$R = \frac{1.96\,\sigma_{TOT}}{Nt}, \qquad r = \frac{1.96\,\sigma_i}{t}$$

Rearranging these two equations, we have

$$\sigma_{TOT} = \frac{NRt}{1.96}, \qquad \sigma_i = \frac{rt}{1.96}$$

And, from statistical theory for the variance of an independent linear sum, as stated above, we have, in general,

$$\sigma_{TOT}^2 = n\,\sigma_i^2$$

For the specific case in which the total relative error must be 0.05, the number of such (identical but statistically independent) suboperations becomes N (see definition of terms above), and we have

$$\sigma_{TOT}^2 = N\,\sigma_i^2$$

We can substitute the expressions for total and individual standard deviation above into this last, giving us the following:

$$\left(\frac{NRt}{1.96}\right)^2 = N\left(\frac{rt}{1.96}\right)^2$$

This expression simplifies into the important relationship between total allowed relative error (taken customarily as 0.05) of a series of (identical but assumed statistically independent) suboperations and the individual allowed relative error of one such sub-operation that will just achieve this overall required standard of accuracy for the balancing period (T):

$$N = \left(\frac{r}{R}\right)^2$$

Rearranging the last equation above, we get

$$\frac{r}{R} = \sqrt{N} \qquad \text{or} \qquad r = R\sqrt{N}$$

But, for the required overall accuracy (relative error) of R over the balancing period T, we must have an additive sequence of N identical but statistically independent sub-operations, which would give us the relationship

$$T = Nt \qquad \text{or} \qquad N = \frac{T}{t}$$

The word "independent" is the important one here, because it is only when additive variables are independent that their positive and negative variations with reference to the measured values can cancel out increasingly as the number of suboperations goes up. If we have 10 repetitions of the same suboperation, there is no opportunity for random errors above and below the table value to cancel in part, since whatever the individual error of a single reading, it simply adds up above or below for all the repetitions—and an individual error of, say, 10 TMU would be a total error of 100 TMU in the same direction for the 10 identical suboperations. In effect, statistically, the 10 identical values correspond to a single value of 10 times the duration, insofar as any leveling effect is concerned; and, for such a case, the above equation becomes

$$N = \frac{T}{nt}$$

And the formula for the allowable individual error becomes

$$r = R\sqrt{\frac{T}{nt}}$$

Now we are able to deal with the meaning of the expression:

$$r^2t = \text{constant}$$

If we square both sides of the expression next above, and rearrange, we have

$$r^2t = \frac{R^2T}{n}$$

Consider each of the three variables on the right side.

 R is given at 0.05 by the requirements of the accuracy convention of work measurement
 T is the balancing time or calculation period for the system in use, and once this system is selected, T is fixed
 n is the number of times the operation takes place, which is fixed by the circumstances of the process

Thus, for all practical purposes, the mathematical expression embodying these three variables is constant for any particular situation.

Using the formula as specified on page 316, the allowed deviation of a suboperation is calculated under two different conditions in the following example.

Example: A typed report required 0.25 hours to perform according to a work measurement analysis. How accurate must this analysis be (i.e., what is the allowed deviation) if the time will be used for setting incentive rates where standards are expected to be within $\pm5\%$ for a 40-hour pay period?

Case 1 The report is typed by a receptionist only twice a day.

$$r_t = \pm r_T \sqrt{\frac{T}{nt}}$$

$$r_t = \pm 5 \sqrt{\frac{40}{10 \times 0.25}}$$

$$r_t = \pm 20\%$$

$r_T = \pm 5\%$

$T = 40$ hours

$n = 2/\text{day} \times 5 \text{ days} = 10$

$t = 0.25$ hours

Case 2 The same report is typed continuously during the 40-hour calculation period by a word processor operator.

$$r_t = \pm r_T \sqrt{\frac{T}{nt}}$$

$$r_t = \pm 5 \sqrt{\frac{40}{160 \times 0.25}}$$

$$r_t = \pm 5\%$$

$r_T = \pm 5\%$

$T = 40$ hours

$n = \dfrac{40 \text{ hours}}{0.25 \text{ hours}} = 160$

$t = 0.25$ hours

In case 1, a deviation of $\pm 20\%$ (0.25 ± 0.05 hours, or between 12 and 18 minutes) can be allowed for the standard time established since the job occurs infrequently and makes up only a small part of the receptionist's total productive time (Fig. A.4). In case 2 the word processor operator types reports during the entire week, causing the relative deviation to remain constant. The allowed deviation in this case is $\pm 5\%$, the same as the requirement for the 40-hour calculation period. This relates to an allowed time of 0.25 ± 0.0125 hours or a "standard time" for the task anywhere from 14.25 to 15.75 minutes (Fig. A.4). These statistically calculated allowed deviations guarantee with 95% confidence that a calculated time that falls within the allowed deviation range will, over the calculation period, produce results within $\pm 5\%$ of a "true time value."

Therefore, frequently occurring suboperations, or those constrained by a shorter leveling or calculation period, have a very limited range of allowed deviation associated with each and as a result can absorb very little in the way of method variations in the operation. For example, the one analysis for case 2 will statistically represent the typing of other reports, or variations of the one analyzed, that fall in a range 14.25–15.75 minutes. On the other hand, the analysis for case 1, with its lower frequency of occurrence, will statistically represent a wider range of variation, for example, the typing of any report or letter taking from 12 to 18 minutes to prepare. This leads to the conclusion that when work has been measured by representative suboperations of sufficient accuracy, fewer data units may be needed to establish the time standards. The data reduction that can result from this higher-level analysis will obviously save time and effort for the industrial engineer or standards applicator. Chapter 7 addresses this subject.

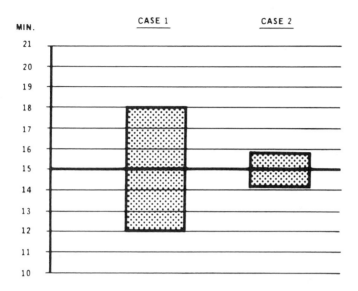

ALLOWED DEVIATION

Figure A.4   Allowed deviation for case 1 and case 2.

Accuracy Test

Previous accuracy calculations were also based on the balancing time and balancing effect theories presented earlier. These are graphically illustrated in Figure A.5.

As Figure A.5 shows, the desired level of accuracy of $\pm 5\%$ (r_T) is required to be reached as the sum of the individual measurements (t) approaches a certain point. The total time at this point is referred to as the balancing time $(T,)$ which in this case is 40 hours. A balancing time of 40 hours, as in this example, allows a wide margin for variation while establishing the time of individual activities in most typical cases. Most of the predetermined motion time systems, including MOST, are capable of far more accuracy than this as a general rule.

As for the balancing effect, it can be tested by evaluating the deviation between the true times for different suboperations and the allowed times for these same suboperations. According to theory, the desired level of accuracy should be achieved at the calculated balancing time.

Figure A.6 lists 10 time ranges covering 0.0–11.0 hours and the allowed time representing each of these ranges. In the middle columns of the table the maximum allowed deviation for each time is shown. All table values were determined from the allowed deviation formula for a 40-hour balancing period with a 95% confidence level.

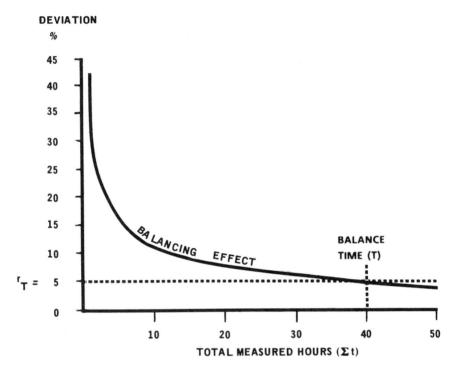

Figure A.5   Balancing time.

RANGE, HOURS	MAXIMUM ALLOWED DEVIATION		ALLOWED TIME VALUE, HOURS
	± HOURS	± %	
0.0 - 0.2	0.1	100	0.1
(0.2) - 0.6	0.2	50	0.4
(0.6) - 1.2	0.3	33	0.9
(1.2) - 2.0	0.4	25	1.6
(2.0) - 3.0	0.5	20	2.5
(3.0) - 4.2	0.6	17	3.6
(4.2) - 5.6	0.7	14	4.9
(5.6) - 7.2	0.8	13	6.4
(7.2) - 9.0	0.9	11	8.1
(9.0) - 11.0	1.0	10	10.0

Figure A.6   Allowed time values for a 40-hour balancing period.

To test the accuracy of this system, a series of random numbers should be used to represent the "true times" to perform certain suboperations. Random numbers are usually generated by a computer program or derived from a table of random values. However, for a simple demonstration, random numbers can be obtained from a telephone book. *Note:* It is recognized that a series of numbers generated from a telephone book may not necessarily be random.

The last two figures of the telephone number may be used to represent the "true" time for the suboperation in hours, with one decimal place. For example, the number 412-2375 would generate the true time of 7.5 hours.

After the true time has been established from the random number table or a telephone book, the next step is to select the appropriate allowed time based on the range into which the actual time falls. Using the table in Figure A.6, it can be seen that the time of 7.5 hours falls within the range greater than 7.2–9.0 hours; therefore, a time of 8.1 hours would be allowed since it is the midpoint of the range. In order to evaluate the balancing effect theory, enough values must be chosen so that the total of the true times is at least 40 hours (the balancing time of Fig. A.5). This is necessary to ensure that the desired level of accuracy is achieved with a 95% confidence level. A complete test example is tabulated in Figure A.7.

Notice that although individual deviations were as large as 20% in one instance, the total deviation was better than the ±5% specified. If we relate this example to a "real" work measurement situation, we can see that calculated

TRUE TIME IN HOURS (from phone book)	ALLOWED TIME IN HOURS (from Figure A.6)	ACTUAL DEVIATION	
		± HOURS	± %
5.3	4.9	− .4	+ 7.5
3.9	3.6	− .3	− 7.7
8.0	8.1	+ .1	+ 1.3
2.0	1.6	− .4	− 20.0
7.8	8.1	+ .3	+ 3.8
1.4	1.6	+ .2	+ 14.3
5.5	4.9	− .6	− 10.9
3.3	3.6	+ .3	+ 9.1
4.8	4.9	+ .1	+ 2.1
42.0	41.3	− .7	− 1.7

Figure A.7   Example of balancing effect.

deviations can be allowed in individual measurements without losing the level of accuracy desired in the final result for a calculation period (1 day, 1 week, and so on). This balancing principle plays an important role in the conceptual design of Basic MOST and the MOST Application System. The balancing effect is fairly well demonstrated in this example. However, a single simulation is rather meaningless to prove the general significance of the balancing effect. Therefore, a computer program for a random simulation was written. Two runs of that program, each with a sample size of 100 simulations, showed that the average percentage error was well within ±5%—2.69% and 2.63%, respectively.

In each of the previous examples, the desired level of accuracy was specified to be ±5%, which is the generally accepted standard for industry. But what about the balancing time? The 40-hour balancing period may be sufficient for calculating incentive standards based on a 40-hour pay period, but hardly acceptable for a line-balancing calculation with cycle times in minutes. The use of the time standard is therefore a very important factor when considering the balancing time of a work measurement system. That is why Basic MOST was designed to have a consistent balancing time of approximately 2 minutes.

Relationship of Balancing Time to the Accuracy of Work Measurement

The concept of balancing time is generally regarded as a means for comparing systems to determine their applicability. For this reason, the following information is provided to ensure that this criterion may be used properly in the selection of MOST Work Measurement Systems.

Every predetermined method time system has a balancing time, which must be calculated from a large collection of operating data by statistical analysis. The relative balancing times for five predetermined motion time systems has been calculated as follows*:

Mini MOST, 500 TMU
Basic MOST, 3235 TMU
MTM-1, 600 TMU (average)
MTM-2, 1600 TMU (average)
MTM-3, 16,000 TMU

At first glance it would seem sufficient to compare the cycle time of the operation to be analyzed with these balancing times to make a system selection. That is, an operation at least 500 TMU long could be analyzed with Mini MOST, an

---

*This list of balancing times plus other information provided in this section of the appendix is based in part on the work of Dr. William D. Brinckloe of the University Research Institute from 1975 to 1981.

operation at least 600 TMU long could be analyzed with MTM-1, and so forth. This general guideline would be technically valid, but a practical choice demands a closer look at several factors, especially since this guideline indicates that any operation shorter than 500 TMU could not be accurately analyzed. These factors are examined here.

As explained at the beginning of this appendix, balancing time is defined as the theoretical total time required of a system for the summation of independent basic elements to attain a desired level of precision. For setting labor standards in most industries the desired level is usually $\pm 5\%$ accuracy with 95% confidence. This means that when a work measurement time equals the system's balancing time, this measurement is expected to be from 0 to 5% less than or greater than the "true" value 95 times in 100. Selection of the appropriate work measurement technique should be based on the most practical (economic) system meeting this criterion.

In general, any analysis with a total time (t) shorter than the balancing time (BT) is less accurate than $\pm 5\%$, and a longer analysis is more accurate than $\pm 5\%$, in accordance with the formula

$$r = \sqrt{\frac{(0.05)^2 \times BT}{t}}$$

where r is the ratio of error for an individual analysis.

For example, if the analyzed time is one-fourth the balancing time, the error ratio doubles to $r = 0.10$ ($\pm 10\%$ accuracy). In contrast, the accuracy improves to $\pm 2.5\%$ if the analyzed time is four times the balancing time. Therefore, since Basic MOST has a balancing time of 3235 TMU, it is reasonable to ask when this system may be used to analyze operations with shorter cycles. This question is answered in the following explanation of the use of the table in Figure A.7 and its graph in Figure A.9. The table lists various operation times less than 2 minutes in the second column and corresponding Basic MOST error ratios in the third column. (Note that a 95% confidence level is assumed throughout this explanation.)

Measuring Short-Cycle Operations with MOST

A Basic MOST analysis of an operation equal in length to the balancing time has an accuracy of $\pm 5\%$. If this same analyzed time is repeated enough times to completely cover a 40-hour period (1236.5×3235 TMU = 4,000,000 TMU = 40 hours) or an 8-hour period (247.3×3235 TMU = 800,000 TMU = 8 hours), the overall accuracy for either period remains $\pm 5\%$. In general, if any operation is repeated identically over an entire period, the measurement accuracy for that period is the same as for one cycle. This also applies to shorter-cycle operations. For example, if the cycle time is only 809 TMU

($r = 0.10$), any number of cycles that fills a 2-hour period has an overall accuracy of $\pm 10\%$ when measured with Basic MOST.

However, because of the balancing effect discussed in this appendix, there is a way to combine short-cycle operations that ensures $\pm 5\%$ accuracy over any balancing period (planning month, pay week, pay-out day, and so on). For example, each day a worker could perform four *different* 809-TMU operations 247 times each and be assured that the Basic MOST analyses covering these operations would collectively be accurate to within $\pm 5\%$. Notice that the performance of each operation occupies 25% of the day (247×809 TMU $= 200,000$ TMU $= 2$ hours) and that 809 TMU is 25% of 3235 TMU. This is a special case, but it illustrates a general principle: If the percentage of the balancing period occupied by repetitions of a short-cycle operation is no greater than the percentage its cycle time is of the balancing time, the *combined* accuracy of the analyses of such operations is $\pm 5\%$ or better, regardless of the accuracy of the individual analyses.

Selecting a MOST System to Assure Overall Accuracy

Figures A.8 and A.9 are based on this important principle. If the analyst knows the most likely percentage of the calculation period occupied by repetitions of the operation and the approximate length of an operation in TMU, he or she can quickly determine whether a Basic MOST analysis of the operation will be sufficiently accurate to ensure $\pm 5\%$ accuracy for the group of analyses covering the entire period. This provides a useful guideline for avoiding the extra work that would be required to analyze a short-cycle operation with a system more detailed than necessary. (If the TMU values under "Operation Time" are multiplied by 10, these charts would be applicable to Maxi MOST, in which case the dotted line on the graph would be ignored.)

For example, using the table in Figure A.9, if two operations are each performed 50% of the week, they should be analyzed with Basic MOST if their cycle times are 1667 TMU (1 minute), since 1667 TMU is greater than 1618 TMU. For another example, using the graph in Figure A.8, if the typical operation in a department takes about 15 seconds (a little over 400 TMU) and is repeated only enough times to occupy about 10% of the day, Basic MOST would suffice, because the intersection of 400 TMU and 10% falls in the Basic MOST region. If each operation is repeated enough times to occupy about 20% of the day, however, Mini MOST should be used, because the intersection of 400 TMU and 20% falls in the Mini MOST region. Figure A.9 also applies to analyses of different lengths. For example, if a day is comprised 70% of a 2265 TMU operation, 25% of an 809 TMU operation, and 5% of a 162 TMU operation, the overall accuracy of their Basic MOST analyses will be $\pm 5\%$.

In each example thus far, the frequency of occurrence happens to be the same for all operations; but the table and graph also apply to relative frequencies

PERCENTAGE OF PERIOD	OPERATION TIME, TMU	ACCURACY OF ANALYSIS, ±r
100	3235	.050
95	3073	.051
90	2912	.053
85	2750	.054
80	2588	.056
75	2426	.058
70	2265	.060
65	2103	.062
60	1941	.065
55	1779	.067
50	1618	.071
45	1456	.075
40	1294	.079
35	1132	.085
30	971	.091
25	809	.100
20	647	.112
15	485	.129
10	324	.158
5	162	.224
4	129	.250
3	97	.289
2	65	.354
1	32	.500

Figure A.8 Limits to ensure $\pm 5\%$ combined accuracy for the Basic MOST analyses of short-cycle operations.

other than 1:1. For example, during each 4000 TMU of a balancing period, a 2000 TMU operation is performed once and a 1000 TMU operation twice. Since each operation occupies 50% of the period, the 2000 TMU operation can be analyzed with Basic MOST, but the 1000 TMU operation should be analyzed with Mini MOST. However, during each 8000 TMU of another balancing period, three different 2000 TMU operations are performed once and a 1000

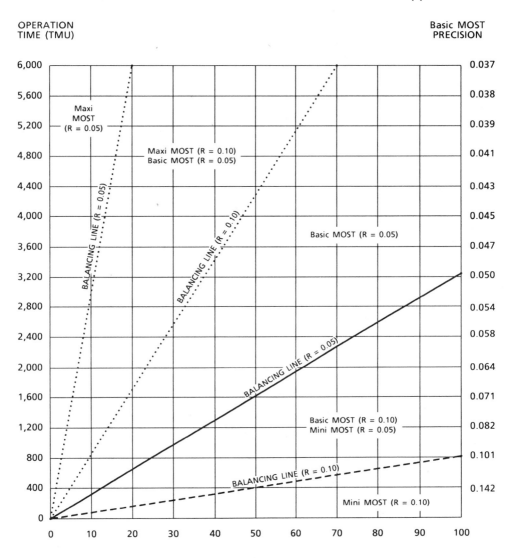

Figure A.9 Selection of MOST version for the analysis of short-cycle operations.

TMU operation twice. Since each operation occupies only 25% of the period, all the operations can be analyzed with Basic MOST.

To summarize, when all analyses of the operations that fill the balancing period fall within the charted limits, overall accuracy within ±5% is assured. This holds true even for an analysis as short as 32 TMU (±50% accuracy), although it is unlikely that Basic MOST would be used to analyze an operation this short. These charts illustrate the principle that the smaller the portion of the balancing period devoted to a particular operation, the less accurate its analysis can be without degrading overall accuracy beyond accepted limits.*

Establishing Overall Accuracy

An accuracy limit of ±5% is too stringent for some applications of work measurement data, such as cost estimating or scheduling. In this case, it is easy to fix a new balancing line on the graph by drawing a straight line from the origin (0, 0) on the left to the appropriate error ratio on the right. The broken line for $R = 0.10$ is an example. This shows that the region for applying Basic MOST is greatly expanded by an increase in allowable error to ±10%. Figure 2.4 (Chap. 2) shows that lowering the confidence requirement also expands this region even more. The balancing time of MOST drops to 570 TMU when the accuracy requirement is ±10% at 90% confidence (this is the requirement established by the Department of Defense for compliance with MIL-STD 1567A). Obviously, the accuracy requirement is an important factor in work measurement system selection.

Whatever its placement, the balancing line represents a limit. Any combination of analyses above the line for $R = 0.05$ has an overall accuracy better than ±5%. Since a typical MOST project has numerous analyses considerably above this balancing line, it would not be unusual to find overall accuracy substantially better than ±5%. Accuracy is maintained even if an occasional analysis falls somewhat below the line.

Although using the graph as explained is by far the simplest way to maintain accuracy, it is possible to confirm the overall ratio of error (R) for any combination of analyses by using the formula

$$R = \frac{\sqrt{(t_1 \times f_1 \times r_1)^2 + (t_2 \times f_2 \times r_2)^2 + \bullet \bullet \bullet + (t_n \times f_n \times r_n)^2}}{BP}$$

---

*Figure A.9 is also useful in another way: If the accuracy of any unit of standard data is known (regardless of its cycle length), its allowable percentage of the balancing period can be determined, and vice versa. Start with the error ratio on the right of the graph, go left to balancing line, and then down to find the percentage.

where: t = cycle time, hours
           f = frequency of occurrence
           r = ratio of error
           n = number of analyses
           BP = balancing period, hours

Occurrence Frequency Grouping for MOST

In accordance with the previous discussion, it is usually safe to expand the region for Basic MOST by lowering the balancing line to $R = 0.055$, because the analyses above $R = 0.050$ compensate for the few Basic MOST analyses that fall between these two lines. The line $R = 0.055$ is equivalent to an operation occurrence frequency of 1500 cycles in a 40-hour period. Operations with higher frequencies fall below this line and should always be analyzed with Mini MOST. In MOST Application Systems the region below $R = 0.055$ is designated OFG 1 (Occurrence Frequency Grouping 1). Basic MOST analyses are usually above this line in OFG 2, where the frequency of occurrence ranges from greater than 150 times per week to 1500 times per week ($150 < f \leq 1500$). On the graph, OFG 2 is bounded above by a line from the origin extending through 6000 TMU at 22.4%. Maxi MOST analyses are usually in the remaining area in OFG 3 ($15 < f \leq 150$) or OFG 4 ($f = 15$ or less). This provides the basis for the operation occurrence frequency guidelines in Chapter 2. (Note that the selection of a MOST system may also be subject to other criteria, as indicated in Chapter 2.)

Effect of Variations Within an Operation Cycle

In a typical operation cycle many subactivities occur. These subactivities are analyzed as Action Distances, Body Motions, Placements, and so on. Each subactivity differs from the others to some extent, even though the same index numbers may be assigned. For example an A_1 may be assigned for a 10-inch reach, a 17-inch move, a 26-inch reach, or a 5-inch move. The time allowed for each of these Action Distances is 10 TMU, which usually differs from the actual time for the subactivity. In accordance with statistical principles, the algebraic sum of these differences approaches zero as more of them are included in the sum. This is equivalent to saying that the measured time approaches the true time for the operation as more subactivities are included in the analysis. This illustrates the balancing effect, which is the basis for the accuracy of MOST. It also illustrates the need for these variations to occur within the operation cycle so there will be a balancing effect.

Balancing time is sufficient measured time to ensure that the precision of the measurement is within acceptable limits. The determination of a system's balancing time is based on the assumption that only independent elements enter into the calculation. This means that each element randomly differs from the others to contribute to the balancing effect. Therefore, any sequence of steps repeated identically makes no contribution to balancing. For this reason repeated steps should be disregarded when using the system selection charts in Figures 2.3, 2.4, A.8, and A.9, which are based on the balancing time. For example, if an operation takes 1000 TMU but 20% of this time is for identical repetitions, use 800 TMU when using the charts. A rough estimate is sufficient to preserve accuracy. (Note that the percentage of the balancing period occupied by repetitions of the operation still should be based on its total time, 1000 TMU.)

Effect of Cycle-to-Cycle Variations

Assuming the system has been applied properly in accordance with these guidelines, any MOST system always provides a combined precision within ±5% with 95% confidence if all the work being analyzed is performed exactly the same from cycle to cycle. However, because of the lack of operator training or practice, differences in parts or their orientations, and numerous other factors, cycle-to-cycle variations are common. How does this affect the accuracy of a MOST analysis?

The answer lies in that when cycle-to-cycle variations fall within the range of the index assigned, there is no significant effect on system precision. In a MOST analysis an index value is assigned for each subactivity (Action Distance, Gain Control, and so on). Each index represents a range of possible times (variations) for the subactivity being analyzed. One of the great benefits in the design of MOST is the optimal selection of index ranges to accommodate ("absorb") most of the cycle-to-cycle variations likely to occur for each subactivity. For example, the Basic MOST A_1 very conveniently includes every Reach and Move Distance from greater than 2 inches (5 cm) to the full extent of the operator's reach. Furthermore, since only the motions actually required to accomplish the work are analyzed, the application of MOST effectively eliminates almost all variations from consideration during the analysis.

Sometimes, however, especially in the use of a lower level system, the expected range of variations still exceeds the index range. This problem is most likely to arise in the application of a detailed system, such as MTM-1, which has many narrow ranges for the data card values. Even though an effort has been made to improve the design, layouts, and method for an operation, variations spanning two or more ranges may occur in some subactivities because of the nature of the work. In these cases, the analyst may separately analyze each variation weighted according to its frequency of occurrence or simply choose an average value on which to base the analysis. The first approach is usually tedious; the second is usually inaccurate. If either approach is needed more than a relatively small number of times in the analysis, then a higher level system should be used.

This recommendation is based not only on practical considerations (which are illustrated in the following section), but also on research that indicates that the balancing time of a system degrades when an analyst's averages include a substantial number of values outside the ranges of the assigned indexes. This is because the calculation of a balancing time is based on the variances *within* index ranges. Therefore, when averaged variations exceed an index range, the variances *between* ranges must be added, which effectively increases the balancing time. If the collective averaging while using a lower level MOST system includes a total range of variations that equals about 50% of the analyzed time for the entire operation, the balancing time degrades to the point at which it actually equals the balancing time of a higher level system. Under these circumstances a Mini MOST analysis, although more detailed, would be no more accurate than a Basic MOST analysis of the same operation.

Fortunately, users of MOST will rarely be concerned with these findings for two reasons: (1) cycle-to-cycle variations are least likely to occur in the most often-repeated operations primarily because operator movements evolve into consistent patterns, and (2) when the system selection guidelines (Chap. 2) are followed, the system used will almost always be the best choice.

Averaging Cycle-to-Cycle Variations

It is well-established that we must deal with averages in most work measurement situations, that is, average distances, average weights, average types of motion, and so on. Consider, for example, this situation. Seated at a punch press, an operator gets a part that has just been formed and moves it to one of 12 spaces in a parts tray within reach to the right. The distance from the press to the spaces

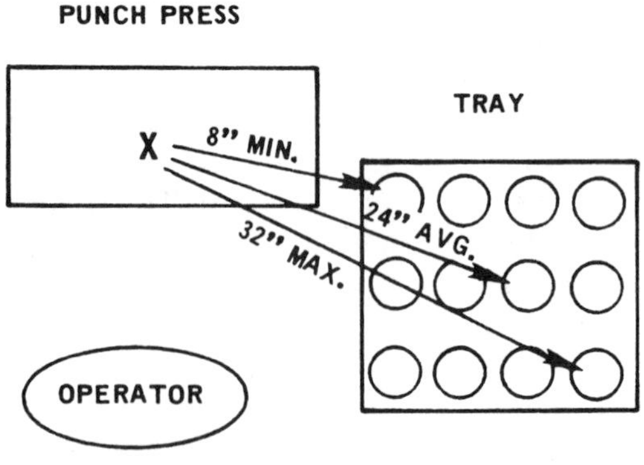

Figure A.10 Punch press operation.

on the tray varies from 8 to 32 inches (20–81 cm). If that were the entire operation to be measured, which work measurement technique would you choose—MTM-1, MTM-2, or Basic MOST? Which technique *could* you choose? The cycle time is obviously very short. To achieve an accurate analysis, your choice should be a very detailed system. Or should it?

An MTM-1 analysis of the punch press operation (Fig. A.10) might be:

MTM-1	TMU
R24A	14.9
G1A	2.0
M24B	20.6
RL1	2.0
Total	39.5

Notice that in this case the MTM-1 analyst assumed an average distance of 24 inches (61 cm) for the operation (an actual case). In actuality, however, the distance varied from a minimum of 8 inches (20 cm) to a maximum of 32 inches (81 cm).

MTM-1 minimum (8 inches, 20 cm)	TMU		MTM-1 maximum (32 inches, 81 cm)	TMU
R8A	7.9		R32A	18.3
G1A	2.0		G1A	2.0
M8B	10.6		M32B	25.5
RL1	2.0		RL1	2.0
Total	22.5		Total	47.8

Deviations
Total deviation (8–32 inches, 20–81 cm), 64%
Minimum to average (8–24 inches, 20–61 cm), 43%
Average to Maximum (24–32 inches, 61–81 cm), 21%

Since variation did exist, the MTM-1 analyst chose to average the distance rather than separately analyzing each of the twelve variations.

An MTM-2 analysis of the same operation will give:

MTM-2	TMU
GB32	23
PA32	20
Total	43

With Basic and Mini MOST using one General Move Sequence Model, the corresponding analyses are:

Basic MOST							TMU
A_1	B_0	G_1	A_1	B_0	P_1	A_0	40

Mini MOST							TMU
A_{16}	B_0	G_6	A_{16}	B_0	P_6	A_0	44

All four time values for the operation (39.5, 43, 40, and 44 TMU) are based on averages.

With MTM-1, the analyst selected an average distance for the reach and move motions based on a subjective judgment. MTM-2 time values are determined from the weighted average of different MTM-1 motion patterns. Index values in MOST are based on statistically calculated averages. The question no longer is "which is the correct analysis?" but "which is the most acceptable average?" No one can say with certainty which average is better. Therefore, when dealing with situations in which variations in the operation occur from cycle to cycle, Basic MOST gives results that are as good as the more detailed systems. In the analysis of an operation that contains substantial variations, MTM-1, MTM-2, Basic MOST, and Mini MOST all produce an acceptable time value from an accuracy standpoint.*

In order to use a detailed work measurement system, like MTM-1, made up of a large number of more or less independent elements, considerable subjectivity is required in making decisions for an analysis. "Subjective averaging" can be good or bad. One thing is certain: It is not a consistent method, and the results are likely to be greatly influenced by the individual's experience and performance. Basic MOST in this respect is definitely more objective and consistent because the averages have been statistically established and can be consistently applied.

Conclusion

When analyzing an operation that varies from cycle to cycle, even the most detailed systems concede accuracy to the analytic technique of averaging. The question is then a subjective one of choosing the average that appears to best fit the situation.

Through the use of MOST Sequence Models, analysts are aided in making the correct decisions. The result is smaller deviations among analysts compared

---

*The practical accuracy of MTM-based standards is discussed in *The Impact of Variation in Method or Workplace on the System Precision of MTM Based Standards.* University Research Institute, March 1979.

to other predetermined motion time systems. The use of a statistically derived index scale further assures the consistency of MOST.

These and other factors discussed in this appendix play an important role in the choice of a technique to use in analyzing an operation. However, the selection of the appropriate version of MOST is as simple as the guidelines provided in Chapter 2, which assure both *accuracy* in analyzing any operation and *economy* in the time and effort required.

appendix B

MOST Calculation Examples

▷ MD	**MOST-calculation**	Code	0 1 0 0 5 1 0 2 0 1
		Date	3/18/75
	Area MACHINE SHOP TURRET LATHE	Sign.	K.Z.
		Page	1 / 1

Activity ADVANCE AND RETRACT DRILL IN TURRET TO WORKPIECE

Conditions

No.	Method	No.	A	B	G	A/M	B/X	P/I	A	Fr	TMU
1	INDEX TURRET										
2	MOVE DRILL (TURRET) TO										
	WORKPIECE										
3	ADJUST COOLANT JET TO										
	WORKPIECE										
4	START AND STOP FEED										
5	CHANGE RPM										
6	RETRACT DRILL (TURRET)										
	FROM WORKPIECE										
		1	A_1	B_0	G_1	M_3	X_0	I_0	A_0		50
		2	A_1	B_0	G_1	M_6	X_0	I_3	A_0		110
		3	A_1	B_0	G_1	M_1	X_0	I_1	A_0		40
		4	A_1	B_0	G_1	M_1	X_0	I_0	A_0	2	60
		5	A_1	B_0	G_1	M_3	X_0	I_0	A_0	2	100
		6	A_1	B_0	G_1	M_6	X_0	I_0	A_0	2	80

TIME = **.26**   ~~millihours (mh)~~ / minutes (min.)   **440**

	MOST-calculation		Code	$1\,09\,03\,05\,3\,02$	
▶			Date	11/13/72	
	Area **MACHINE SHOP. VERTICAL LATHE**		Sign.	A.A.	
			Page	1/1	

Activity CHANGE WORKPIECE ON FACEPLATE WITH JIB CRANE

Conditions

No.	Method	No.	Sequence Model	Fr	TMU
1	GET LIFT STRAPS	1	$A_{10} B_6 G_3 A_{10} B_0 P_0 A_0$	1/2	145
		2	$A_{10} B_6 G_3 A_{10} B_0 P_0 A_0$	1/2	145
2	GET CRANE HOOK	5	$A_1 B_6 G_3 A_{10} B_0 P_3 A_{10}$	1/2	165
		6	$A_1 B_0 G_3 A_{10} B_0 P_3 A_{10}$	1/2	135
3	USING JIB CRANE. REMOVE		A B G A B P A		
			A B G A B P A		
	WORKPIECE FROM LATHE		A B G A B P A		
			A B G A B P A		
	AND PLACE ON WORKBENCH		A B G A B P A		
			A B G A B P A		
4	USING JIB CRANE. MOVE NEW		A B G A B P A		
			A B G A B P A		
	WORKPIECE TO LATHE		A B G A B P A		
			A B G A B P A		
5	ASIDE LIFT STRAPS		A B G A B P A		
			A B G A B P A		
6	ASIDE CRANE HOOK		A B G A B P A		
			A B G A B P A		
7	CLEAN WORKPIECE WITH AIR		A B G M X I A		
			A B G M X I A		
	HOSE		A B G M X I A		
			A B G M X I A		
			A B G M X I A		
			A B G M X I A		
			A B G M X I A		
			A B G M X I A		
		7	$A_3 B_0 G_1 A_3 B_0 P_1 S_{32} A_3 B_0 P_3 A_0$	2	920
			A B G A B P A B P A		
			A B G A B P A B P A		
			A B G A B P A B P A		
			A B G A B P A B P A		
			A B G A B P A B P A		
			A B G A B P A B P A		
			A B G A B P A B P A		
			A B G A B P A B P A		
			A B G A B P A B P A		
			A B G A B P A B P A		
			A B G A B P A B P A		
			A B G A B P A B P A		
		3	$A_{16} T_{54} K_{220} F_{24} V_{32} L_{81} V_{10} R_{24} T_{42} A_0$		5030
		4	$A_{16} T_{54} K_{220} F_{24} V_{10} L_{81} K_{32} R_{42} T_{42} A_{10}$		5050

TIME = **6.9**   ~~millihours (mh.)~~ / minutes (min.) | 11590

	MOST-calculation		Code	$1\ 1\ 1\ 0\ 4\ 1\ 0\ 2\ 0\ 6$
▷			Date	11/28/77
	Area MACHINING – ENGINE LATHE		Sign.	WMY
			Page	1/1

Activity: CHANGE TOOL IN DRILL CHUCK

Conditions: JACOBS CHUCK, TOOL ON SHELF OR RACK

No.	Method	No.	Sequence Model	Fr	TMU
1	LOOSEN CHUCK WITH CHUCK	3	$A_1\ B_0\ G_1\ A_6\ B_0\ P_1\ A_0$		90
	WRENCH	4	$A_3\ B_0\ G_1\ A_6\ B_0\ P_3\ A_1$		140
2	OPEN CHUCK JAWS WITH		A B G A B P A		
	FINGERS		A B G A B P A		
3	REMOVE TOOL AND LAY ASIDE		A B G A B P A		
4	OBTAIN TOOL AND POSITION		A B G A B P A		
	IN CHUCK		A B G A B P A		
5	HAND TIGHTEN CHUCK		A B G A B P A		
6	TIGHTEN CHUCK WITH		A B G A B P A		
	CHUCK WRENCH		A B G M X I A		
			A B G M X I A		
			A B G M X I A		
			A B G M X I A		
			A B G M X I A		
			A B G M X I A		
		1	$A_1\ B_0\ G_1\ A_1\ B_0\ P_3\ L_{16}\ A_1\ B_0\ P_1\ A_0$		240
		2	$A_0\ B_0\ G_0\ A_1\ B_0\ P_1\ L_3\ A_0\ B_0\ P_0\ A_0$		50
		5	$A_0\ B_0\ G_0\ A_1\ B_0\ P_1\ F_3\ A_0\ B_0\ O_0\ O_0$		50
		6	$A_1\ B_0\ G_1\ A_1\ B_0\ P_3\ F_{16}\ A_1\ B_0\ P_1\ A_0$		240
			A B G A B P A B P A		
			A B G A B P A B P A		
			A B G A B P A B P A		
			A B G A B P A B P A		
			A B G A B P A B P A		
			A B G A B P A B P A		

TIME = 8.1   millihours (mh.)   **810**

MOST-calculation	Code	1 0 3 0 3 1 0 2 0 1
	Date	2/10/75
Area MACHINING	Sign.	KZ
	Page	1 1

Activity CHANGE WORKPIECE IN 3-JAW CHUCK WITH T-WRENCH AT ENGINE LATHE

Conditions

No.	Method	No.	Sequence Model							Fr	TMU
1	LOOSEN WORKPIECE WITH	2	A₁ B₀ G₁ A₆ B₆ P₁ A₀ A B G A B P A								150
	T-WRENCH	3	A₃ B₆ G₁ A₁₀ B₀ P₃ A₀ A B G A B P A								230
			A B G A B P A								
2	MOVE WORKPIECE FROM		A B G A B P A								
	3-JAW CHUCK TO PALLET 1		A B G A B P A								
3	PLACE WORKPIECE FROM		A B G A B P A								
	PALLET 2 TO 3-JAW CHUCK		A B G A B P A								
4	FASTEN WORKPIECE IN		A B G A B P A								
	3-JAW CHUCK WITH T-WRENCH		A B G A B P A								
5	PULL LEVER ON LATHE		A B G A B P A								
	TO START SPINDLE FOR	5	A₁ B₀ G₁ M₃ X₃ I₀ A₀ A B G M X I A								80
	CENTRICITY CHECK, PT. 1 SEC		A B G M X I A								
			A B G M X I A								
			A B G M X I A								
			A B G M X I A								
			A B G M X I A								
		1	A₁ B₀ G₁ A₁ B₀ P₃ L₁₆ A₁ B₀ P₁ A₀ A B G A B P A B P A								240
		4	A₁ B₀ G₁ A₁ B₀ P₃ F₁₆ A₁ B₀ P₁ A₀ A B G A B P A B P A								240
			A B G A B P A B P A								
			A B G A B P A B P A								
			A B G A B P A B P A								
			A B G A B P A B P A								
			A B G A B P A B P A								
			A B G A B P A B P A								
			A B G A B P A B P A								
			A B G A B P A B P A								

TIME = .564   minutes (min.)   940

MOST-calculation			
Area 4 - SPINDLE GANG DRILL	**Code** $|3|0|0|0|5|1|0|3|0|1|$ **Date** 9/29/76 **Sign.** KZ **Page** 1 / 1		

Activity DRILL HOLE IN DRIVE GEAR

Conditions

No.	Method	No.	Sequence Model	Fr	TMU
1	PLACE PART IN FIXTURE	1	$A_1 B_0 G_3 A_1 B_0 P_3 A_0$		80
		5	$A_3 B_6 G_3 A_3 B_0 P_3 A_0$	1/4	(45)
2	PUSH LEVER TO HOLD PART	7	$(A_1 B_0 G_1) A_1 B_0 P_1 A_0$		20
			A B G A B P A		
3	APPROACH SPINDLE TO		A B G A B P A		
			A B G A B P A		
	PART		A B G A B P A		
			A B G A B P A		
4	START DRILLING OPERATION		A B G A B P A		
			A B G A B P A		
5	PLACE PARTS ON MACHINE		A B G A B P A		
			A B G A B P A		
	TABLE, SIMO		A B G A B P A		
			A B G A B P A		
6	PULL LEVER ON FIXTURE		A B G A B P A		
			A B G A B P A		
	TO LOOSEN PART		A B G A B P A		
7	REMOVE PART TO TOTE	2	$A_1 B_0 G_1 M_1 X_0 I_0 A_0$		30
		3	$A_1 B_0 G_1 M_{10} X_0 I_0 A_0$		120
	BOX	4	$(A_1) B_0 G_1 M_1 X_{113} I_0 A_0$		1150
		6	$A_1 B_0 G_1 M_1 X_0 I_0 A_0$		30
8	CLEAN FIXTURE w/AIR		A B G M X I A		
			A B G M X I A		
			A B G M X I A		
			A B G M X I A		
		8	$A_1 B_0 G_1 A_1 B_0 P_1 56 A_1 B_0 P_1 A_0$		120
			A B G A B P A B P A		
			A B G A B P A B P A		
			A B G A B P A B P A		
			A B G A B P A B P A		
			A B G A B P A B P A		
			A B G A B P A B P A		
			A B G A B P A B P A		
			A B G A B P A B P A		
			A B G A B P A B P A		
			A B G A B P A B P A		
			A B G A B P A B P A		
			A B G A B P A B P A		

TIME = .93   minutes (min.)   **1,550**

MOST-calculation				Code	2011265402

Area: **WIRE ELEMENT DEPT.** Date: **1/13/77** Sign. **K.Z.** Page **1/1**

Activity: **SPOTWELD X-METAL CYLINDER**

Conditions:

No.	Method	No.	Sequence Model							Fr	TMU
1	PLACE X-METAL	1	A1 B0 G3	A1 B0	P3 A1					90
		2	A0 B0 G1	A1 B0	P6 A0					80
	CYLINDER ON CYLINDER	4	A0 B0 G0	A1 B0	P6 A0					70
		5	A1 B0 G3	A1 B0	P1 A0					60
	FIXTURE	6	A0 B0 G0	A1 B0	P3 A0					40
		8	A0 B0 G0	A1 B3	P1 A0					50
2	PLACE GUN TO		A B G	A B	P A					
			A B G	A B	P A					
	CYLINDER		A B G	A B	P A					
			A B G	A B	P A					
3	SPOTWELD ENDS (2)		A B G	A B	P A					
			A B G	A B	P A					
4	TURN CYLINDER		A B G	A B	P A					
			A B G	A B	P A					
5	REMOVE FIXTURE TO		A B G	A B	P A					
			A B G	A B	P A					
	BENCH		A B G	A B	P A					
6	REPOSITION CYLINDER	3	A1 B0 G1	M1 X1	I0 A0			2		80
		7	A1 B0 G1 (M1 X1)	I0 A0				(10)		220
7	SPOTWELD 10 POINTS		A B G	M X	I A					
8	PLACE CYLINDER ON		A B G	M X	I A					
			A B G	M X	I A					
	FLOOR		A B G	M X	I A					
			A B G	M X	I A					
			A B G A B P		A B P A					
			A B G A B P		A B P A					
			A B G A B P		A B P A					
			A B G A B P		A B P A					
			A B G A B P		A B P A					
			A B G A B P		A B P A					
			A B G A B P		A B P A					
			A B G A B P		A B P A					
			A B G A B P		A B P A					
			A B G A B P		A B P A					
			A B G A B P		A B P A					
			A B G A B P		A B P A					
			A B G A B P		A B P A					

TIME = **.414**　　　minutes (min.)　　　　　　　　　　　　**690**

MOST-calculation

Code	402b0022l01	
Date	3/19/75	
Sign.	K.Z.	
Page	1 / 1	

Area FABRICATION

Activity PUNCH HOLES IN PLATE AT STRIPPIT PUNCH PRESS, PER 2-4 HOLES, PLATE SIZE = 24 X 30"

Conditions

No.	Method	No.	Sequence Model	Fr	TMU
1	POSITION PLATE FROM HAND-	1	$A_3 B_0 G_1 A_3 B_0 P_6 A_0$		130
	TRUCK TO PUNCH PRESS	4	$A_1 B_0 G_1 A_6 B_0 P_1 A_6$		150
			A B G A B P A		
2	PUSH BUTTONS FOR PUNCHING		A B G A B P A		
	HOLES F₃		A B G A B P A		
			A B G A B P A		
3	SLIDE PLATE AGAINST STOP		A B G A B P A		
	AT PRESS F₂		A B G A B P A		
			A B G A B P A		
4	MOVE PLATE FROM PRESS TO		A B G A B P A		
	HANDTRUCK 2		A B G A B P A		
			A B G A B P A		
5	CHECK HOLE LOCATIONS WITH		A B G A B P A		
	CALIPER AND RETURN TO	2	$A_1 B_0 G_1 M_1 X_1 I_0 A_0$	3	120
	HANDTRUCK 2, F 1/4	3	$A_1 B_0 G_1 M_3 X_0 I_0 A_0$	3	100
		6	$A_1 B_0 G_1 M_3 X_0 I_0 A_0$	1/4	13
6	SLIDE PLATE AT HANDTRUCK		A B G M X I A		
	2, F 1/4		A B G M X I A		
			A B G M X I A		
		5	$A_3 B_0 G_1 A_3 B_0 P_1 M_{24} A_3 B_0 P_1 A_3$	1/4	98
			A B G A B P A B P A		
			A B G A B P A B P A		
			A B G A B P A B P A		
			A B G A B P A B P A		
			A B G A B P A B P A		
			A B G A B P A B P A		
			A B G A B P A B P A		
			A B G A B P A B P A		
			A B G A B P A B P A		
			A B G A B P A B P A		
			A B G A B P A B P A		

TIME = . 367   minutes (min.)   **611**

<table>
<tr><td colspan="2" rowspan="2">MOST-calculation</td><td>Code</td><td>| 0 0 7 | 8 3 6 2 | 2 0 3</td></tr>
<tr><td>Date</td><td>3/19/75</td></tr>
</table>

	MOST-calculation	Code	0 0 7 8 3 6 2 2 0 3
m▷		Date	3/19/75
	Area ASSEMBLY	Sign.	K.Z.
		Page	1/1

Activity **ASSEMBLE RESISTOR OR DIODE ON PC-BOARD**

Conditions

No.	Method	No.	Sequence Model							Fr	TMU
1	TURN CAROUSEL TRAY	2	A₁ B₀ G₃ A₁ B₀ P₁ A₀							¼	15
	WITH COMPONENTS F - ⅛	3	A₁ B₀ G₁ A₁ B₀ P₀ A₀								30
		5	A₀ B₀ G₀ A₁ B₀ P₁ A₀								20
2	GET AND MOVE 4	7	A₁ B₀ G₁ A₁ B₀ P₆ A₀								90
			A B G A B P A								
	COMPONENTS FROM		A B G A B P A								
			A B G A B P A								
	TRAY BIN TO BENCH, F - ¼		A B G A B P A								
3	PICK UP COMPONENT		A B G A B P A								
			A B G A B P A								
4	BEND LEGS ON COMPONENT		A B G A B P A								
			A B G A B P A								
	WITH PLIERS		A B G A B P A								
5	MOVE COMPONENT TO		A B G A B P A								
		1	A₁ B₀ G₁ M₃ X₀ I₃ A₀							⅛	10
	BENCH		A B G M X I A								
6	READ DRAWING, 10 DIGITS,		A B G M X I A								
			A B G M X I A								
	TO LOCATE COMPONENT TO		A B G M X I A								
	PC-BOARD		A B G M X I A								
7	POSITION COMPONENT TO	4	A₁ B₀ G₁ A₁ B₀ (F₃ C₁) A₁ B₀ P₁ A₀ (8) ¼								92
		6	A₀ B₀ G₀ A₀ B₀ P₁ I₀ A₀ B₀ P₀ A₀								100
	PC-BOARD	8	A₁ B₀ G₁ A₁ B₀ (P₁ C₃) A₁ B₀ P₁ A₀ (2)								130
8	FASTEN COMPONENT LEGS	9	A₁ B₀ G₁ A₁ B₀ (F₃ C₁) A₁ B₀ P₁ A₀ (8) ¼								92
			A B G A B P A B P A								
	WITH PLIERS		A B G A B P A B P A								
9	CUTOFF EXCESS WIRE		A B G A B P A B P A								
			A B G A B P A B P A								
	WITH DIKE		A B G A B P A B P A								
			A B G A B P A B P A								
			A B G A B P A B P A								
			A B G A B P A B P A								

TIME = **.347**   minutes (min.)   **579**

MOST-calculation

Code	$1\,0\,|\,5\,3\,7\,3\,|\,3\,0\,2$
Date	3/25/77
Sign.	S
Page	1/1

Area: AUTO ASSEMBLY

Activity: ASSEMBLE 4 SHOCKABSORBERS (FRONT) TO FRAME

Conditions:

No.	Method	No.	Sequence Model	Fr	TMU
1	GET AND PICK UP 4 SHOCK-	1	$(A_1\ B_0\ G_3)\ A_6\ B_0\ P_0\ A_0$	(2)	140
	ABSORBERS	2	$A_0\ B_0\ G_0\ A_1\ B_0\ P_3\ A_0$	3	120
		4	$A_1\ B_0\ G_1\ A_1\ B_0\ P_0\ A_0$		30
2	HOLD AND PLACE 3	5	$A_0\ B_0\ G_0\ A_1\ B_6\ P_3\ A_0$	4	400
	SHOCKABSORBERS TO	6	$A_0\ B_0\ G_0\ A_1\ B_0\ P_3\ A_0$	4	160
		8	$A_1\ B_0\ G_1\ A_1\ B_0\ P_0\ A_0$		30
	FRAME	9	$A_1\ B_0\ G_3\ A_{16}\ B_0\ P_0\ A_0$		200
		10	$A_0\ B_0\ G_0\ A_1\ B_0\ P_1\ A_0$		20
3	LOOSEN 4 NUTS 5 SPINS		A B G A B P A		
	WITH FINGERS		A B G A B P A		
4	PICK UP RETAINER AND		A B G A B P A		
	BUSHING FROM SHOCK-		A B G A B P A		
	ABSORBER		A B G M X I A		
5	HOLD AND PLACE SHOCK-		A B G M X I A		
	ABSORBER IN BRACKET		A B G M X I A		
6	HOLD AND PLACE BUSHING		A B G M X I A		
	AND RETAINER TO	3	$A_0\ B_0\ G_0\ A_1\ B_0\ P_{10}\ A_0\ A_0\ B_0\ P_0\ A_0$	4	480
	SHOCKABSORBERS	7	$A_0\ B_0\ G_0\ A_1\ B_0\ P_3\ A_0\ A_0\ B_0\ P_0\ A_0$	4	560
7	HOLD AND FASTEN 4 NUTS		A B G A B P A B P A		
	5 SPINS WITH FINGERS		A B G A B P A B P A		
	TO SHOCKABSORBER		A B G A B P A B P A		
8	PICK UP SHOCKABSORBERS		A B G A B P A B P A		
9	GET AND PICK UP 2 SHOCKAB		A B G A B P A B P A		
10	HOLD AND MOVE SHOCK-				
	ABSORBERS TO FRAME				

TIME = 1.28   minutes (min.)   **2140**

MOST-calculation	Code	0 0 5 0 6 0 5 2 0 1
	Date	9/13/74
Area ELECTRICAL MAINTENANCE	Sign.	K.Z.
	Page	1/1

Activity REPLACE LIGHT SWITCH

Conditions

No.	Method	No.	Sequence Model							Fr	TMU
1	REMOVE COVER PLATE WITH	2	A1	B0 G3	A1	B0	P1	A0			60
	SCREWDRIVER (2 SCREWS)	5	A1	B0 (G3)	A1	B6	P1	A0	(2)	150
		7	A1	B0 G3	A1	B0	P6	A0		110
2	REMOVE SWITCH FROM BOX	9	A0	B0 G0	A1	B0	P6	A0		70
		10	A1	B6 G3	A1	B0	P3	A0		140
3	REMOVE 2 SCREWS WITH		A	B G	A	B	P	A		
	SCREWDRIVER		A	B G	A	B	P	A		
4	DISCONNECT 2 WIRES		A	B G	A	B	P	A		
			A	B G	A	B	P	A		
5	ASIDE SWITCH TO POCKET		A	B G	A	B	P	A		
			A	B G	A	B	P	A		
6	STRAIGHTEN 2 WIRES		A	B G	A	B	P	A		
			A	B G	A	B	P	A		
7	GET NEW SWITCH FROM		A	B G	A	B	P	A		
	POCKET TO WIRES		A	B G	M	X	I	A		
8	CONNECT 2 WIRES		A	B G	M	X	I	A		
			A	B G	M	X	I	A		
9	POSITION SWITCH IN BOX		A	B G	M	X	I	A		
			A	B G	M	X	I	A		
10	PLACE COVER PLATE		A	B G	M	X	I	A		
			A	B G	M	X	I	A		
11	FASTEN COVER PLATE WITH	1	A1 B0 G1 A1 B0 (3 A0 L16) A1 B6 P1 A0	(2)	490
	SCREWDRIVER	3	A0 B0 G0 A0 B0 (3 A1 L54) A0 B0 P0 A0	(2)	1160
		4	A0 B0 G0 A0 B0 (3 A1 L10) A1 B0 P1 A0	(2)	300
		6	A1 B0 G1 A0 B0 (3 A1 F16) A1 B0 P1 A0	(2)	400
		8	A1 B0 G1 A0 B0 (3 A1 F16) A0 B0 P0 A0	(2)	420
		11	A1 B0 G1 A0 B0 (3 A1 F16) A1 B0 P1 A0	(2)	320
			A B G A B P	A B P A		
			A B G A B P	A B P A		
			A B G A B P	A B P A		
			A B G A B P	A B P A		
			A B G A B P	A B P A		
			A B G A B P	A B P A		
			A B G A B P	A B P A		
			A B G A B P	A B P A		

| TIME = 2.2 | ~~millihours (mhr)~~ / minutes (min.) | 3620 |

	MOST-calculation		Code	5 0d0001 1 01
m			Date	6/20/77
	Area PIPE SHOP		Sign.	W.N.Y.
			Page	1 / 1

Activity BEND TUBE FOR CHAIR FRAME AT ROTARY COMPRESSION BENDING MACHINE (PER TUBE)

Conditions

No.	Method	No.	Sequence Model								Fr	TMU
1	REMOVE TAPE FROM TUBES	1	(A₁	B₀	G₃	A₁	B₀	P₁)	A₀ (5)	½	12
		2	A₀	B₀	G₀	A₃	B₀	P₀	A₃	1/25	2
2	ASIDE TAPE TO TRASH BIN	3	A₁	B₀	G₁	A₁	B₀	P₁	A₀		40
		10	A₁	B₀	G₁	A₃	B₆	P₁	A₃		150
	AND RETURN TO WORK BENCH		A	B	G	A	B	P	A		
			A	B	G	A	B	P	A		
3	GET TUBE FROM WORK BENCH		A	B	G	A	B	P	A		
			A	B	G	A	B	P	A		
	AND PLACE IN BENDING		A	B	G	A	B	P	A		
			A	B	G	A	B	P	A		
	MACHINE		A	B	G	A	B	P	A		
			A	B	G	A	B	P	A		
4	PULL LEVER 1 WITH		A	B	G	A	B	P	A		
			A	B	G	A	B	P	A		
	LEFT HAND (L.H.)		A	B	G	A	B	P	A		
			A	B	G	A	B	P	A		
5	PULL SUPPORT WITH		A	B	G	A	B	P	A		
			A	B	G	A	B	P	A		
	RIGHT HAND (R.H.)	4	A₁	B₀	G₁	M₁	X₀	I₀	A₀		30
		5	(A₁)	B₀	G₁	M₁	X₀	I₀	A₀		20
6	PULL LEVER 2 WITH L.H.	6	(A₁)	B₀	G₁	M₁	X₀	I₀	A₀		20
		7	(A₁)	B₀	G₁	M₁	X₃	I₀	A₀		50
7	PUSH ACTIVATING LEVER	8	A₀	B₀	G₀	M₁	X₀	I₀	A₀		10
		9	A₁	B₀	G₁	M₁	X₀	I₀	A₀		30
	WITH R.H. TO BEND TUBE	11	A₁	B₀	G₁	M₃	X₃	I₀	A₀		(80)
			A	B	G	M	X	I	A		
8	PUSH LEVER 2 WITH L.H.		A B G A B P				A B P A				
			A B G A B P				A B P A				
9	PUSH LEVER 1 WITH L.H.		A B G A B P				A B P A				
			A B G A B P				A B P A				
10	REMOVE TUBE AND ASIDE		A B G A B P				A B P A				
			A B G A B P				A B P A				
	TO LOWER SHELF		A B G A B P				A B P A				
			A B G A B P				A B P A				
11	PULL ACTIVATING LEVER		A B G A B P				A B P A				
			A B G A B P				A B P A				
	WITH R.H. TO RESET		A B G A B P				A B P A				
			A B G A B P				A B P A				
	MACHINE (SIMO TO		A B G A B P				A B P A				
	REMOVE TUBE)										

TIME = .22   minutes (min.)   **364**

MOST-calculation

Area: YARN HAULER / CHECKER	Code: |006|20 70|3|04
	Date: 11/17/76
	Sign. D. D.
	Page: 1/1

Activity: UNLOAD EMPTY BOBBINS

Conditions: FROM BINS ON AUTOCONER

No.	Method	No.	Sequence Model							Fr	TMU
1	OBTAIN EMPTY TRUCK FROM STORAGE AREA, PUSH TO FRONT ALLEY OF AUTO-CONERS; INCLUDES RETURN AT END OF ACTIVITY.	4	A0	B0	G0	A1	B0	P1	A0	10	200
		6	A0	B0	G0	A1	B6	P3	A0	10	1000
			A	B	G	A	B	P	A		
			A	B	G	A	B	P	A		
			A	B	G	A	B	P	A		
2	PUSH TRUCK FROM BIN TO BIN IN ALLEY.		A	B	G	A	B	P	A		
			A	B	G	A	B	P	A		
			A	B	G	A	B	P	A		
3	REMOVE BOBBIN BIN ON AUTOCONER.		A	B	G	A	B	P	A		
			A	B	G	A	B	P	A		
			A	B	G	A	B	P	A		
4	LIFT BIN TO TRUCK.	2	A1	B0	G3	M3	X0	I0	A10	4	680
		3	A1	B6	G1	M3	X0	I0	A0	10	1100
5	DUMP BOBBINS INTO TRUCK.	5	A0	B0	G0	M1	X10	I0	A0	10	1100
			A	B	G	M	X	I	A		
			A	B	G	M	X	I	A		
6	REPLACE BIN ON AUTO-CONER.		A	B	G	M	X	I	A		

No.	Sequence Model												Fr	TMU
	A	B	G	A	B	P		A	B	P	A			
1	A3	S3	T6	L0	T0	L	T6	A9						2100

TIME = 3.71 minutes (min.)   6/80

⏵	MOST-calculation	Code	2 0 5 5 0 1 1 4 0 1
		Date	12/16/75
Area COAT DEPARTMENT		Sign.	K.Z.
		Page	1 / 1

Activity **SEW SLEEVE IN LINER**

Conditions

No.	Method	No.	Sequence Model							Fr	TMU
		1	A_1	B_0	G_1	A_1	B_0	P_1	A_0		40
1	PLACE LINER IN MACHINE	2	A_1	B_0	G_1	A_1	B_0	P_3	A_0	2	120
2	PLACE 2 SLEEVES IN	5	A_0	B_0	G_1	A_1	B_0	P_3	A_0		50
	LINER		A	B	G	A	B	P	A		
			A	B	G	A	B	P	A		
3	SEW SLEEVE IN LINER		A	B	G	A	B	P	A		
			A	B	G	A	B	P	A		
4	CUT OFF THREAD WITH		A	B	G	A	B	P	A		
	SCISSORS		A	B	G	A	B	P	A		
5	ASIDE LINER		A	B	G	A	B	P	A		
			A	B	G	A	B	P	A		
			A	B	G	A	B	P	A		
			A	B	G	A	B	P	A		
			A	B	G	A	B	P	A		
		3	A_0	B_0	G_0	M_1	$X_{32(13)}$	A_1	(2) A	2	800
			A	B	G	M	X	I	A		
			A	B	G	M	X	I	A		
			A	B	G	M	X	I	A		
			A	B	G	M	X	I	A		
			A	B	G	M	X	I	A		
		4	A_1	B_0	G_1	A_1	B_0	P_1	G_1	A_1	B_0	P_0	A_0	2	120
			A	B	G	A	B	P	A	B	P	A		
			A	B	G	A	B	P	A	B	P	A		
			A	B	G	A	B	P	A	B	P	A		
			A	B	G	A	B	P	A	B	P	A		
			A	B	G	A	B	P	A	B	P	A		
			A	B	G	A	B	P	A	B	P	A		
			A	B	G	A	B	P	A	B	P	A		
			A	B	G	A	B	P	A	B	P	A		
			A	B	G	A	B	P	A	B	P	A		
			A	B	G	A	B	P	A	B	P	A		
			A	B	G	A	B	P	A	B	P	A		

TIME = **.68**	minutes (min.)	**1130**

	MOST-calculation		Code	1185109301
m			Date	9/23/76
	Area APPAREL CUTTING		Sign.	KZ
			Page	1/1

Activity HAND LAY UP 24 LAYERS HIGH (2 OPERATORS)

Conditions

No.	Method	No.	Sequence Model							Fr	TMU
1	REMOVE CORE TUBE	1	A_1	B_0	G_3	A_1	B_0	P_0	A_0	2	100
2	PULL OUT TUBE	3	A_0	B_6	G_0	A_1	B_0	P_1	A_0	2	40
		4	A_6	B_6	G_3	A_1	B_0	P_3	A_0	2	380
3	ASIDE TUBE	6	A_1	B_0	G_3	A_6	B_0	P_3	A_0	2	260
		7	A_1	B_0	G_1	A_1	B_0	P_6	A_0	24	2,160
4	PLACE ROLL OF FABRIC	8	A_1	B_0	G_1	A_1	B_0	P_1	A_0	48	1,920
	ON MACHINE (LEFT END)	10	A_1	B_0	G_1	A_0	B_0	P_1	A_0	48	7,200
		12	A_1	B_0	G_1	A_0	B_0	P_0	A_0	2	80
5	ADJUST CLAMPS (BOTH	13	A_3	B_0	G_1	A_3	B_0	P_3	A_0		100
	ENDS)		A	B	G	A	B	P	A		
			A	B	G	A	B	P	A		
6	PLACE ROLL OF FABRIC		A	B	G	A	B	P	A		
	ON MACHINE (RIGHT END)		A	B	G	A	B	P	A		
			A	B	G	A	B	P	A		
7	PLACE END OF FABRIC	2	A_1	B_0	G_1	M_3	X_0	I_0	A_0	2X2	200
		5	A_1	B_0	G_1	M_3	X_0	I_0	A_0	2X2	200
8	PLACE WEIGHTS TO HOLD	9	A_1	B_0	G_1	M_3	X_0	I_0	A_{16}	24X2	10,080
	END OF FABRIC		A	B	G	M	X	I	A		
			A	B	G	M	X	I	A		
9	LAY UP FABRIC ON		A	B	G	M	X	I	A		
	TABLE	11	A_1 B_0 G_3	A_1 B_0 P_1	C_{10}	A_1 B_0 P_3 A_0				25	5,000
			A B G	A B P		A B P A					
10	ALIGN FABRIC EDGES (SIMO		A B G	A B P		A B P A					
	TO 9)		A B G	A B P		A B P A					
			A B G	A B P		A B P A					
11	CUT OFF FABRIC W/SCISSORS		A B G	A B P		A B P A					
			A B G	A B P		A B P A					
12	PUT WEIGHTS ON MACHINE		A B G	A B P		A B P A					
			A B G	A B P		A B P A					
13	PLACE PATTERN PAPER ON		A B G	A B P		A B P A					
	TOP OF BATCH		A B G	A B P		A B P A					
			A B G	A B P		A B P A					

TIME = 12.31 minutes (min.) **20520**

	MOST-calculation	Code 1 01 60 1 34 05
⏩		Date 12/7/77
	Area COLLECTIONS	Sign. A.M.G.
		Page 1/1

Activity ASSEMBLE CHECKS IN INSIDE COLLECTIONS

Conditions

No.	Method	No.	Sequence Model							Fr	TMU
1	GET CHECK AND NOTICE	1	A_1	B_0	G_1	A_1	B_0	P_0	A_0	3	90
		2	ⓐ$_0$	B_0	G_1	A_1	B_0	P_1	A_0	3	90
2	REMOVE AND ASIDE	3	A_0	B_0	G_0	A_1	B_0	P_0	A_0	3	60
	PAPER CLIP	4	ⓐ$_1$	B_0	G_1	A_1	B_0	P_1	A_0	3	60
		5	A_1	B_0	G_3	ⓐ$_1$	B_0	P_1	A_0	3	120
3	PLACE CHECK AND NOTICE	6	A_0	B_0	G_0	A_1	B_0	P_1	A_0	3	60
	ON DESK	7	A_1	B_0	G_1	A_1	B_0	P_1	A_0	3	90
		9	ⓐ$_1$	B_0	G_1	A_1	B_0	ⓟ$_1$	A_0	3	90
4	PICK UP FORM	10	A_1	B_0	G_1	A_1	B_0	P_3	A_0	3	180
5	REMOVE CARBON AND	11	A_0	B_0	G_0	A_1	B_0	P_1	A_0	3	60
	ASIDE	12	A_1	B_0	G_1	A_1	B_0	P_1	A_0		40
			A	B	G	A	B	P	A		
6	PLACE NOTICE ON DESK		A	B	G	A	B	P	A		
7	PLACE TOP COPY OF		A	B	G	M	X	I	A		
	NOTICE ON CHECK		A	B	G	M	X	I	A		
8	GET CHECK AND NOTICE		A	B	G	M	X	I	A		
	AND STAPLE		A	B	G	M	X	I	A		
9	GET COPIES OF NOTICE	8	A_0 B_0 G_1 A_1 B_0 P_1 M_3 A_1 B_0 P_0 A_0							3	210
	AND PLACE WITH CHECK		A B G A B P			A B P A					
10	GET AND PLACE PAPER		A B G A B P			A B P A					
	CLIP ON NOTICE		A B G A B P			A B P A					
11	ASIDE PAPERS		A B G A B P			A B P A					
12	THROW AWAY CARBONS		A B G A B P			A B P A					

TIME = .6540	minutes (min.)	1090

Copyright: Maynard 1974 M101 - REV. 1

MOST-calculation

Code	9 0 4 6 1 0 2 3 0 1
Date	12/13/77
Sign.	B. B.
Page	1 / 1

Area: **CASH AND MAIL**

Activity: **PREPARE DUPLICATE BILL FOR PAYMENT**

Conditions

No.	Method	No.	Sequence Model							Fr	TMU
			A	B	G	A	B	P	A		
1	OBTAIN PEN, WRITE DATE		A	B	G	A	B	P	A		
	ON DUPLICATE BILL		A	B	G	A	B	P	A		
			A	B	G	A	B	P	A		
2	COPY ACCOUNT NUMBER		A	B	G	A	B	P	A		
	(11 DIGITS)		A	B	G	A	B	P	A		
			A	B	G	A	B	P	A		
3	COPY SYMBOL FOR		A	B	G	A	B	P	A		
	STATUS OF PAYMENT		A	B	G	A	B	P	A		
			A	B	G	A	B	P	A		
4	COPY AMOUNT OF PAYMENT		A	B	G	A	B	P	A		
			A	B	G	A	B	P	A		
5	COPY SYMBOL FOR TYPE		A	B	G	A	B	P	A		
	OF PAYMENT		A	B	G	A	B	P	A		
			A	B	G	M	X	I	A		
6	WRITE NAME OF		A	B	G	M	X	I	A		
	CUSTOMER		A	B	G	M	X	I	A		
			A	B	G	M	X	I	A		
7	WRITE SYMBOL ABOVE		A	B	G	M	X	I	A		
	LAST NAME		A	B	G	M	X	I	A		
8	WRITE ADDRESS OF	1	$A_1 B_0 G_0 A_1 B_0 P_1$	R_{16}	$A_0 B_0 P_0 A_0$						200
		2	$A_0 B_0 G_0 A_1 B_0 P_1$	R_{24}	$A_0 B_0 P_0 A_0$						250
	CUSTOMER	3	$A_0 B_0 G_0 A_1 B_0 P_1$	R_3	$A_0 B_0 P_0 A_0$						40
		4	$A_0 B_0 G_0 A_1 B_0 P_1$	R_6	$A_0 B_0 P_0 A_0$						70
9	WRITE CITY AND STATE	5	$A_0 B_0 G_0 A_1 B_0 P_1$	R_3	$A_0 B_0 P_0 A_0$						40
	OF CUSTOMER	6	$A_0 B_0 G_0 A_1 B_0 P_1$	R_{16}	$A_0 B_0 P_0 A_0$						180
		7	$A_0 B_0 G_0 A_1 B_0 P_1$	R_3	$A_0 B_0 P_0 A_0$						40
		8	$A_0 B_0 G_0 A_1 B_0 P_1$	R_{32}	$A_0 B_0 P_0 A_0$						330
10	WRITE INITIALS ON	9	$A_0 B_0 G_0 A_1 B_0 P_1$	R_{16}	$A_0 B_0 P_0 A_0$						170
	DUPLICATE BILL (2	10	$A_0 B_0 G_0 A_1 B_0 P_1$	R_3	$A_1 B_0 P_0 A_0$						70
			A	B	G	A	B	P		A	B	P	A		
	LETTERS) AND ASIDE		A	B	G	A	B	P		A	B	P	A		
			A	B	G	A	B	P		A	B	P	A		
	PEN		A	B	G	A	B	P		A	B	P	A		

TIME = **.834**   minutes (min.)   **1390**

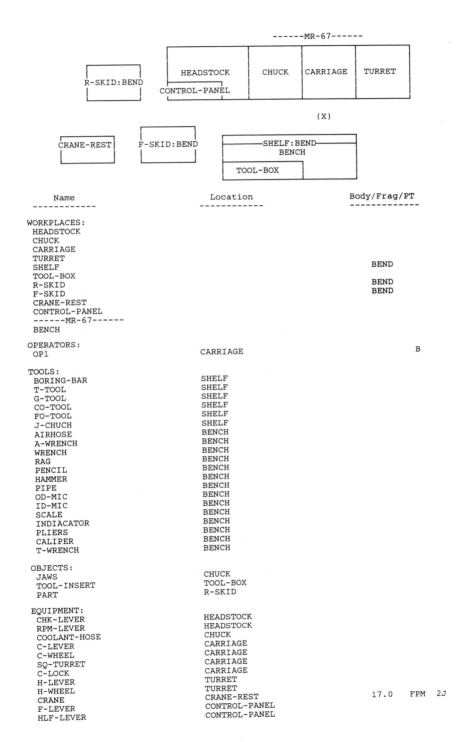

```
                            ------MR-67------

                 ┌──────────┬──────┬──────────┬────────┐
  ┌────────────┐ │ HEADSTOCK│ CHUCK│ CARRIAGE │ TURRET │
  │R-SKID:BEND │ ├──────────┤      │          │        │
  └────────────┘ │CONTROL-PANEL    │          │        │
                 └──────────┴──────┴──────────┴────────┘

                                          (X)

  ┌────────────┐ ┌────────────┐ ┌──────────────────────┐
  │ CRANE-REST │ │F-SKID:BEND │ │──────SHELF:BEND───────│
  └────────────┘ └────────────┘ │        BENCH          │
                                 ├──────────────┐        │
                                 │  TOOL-BOX    │        │
                                 └──────────────┴────────┘
```

Name	Location	Body/Frag/PT
WORKPLACES:		
HEADSTOCK		
CHUCK		
CARRIAGE		
TURRET		
SHELF		BEND
TOOL-BOX		
R-SKID		BEND
F-SKID		BEND
CRANE-REST		
CONTROL-PANEL		
------MR-67------		
BENCH		
OPERATORS:		
OP1	CARRIAGE	B
TOOLS:		
BORING-BAR	SHELF	
T-TOOL	SHELF	
G-TOOL	SHELF	
CO-TOOL	SHELF	
FO-TOOL	SHELF	
J-CHUCH	SHELF	
AIRHOSE	BENCH	
A-WRENCH	BENCH	
WRENCH	BENCH	
RAG	BENCH	
PENCIL	BENCH	
HAMMER	BENCH	
PIPE	BENCH	
OD-MIC	BENCH	
ID-MIC	BENCH	
SCALE	BENCH	
INDIACATOR	BENCH	
PLIERS	BENCH	
CALIPER	BENCH	
T-WRENCH	BENCH	
OBJECTS:		
JAWS	CHUCK	
TOOL-INSERT	TOOL-BOX	
PART	R-SKID	
EQUIPMENT:		
CHK-LEVER	HEADSTOCK	
RPM-LEVER	HEADSTOCK	
COOLANT-HOSE	CHUCK	
C-LEVER	CARRIAGE	
C-WHEEL	CARRIAGE	
SQ-TURRET	CARRIAGE	
C-LOCK	CARRIAGE	
H-LEVER	TURRET	
H-WHEEL	TURRET	
CRANE	CRANE-REST	17.0 FPM 2J
F-LEVER	CONTROL-PANEL	
HLF-LEVER	CONTROL-PANEL	

Basic MOST.   Work area—horizontal turret lathe.   (*Continues*)

From	To	Steps
HEADSTOCK	CHUCK	2
HEADSTOCK	CARRIAGE	4
HEADSTOCK	TURRET	6
HEADSTOCK	SHELF	3
HEADSTOCK	TOOL-BOX	3
HEADSTOCK	R-SKID	4
HEADSTOCK	F-SKID	4
HEADSTOCK	CRANE-REST	6
HEADSTOCK	CONTROL-PANEL	0
HEADSTOCK	------MR-67------	0
HEADSTOCK	BENCH	3
CHUCK	CARRIAGE	2
CHUCK	TURRET	5
CHUCK	SHELF	3
CHUCK	TOOL-BOX	3
CHUCK	R-SKID	6
CHUCK	F-SKID	6
CHUCK	CRANE-REST	8
CHUCK	CONTROL-PANEL	2
CHUCK	------MR-67------	0
CHUCK	BENCH	3
CARRIAGE	TURRET	4
CARRIAGE	SHELF	3
CARRIAGE	TOOL-BOX	3
CARRIAGE	R-SKID	7
CARRIAGE	F-SKID	7
CARRIAGE	CRANE-REST	10
CARRIAGE	CONTROL-PANEL	4
CARRIAGE	------MR-67------	0
CARRIAGE	BENCH	3
TURRET	SHELF	3
TURRET	TOOL-BOX	3
TURRET	R-SKID	9
TURRET	F-SKID	9
TURRET	CRANE-REST	12
TURRET	CONTROL-PANEL	6
TURRET	------MR-67------	0
TURRET	BENCH	3
SHELF	TOOL-BOX	0
SHELF	R-SKID	6
SHELF	F-SKID	6
SHELF	CRANE-REST	7
SHELF	CONTROL-PANEL	3
SHELF	------MR-67------	0
SHELF	BENCH	0
TOOL-BOX	R-SKID	6
TOOL-BOX	F-SKID	6
TOOL-BOX	CRANE-REST	7
TOOL-BOX	CONTROL-PANEL	3
TOOL-BOX	------MR-67------	0
TOOL-BOX	BENCH	0
R-SKID	F-SKID	4
R-SKID	CRANE-REST	4
R-SKID	CONTROL-PANEL	5
R-SKID	------MR-67------	0
R-SKID	BENCH	6
F-SKID	CRANE-REST	2
F-SKID	CONTROL-PANEL	4
F-SKID	------MR-67------	0
F-SKID	BENCH	6
CRANE-REST	CONTROL-PANEL	6
CRANE-REST	------MR-67------	0
CRANE-REST	BENCH	7
CONTROL-PANEL	------MR-67------	0
CONTROL-PANEL	BENCH	3
------MR-67------	BENCH	0

Basic MOST. Work area—horizontal turret lathe (*continued*).

```
42. LOAD PART IN 3 JAW CHUCK AT HORIZONTAL TURRET LATHE
    PER PART OFG: 2 12-APR-83
              SMALL PART
    OP1 BEGINS AT BENCH

  1 GRASP WORKPIECE FROM BENCH AND HOLD
                    A1  B0  G1  A0  B0  P0  A0      1.00      20.
  2 AIRCLEAN CHUCK 1 SQ.FT. USING AIR-HOSE AT HEADSTOCK AND RETURN TO
    HEADSTOCK
       A6  B0  G1  A3  B0  P1  S6  A3  B0  P1  A0   1.00     210.
  3 PLACE CHUCK-WRENCH FROM HEADSTOCK TO CHUCK
                    A1  B0  G1  A3  B0  P3  A0      1.00      80.
  4 HOLD+PLACE WORKPIECE FROM OP1 TO CHUCK
                    A0  B0  G0  A1  B0  P3  A0      1.00      40.
  5 HOLD+FASTEN CHUCK 3 ARM-STROKES USING CHUCK-WRENCH AT HEADSTOCK AND
    RETURN TO HEADSTOCK AND INSERT SIMO 4 5 6
       A0  B0  G0  <A3  B0  P3  >F16  A3  B0  P1  A0  1.00    200.
  6 SLIDE LEVER AT CHUCK FOR STARTING SPINDLE
                    A3  B0  G1  M3  X0  I0  A0      1.00      70.
  7 SLIDE SAFETY SHIELD AT CHUCK OVER WORKPIECE AND RETURN TO CARRIAGE
                    A1  B0  G1  M3  X0  I0  A3      1.00      80.


                                    TOTAL TMU          700.
```

Basic MOST.   Analysis—horizontal turret lathe.

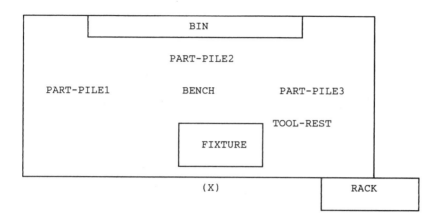

(*above and facing page*) Mini MOST.   Work area—assembly bench.

```
280. INSERT 2-LEAD COMPONENT ON BOARD WITH PLIERS AT BENCH
     PER COMPONENT OFG: 2 27-JUL-87
              MINIMOST SUBOP. FREQ. = # OF COMPONENTS PER BD. VALID FOR
     JUMPERS OR AXIALS THAT REQUIRE PLACEMENT WITH PLIERS. USE LN1 TO
     GET/ASIDE PLIERS
     OP BEGINS AT FIXTURE

     1 LH CONTACT AND PUSH UP COMPONENT. AT PART-PILE1
                        A10 B0   G3   M3   X0   I0   A0        1.00      16.
     2 RH HOLD AND PLACE PLIERS. FROM TOOL-REST TO AXIAL AT PART-PILE1 SIMO
        1 2 3
                        <A10B0   G0  >A6   B0   P6   A0        1.00      12.
     3 RH HOLD AND POSITION ACCURATE DIFFICULT ENTER AXIAL FROM SELF TO
       BOARD. AT FIXTURE WITH EYE-MOTION
                        A0   B0   G0   A10  B10  P32  A0       1.00      52.


                                              TOTAL TMU             80.
```

Mini MOST.   Analysis—assembly bench.

Name	Location	Frag/PT
------------	------------	--------------

WORKPLACES:
 BENCH
 BIN
 PART-PILE2
 PART-PILE1
 PART-PILE3
 FIXTURE
 TOOL-REST
 RACK

OPERATORS:		
OP	FIXTURE	B
LH	FIXTURE	
RH	FIXTURE	
LF	FIXTURE	
RF	FIXTURE	

TOOLS:	
PLIERS	TOOL-REST
SOLDERING-STICK	TOOL-REST
SCREWDRIVER	TOOL-REST
NUTDRIVER	TOOL-REST

OBJECTS:	
COMPONENTS	BIN
HARDWARE	BIN
BOARD	FIXTURE

From	To	Inches
------------	------------	---------
BENCH	BIN	0
BENCH	PART-PILE2	0
BENCH	PART-PILE1	0
BENCH	PART-PILE3	0
BENCH	FIXTURE	0
BENCH	TOOL-REST	0
BENCH	RACK	30
BIN	PART-PILE2	14
BIN	PART-PILE1	14
BIN	PART-PILE3	14
BIN	FIXTURE	24
BIN	TOOL-REST	14
BIN	RACK	30
PART-PILE2	PART-PILE1	8
PART-PILE2	PART-PILE3	8
PART-PILE2	FIXTURE	14
PART-PILE2	TOOL-REST	10
PART-PILE2	RACK	23
PART-PILE1	PART-PILE3	8
PART-PILE1	FIXTURE	14
PART-PILE1	TOOL-REST	8
PART-PILE1	RACK	15
PART-PILE3	FIXTURE	14
PART-PILE3	TOOL-REST	8
PART-PILE3	RACK	30
FIXTURE	TOOL-REST	14
FIXTURE	RACK	30
TOOL-REST	RACK	15

```
        ┌─────────────┐      ┌────────────────┬─────────┐
        │  TOOL-AREA  │      │  STORAGE-AREA  │  PARTS  │
        └─────────────┘      └────────────────┴─────────┘


                        ┌─────────────────┐   ┌──────────────────────┐
                        └TEAR-D-AREA──────┘   │                      │
                        └─TEAR-D-AREA──┘  (X) │     WORK-BENCH        │
                                              │                      │
                                              └──────────────────────┘
   ┌────────────────────┐
   │  RECEIVING-AREA    │
   └────────────────────┘
```

(*above and facing page*) Maxi MOST.   Work area—motor repair shop.


```
28. REMOVE BEARING FROM ONE END WITH TYPE VII BEARING PULLER AT MOTOR
        REPAIR SHOP 51A
    PER MOTOR OFG: 1 24-MAR-83
          BM # 03
      OP BEGINS AT TEAR-D-AREA

    1 MOVE BEARING PULLER BOX FROM PARTS TO TEAR-D-AREA
                                A3  B0  P1      1.00      400.
    2 MANIPULATE 2 FLAPS ON BOX FROM TEAR-D-AREA TO TEAR-D-AREA WITH
        ADJUSTMENT
                                A0  B0  P6      1.00      600.
    3 DISASSEMBLE 4 NUTS 3 / 4 IN DIA TO-OPEN CLAM SHELL USING WRENCH AND
        ASIDE ; 3 STEPS
                                A1  B0  T42     1.00     4300.
    4 PLACE CLAM-SHELL ON TO SHAFT WITH ADJUSTMENT ( INCLUDES CLOSING CLAM
        SHELL )
                                A0  B0  P3      1.00      300.
    5 ASSEMBLE 4 NUTS 3 / 4 IN DIA AT CLAM-SHELL USING WRENCH AND ASIDE
                                A0  B0  T42     1.00     4200.
    6 PLACE 2 OBJECTS : EXTENSION-ARM AND ARM WASHERS ON TO CLAM-SHELL WITH
        ADJUSTMENT
                                A0  B0  P3      1.00      300.
    7 TURN EYE BOLT AT EXTENSION-ARM 5 WRIST-TURNS USING HAND F 6
                                A0  B0  T3      6.00     1800.
    8 POSITION 3 OBJECTS : JACKING STUD , WASHER AND STRONG BACK ON TO
        EXTENSION-ARM WITH ADJUSTMENT ; 3 STEPS
                                A1  B0  P6      1.00      700.
    9 PLACE 4 OBJECTS : 2 NUTS AND 2 WASHERS ON TO EXTENSION-ARM
                                A0  B0  P3      1.00      300.
   10 TURN NUTS AT EXTENSION-ARM 17 ARM-TURNS USING HAND F 2
                                A0  B0  T6      2.00     1200.
   11 ADJUST 2 NUTS 1 IN DIA AT EXTENSION-ARM USING WRENCH AND ASIDE ;
        BEND
                                A0  B1  T16     1.00     1700.
   12 PLACE SOFT CENTER FROM TEAR-D-AREA IN TO STUD ; BEND
                                A0  B1  P1      1.00      200.
   13 ASSEMBLE 1 JACKING STUD 1 IN DIA USING HAND
                                A0  B0  T6      1.00      600.
   14 PLACE STUD WRENCH ON TO STUD WITH ADJUSTMENT
                                A0  B0  P3      1.00      300.
   15 ADJUST-LONG 1 JACKING NUT 1 IN DIA 4 IN USING WRENCH AND ASIDE
                                A0  B0  T42     1.00     4200.
   16 PLACE 2 OBJECTS : BEARING AND PULLER FROM SHAFT TO WORK-BENCH
                                A1  B0  P1      1.00      200.
   17 PLACE 2 : BEARING AND PULLER FROM SHAFT TO PARTS-PAN WITH ADJUSTMENT
        ( INCLUDES TAGGING )
                                A1  B0  P3      1.00      400.


                                TOTAL TMU       21700.
```

Maxi MOST.   Analysis—motor repair shop.

```
WORKPLACES:
 TOOL-AREA
 STORAGE-AREA
 PARTS
 WORK-BENCH
 TEAR-D-AREA
 RECEIVING-AREA


OPERATORS:
 OP                        TEAR-D-AREA                              B


TOOLS:
 HAMMER                    TOOL-AREA
 MALLET                    TOOL-AREA
 WRENCH                    TOOL-AREA
 RATCHET                   TOOL-AREA
 PUNCH                     TOOL-AREA
 JACK                      TOOL-AREA
 V-BLOCK                   TOOL-AREA
 SCREWDRIVER               TOOL-AREA


OBJECTS:
 TABLE                     TEAR-D-AREA
 BOLTS                     TEAR-D-AREA
 COVER                     TEAR-D-AREA
 GASKET                    TEAR-D-AREA
 SHAFT                     TEAR-D-AREA
 ROTOR                     TEAR-D-AREA
 STATOR                    TEAR-D-AREA
 CLAM-SHELL                TEAR-D-AREA
 EXTENSION-ARM             TEAR-D-AREA
 COUPLING-PULLER           TEAR-D-AREA
 TAG                       TEAR-D-AREA
 MOTOR                     RECEIVING-AREA


EQUIPMENT:
 ELECTRIC-HOISST           RECEIVING-AREA                      10B
```

From	To	Steps
TOOL-AREA	STORAGE-AREA	0
TOOL-AREA	PARTS	0
TOOL-AREA	WORK-BENCH	0
TOOL-AREA	TEAR-D-AREA	5
TOOL-AREA	RECEIVING-AREA	0
STORAGE-AREA	PARTS	0
STORAGE-AREA	WORK-BENCH	0
STORAGE-AREA	TEAR-D-AREA	7
STORAGE-AREA	RECEIVING-AREA	0
PARTS	WORK-BENCH	0
PARTS	TEAR-D-AREA	9
PARTS	RECEIVING-AREA	0
WORK-BENCH	TEAR-D-AREA	4
WORK-BENCH	RECEIVING-AREA	0
TEAR-D-AREA	RECEIVING-AREA	10

appendix C

Data Cards

Basic MOST® System

INDEX X 10	A — ACTION DISTANCE		B — BODY MOTION	
	PARAMETER VARIANT	KEYWORD	PARAMETER VARIANT	KEYWORD
0	≤ 2 in. ≤ 5 cm.	CLOSE		
1	Within reach			
3	1 - 2 steps	1 STEP 2 STEPS	Bend and arise 50 % occ.	PBEND
6	3 - 4 steps	3 STEPS 4 STEPS	Bend and arise	BEND
10	5 - 7 steps	5 STEPS 6 STEPS 7 STEPS	Sit or stand	SIT STAND
16	8 - 10 steps	8 STEPS 9 STEPS 10 STEPS	Through Door Climb on or off Stand and bend Bend and sit	DOOR CLIMB / DESCEND STAND AND BEND BEND AND SIT

General Move data card.   (Fig. 3.1, pp. 30–31)

A B G A B P A					GENERAL MOVE

G		P		INDEX X 10
GAIN CONTROL		PLACEMENT		
PARAMETER VARIANT	KEYWORD	PARAMETER VARIANT	KEYWORD	
		Hold Toss	THROW TOSS CARRY PICKUP	0
Light object Light objects simo	GRASP (optional)	Lay aside Loose fit	MOVE PUT	1
Non Simo Obstructed Heavy / Bulky Interlocked Blind Collect Disengage	GET DISENGAGE FREE COLLECT	Adjustments Light pressure Double placement	PLACE REPLACE	3
		Care Precision Blind Obstructed Heavy pressure Intermediate moves	POSITION REPOSITION	6
				10
				16

Basic MOST® System   A B G M X I A   **CONTROLLED MOVE**

INDEX X 10	MOVE CONTROLLED (M)		CRANK (REVS.)	PROCESS TIME (X)			ALIGNMENT (I)		INDEX X 10
	PUSH / PULL / PIVOT	KEYWORD		SECONDS	MINUTES	HOURS	OBJECT	KEYWORD	
1	≦ 12 Inches (30 cm) Button/Switch/Knob	PUSH PULL ROTATE		.5	.01	.0001	To 1 Point	ALIGN - POINT	**1**
3	>12 Inches (30 cm) Resistance Seat or Unseat High Control 2 Stages ≦ 12 Inches (30 cm)	SLIDE SEAT TURN UNSEAT OPEN SHIFT SHUT PRESS PUSH + PULL (INCHES,CM. OR STAGES)	1	1.5	.02	.0004	To 2 Points ≦ 4 Inches (10 cm)	ALIGN - POINTS CLOSE	**3**
6	2 Stages >12 Inches (30cm) With 1 - 2 Steps	OPEN + SHUT OPERATE PUSH OR PULL WITH 1 or 2 PACES	3	2.5	.04	.0007	To 2 Points >4 Inches (10 cm)	ALIGN - POINTS	**6**
10	3 - 4 Stages With 3 - 5 Steps	MANIPULATE MANEUVER PUSH OR PULL WITH 3, 4 or 5 PACES	6	4.5	.07	.0012			**10**
16	With 6 - 9 Steps	PUSH OR PULL WITH 6, 7, 8 or 9 PACES	11	7.0	.11	.0019	Precision	ALIGN -PRECISION	**16**

Controlled Move data card. (Fig. 3.10, p. 54)

Basic MOST® System — **FASTEN (F) or LOOSEN (L)** — **TOOL USE**

Index X 10	Finger Action	Wrist Action				Arm Action				Tool Action	Index X 10
	SPINS	TURNS	STROKES	CRANKS	TAPS	TURNS	STROKES	CRANKS	STRIKES	SCREW DIAMETER	
	Fingers, Screw-driver	Hand, Screw-driver, Ratchet, T-Wrench	Wrench, Allen Key	Wrench, Allen Key, Ratchet	Hand, Hammer	Ratchet	Wrench, Allen Key	Wrench, Allen Key, Ratchet	Hand, Hammer	Power Wrench	
1	1	-	-	-	1	-	-	-	-	-	1
3	2	1	1	1	3	1	1	-	1	1/4" (6 mm)	3
6	3	3	2	3	6	2	-	1	3	1" (25 mm)	6
10	8	5	3	5	10	4	2	2	5		10
16	16	9	5	8	16	6	3	3	8		16
24	25	13	8	11	23	9	4	5	12		24
32	35	17	10	15	30	12	6	6	16		32
42	47	23	13	20	39	15	8	8	21		42
54	61	29	17	25	50	20	10	11	27		54

Tool Use data card for Fasten or Loosen. (Fig. 3.19, p. 73)

Basic MOST® System — Cut(C), Surface Treat(S), Measure(M), Record(R), Think(T) — TOOL USE

INDEX X10	Activity (Pliers)	CUT (Scissors) CUT(S)	SLICE (Knife) SLICE(S)	AIR-CLEAN (Nozzle) SQ.FT. (0.1M²)	BRUSH-CLEAN (Brush) SQ.FT. (0.1M²)	WIPE (Cloth) SQ.FT. (0.1M²)	MEASURE (Measuring Device) IN.(CM) FT.(M)	WRITE (Pencil) DIGITS	WRITE (Pencil) WORDS	MARK (Marker) DIGITS	INSPECT (Eyes, Fingers) POINTS	READ (Eyes) DIGITS, SINGLE WORDS	READ (Eyes) TEXT OF WORDS	INDEX X10
1	GRIP	1	·	·	·	·		1	·	CHECK MARK	1	1	3	1
3	SOFT	2	1	·	·	1/2		2	·	1 SCRIBE LINE	3	3	8	3
6	MEDIUM	4		1 SPOT POINT CAVITY	1 SMALL OBJECT	·		4	1	2	5 TOUCH FOR HEAT	6 SCALE VALUE DATE/TIME	15	6
10	HARD	7	3	·	·	1	PROFILE-GAUGE	6	·	3	9 FEEL FOR DEFECT	12	24	10
16	BEND-COTTER PIN	11	4	3	2	2	FIXED SCALE / CALIPER 12 IN (30CM)	9	2 SIGNATURE, DATE	5		VERNIER-SCALE	38 TABLE VALUE	16
24		15	6	4	3	·	FEELER-GAUGE	13	3	7			54 TABLE VALUE	24
32		20	9	7	5	5	STEEL-TAPE 6 FT. (2M) / DEPTH MICROMETER	18	4	10			72	32
42		27	11	10	7	7	OD-MICROMETER 4 IN. (10CM)	23	5	13			94	42
54		33			7	7	ID-MICROMETER 4 IN. (10CM)	29	7	16			119	54

Left-column activity labels for the Cut (Pliers) section: TWIST BEND, TWIST BEND-LOOP, BEND-COTTER PIN; Pliers CUTOFF column = WIRE.

Tool Use data card for cutting, cleaning, gauging, reading, writing, and other activities. (Fig. 3.20, p. 74)

Basic MOST® System

A T K F V L V P T A

MANUAL CRANE

INDEX X 10	A ACTION DISTANCE STEPS	T / L TRANSPORTATION UP TO 2 TON FEET (M)		K HOOK-UP AND UNHOOK	F FREE OBJECT	V VERTICAL MOVE INCHES (CM)	P PLACEMENT	INDEX X 10
		EMPTY	LOADED					
3	2				Without direction change	9 (20)	Without direction change	3
6	4				With single direction change	15 (40)	Align with one hand	6
10	7	5 (1.5)	5 (1.5)		With double direction change	30 (75)	Align with two hands	10
16	10	13 (4)	12 (3.5)		With one or more direction changes, care in handling or apply pressure	45 (115)	Align and place with one adjustment	16
24	15	20 (6)	18 (5.5)	Single or double hook		60 (150)	Align and place with several adjustments	24
32	20	30 (9)	26 (8)	Sling			Align and place with several adjustments + apply pressure	32
42	26	40 (12)	35 (10)					42
54	33	50 (15)	45 (13)					54

Manual crane data card. (Fig. 3.27, p. 103)

Mini MOST® System   A B G A B P A   GENERAL MOVE

INDEX ×1	A — ACTION DISTANCE			B	G	P	INDEX ×1
	HAND Inches (cm)	HAND Degrees	LEG Inches (cm)	BODY MOTION	GAIN CONTROL	PLACEMENT	
0	1 (2.5)	30			SWEEP	DROP, PICK UP, KEEP	0
1	2 (5)	60					1
3	4 (10)	120	8 (20)		CONTACT (hand or foot)	TOSS / SET AND RETAIN	3
6	8 (20)	180	12 (30)		GRASP REGRASP	SET ASIDE; SET AND SLIDE; PLACE	6
10	14 (35)		18 (45) 1 STEP	EYE-MOTION	TRANSFER SELECT	POSITION	10
16	24 (60)		26 (65)		DISENGAGE SELECT-SMALL	ORIENT	16
24	>24 (60)		>26 (65) 2 STEPS				24
32				BEND ARISE			32

NOTES:

(1) When hand reaches more than 8 inches (20 cm) to an object in a fixed location or to the other hand, use the next lower index value

(1) ENW = Effective Weight (max. 2.5 lbs., 1 kg.)

(2) For an ENW of 2.6 - 10.0 lbs. (1 - 5 kgs.) use the next higher index value accept for "Grasp"

(1) For accurate positioning (ACCURATE) or difficult handling (DIFFICULT) or insertion 1/8"-1" (.3-2.5 cm) (ENTER, INSERT) use the next *higher* index value.

(2) For binding or applying pressure go up two index values per occurence (BIND, DOUBLE BIND).

(3) For insertions > 1" (2.5 cm) use an *additional* Controlled Move Sequence Model.

General Move Sequence Model data card.   (Fig. 4.4, p. 134)

Mini MOST® System   **A B G M X I A**   **CONTROLLED MOVE**

INDEX X 1	M — MOVE CONTROLLED					X — PROCESS TIME	I — ALIGNMENT		INDEX X 1
	PUSH, PULL, SLIDE, ROTATE			SMALL CRANK, CRANK			TO POINT OR LINE		
	HAND		FOOT OR LEG	SMALL-CRANK ≤ 5 INCHES (13 cm)	CRANK ≤ 20 INCHES (50 cm)		WITHIN AREA OF NORMAL VISION	OUTSIDE AREA OF NORMAL VISION	
	INCHES (cm)	DEGREES	INCHES (cm)	REVOLUTIONS	REVOLUTIONS	TMU			
0									0
1	1 (2.5) BUTTON					1.7			1
3		90				4.2			3
6	4 (10)					7.7	ALIGN, CHECK INSPECT		6
10	10 (25)	180	10 (25)			12.6	ALIGN-ACCURATE ALIGN-POINTS		10
16	18 (45) SEAT, UNSEAT		16 (40) FOOT-PRESS	1		19.6	ALIGN-POINTS-ACCURATE	ALIGN-OUT, CHECK-OUT INSPECT-OUT	16
24	30 (75)		22 (55)		1	27.7		ALIGN-ACCURATE-OUT ALIGN-POINTS-OUT	24
32			30 (75)	2		36.6		ALIGN-POINTS-ACCURATE-OUT	32
42				3	2	47.6			42
54				4	3	60.1			54

Controlled Move Sequence Model data card.   (Fig. 4.5, p. 155)

Maxi MOST® System				A - ACTION DISTANCE
INDEX X 100	SEGMENTED WALKING	STRAIGHT WALKING		INDEX X 100
	STEPS	FEET	METERS	
0	2	6	2	0
1	9	24	7	1
3	23	60	18	3
6	42	120	36	6
10	70	190	60	10
16	108	300	90	16
24	153	420	130	24
32	203	550	170	32
42	264	720	220	42
54	333	920	280	54
67	408	1120	340	67
81	489	1350	410	81
96	578	1590	490	96
113	675	1860	570	113
131	784	2160	670	131
152	901	2480	770	152
173	1023	2820	870	173
196	1153	3170	980	196

Action Distance data card.   (Fig. 5.8, p. 192)

Maxi MOST® System

B - BODY MOTIONS

INDEX X 100	ONE OR TWO WAY BODY MOTION	PASS THROUGH OPENINGS	COMBINATIONS OCCURRING IN SEQUENCE	LADDER		OBSTR-LADDER		INDEX X 100
				LIGHT LOAD	HEAVY LOAD	LIGHT LOAD	HEAVY LOAD	
				NUMBER OF RUNGS				
1	1 OR 2 BENDS KNEEL SIT STAND CLIMB	DOOR HATCH	BEND + SIT STAND + BEND					1
3	SIT + STAND CRAWL CREEP 2 KNEELS 2 CLIMBS 3 BENDS CLIMB - OBJECT ON FLOOR	2 DOORS 2 HATCHES OP - DOOR MANHOLE	SIT + BENDS STAND + BENDS SIT + STAND + BENDS CLIMB + BENDS DOOR + BENDS HATCH + BENDS HATCH + ON - FLOOR 2 CLIMBS + BENDS	10	3	5		3
6	FLAT - CRAWL 2 ON - FLOOR	2 MANHOLES 2 OP - DOORS OBSTR - MANHOLE	2 DOORS + BENDS 2 HATCHES + BENDS 2 HATCHES + ON - FLOOR	25	8	20	6	6
10		2 OBSTR - MANHOLES		45	17	40	14	10
16					29		26	16
24					42		40	24

Body Motions data card.   (Fig. 5.10, p. 195)

Maxi MOST® System

INDEX X 100	GENERAL PART HANDLING — HANDLE PART(S) ONLY							GENERAL PART HANDLING — HANDLE PART(S) WITH ADJUSTMENT						
	SMALL PART(S)	SMALL LIGHT PART(S) OR MEDIUM SIZE AND WEIGHT		MEDIUM OR HEAVY WEIGHT	HEAVY, LARGE AND BULKY OR SPECIAL	HEAVY AND BULKY OR SPECIAL		SMALL PARTS	SMALL LIGHT PARTS OR MEDIUM SIZE AND WEIGHT		MEDIUM OR HEAVY WEIGHT	HEAVY, LARGE AND BULKY OR SPECIAL	HEAVY AND BULKY OR SPECIAL	
	GRASP OR HOLD + MOVE	COLLECT + MOVE	MOVE	PLACE	POSITION	SITUATE	MANIPULATE	GRASP OR HOLD + MOVE	COLLECT + MOVE	MOVE	PLACE	POSITION	SITUATE	MANIPULATE
	NUMBER OF ACTIONS			NUMBER OF OBJECTS				NUMBER OF ACTIONS			NUMBER OF OBJECTS			
1	2	2	3	2	1			2		1				
3		8	10	6	3	2	1		6	7	4	2	1	
6		17		6	4	2			15	16	10	5	3	2
10				10	7	4						10	7	3
16					12	6							11	6

Part Handling data card.   (Fig. 5.11, pp. 200–201)

						P - PART HANDLING
MOVE OBJECT(S) ON SURFACE				LINE HANDLING		
MOVE ONLY		MOVE AND ADJUST		HANDLE		
LIGHT WEIGHT CART, CONVEYOR TABLE	MEDIUM OR HEAVY WEIGHT RAILS, TABLE CONVEYOR	LIGHT WEIGHT CART, CONVEYOR TABLE	MEDIUM OR HEAVY WEIGHT RAILS, TABLE CONVEYOR	STRAIGHT	INTO HAND OR ON FLOOR	INDEX X 100
PUSH OR PULL	SLIDE	PUSH OR PULL	SLIDE	TUGS	COILS	
DISTANCE IN FEET (M)				NUMBER OF TUGS / COILS		
8 (2.5)	3 (1)			2	1	**1**
29 (9)	13 (4)	21 (6.5)	10 (3)	8	3	**3**
58 (17.5)	28 (8.5)	50 (15)	24 (7.5)	16	7	**6**
99 (30)	48 (14.5)	91 (28)	45 (14)	28	13	**10**
157 (48)	78 (24)	150 (46)	74 (22.5)	44	21	**16**

Maxi MOST® Systems										
					VERNIER CALIPER			MICRO-METER		
INDEX X 100	FLAT-RULE OR SCALE	TAPE-RULE	FOLDING WOOD-RULE	PROFILE GAUGE	12" (30 cm)	36" (90 cm)	FEELER-GAUGE	4" (10 cm)	36" (90 cm)	RING-GAUGE
3	2	1		3	2		1			1
6	3	2	3	5	3	1	2	1	1	2
10	6	3	7	10	6	2	4	2		3
16	10	6	14	15	10	3	7	4	3	5
24		8	21		15	5	10	5	4	8
32						7		7	5	11
42						9			7	
54						12			9	
67									11	

Maxi MOST—Tool Use data card: Measuring Tools.   (Fig. 5.19, pp. 232–233)

MEASURING TOOLS											T - TOOL USE	
PLUG GAUGE		THREAD GAUGE		SQUARE	SET TO MEASURE			SNAP-GAUGE	DIAL INDICATOR	TAPER GAUGE	DEVICE	INDEX X 100
1" (25 mm)	8" (200 mm)	4" (100 mm)	8" (200 mm)		TELESCOPE GAUGE	CALIPER SPRING-JOINT	CALIPER FIRM-JOINT	16" (400 mm)				
2				2	1			2				3
3	1	1		4	2	1	1	5		1	Telescope Gauge Firm Joint Calipers 12" (30 cm) Vernier Calipers 36" (90 cm) Vernier Calipers	6
6		2		7	3	2		9			Combination Square Bevel Protractor 4" (10 cm)	10
10	3	4	1	11	5	4	2	14	1	2	4" (10 cm) Micrometer Spring Joint Caliper 36" (90 cm)	16
15	4	6	2		8	6	3			4	36" (90 cm) Micrometer	24
	5	8			10	8	5		2	5		32
	7	10	3			11	6			7		42
	9		4				8		3	8		54
			5				10		4	10		67

Maxi MOST® System — ASSEMBLE OR DISASSEMBLE STANDARD THREADED FASTENER(S) COMPLETE — T - TOOL USE

NUMBER OF FASTENERS

THREAD DIAMETER (UP TO) INDEX X 100	SCREWDRIVER MACHINE SCREW ALL	SCREWDRIVER SHEET-METAL SCREW ALL	WRENCH 3/4" (20 mm)	WRENCH 1-1/2" (40 mm)	WRENCH >1-1/2" (>40 mm)	RATCHET 3/4" (20 mm)	RATCHET 1-1/2" (40 mm)	POWER TOOL 1/4" (6 mm)	POWER TOOL 1" (25 mm)	POWER TOOL >1" (>25 mm)	POWER TOOL START ONLY N/A	HAND RUN DOWN LOOSE 1/4" (6 mm)	HAND RUN DOWN LOOSE 1" (25 mm)	HAND RUN DOWN LOOSE 1-1/2" (40 mm)	HAND RUN DOWN LOOSE >1-1/2" (>40 mm)	HAND TIGHT 1/4" (6 mm)	THREAD DIAMETER (UP TO) INDEX X 100
1											2						**1**
3	1										4	1					**3**
6	2	1				1		1	1	1	6	2	1			1	**6**
10	3	2				2		2	2		10	3	2		1	2	**10**
16	4	3	1			2	1	4	3	3		5	4	1	2	3	**16**
24	6	5	2	1	1	3	2	6	6	4		8	6	2	3	5	**24**
32	8	6	3	2		4	3	9	8	6		10	8	3	4	7	**32**
42		9	4	3	2	6	4	12	11	9			11	4	6	9	**42**
54	10	11	6	4	3	8	5			12				5	7	11	**54**
67			7			9								7	9		**67**
81			9	5		11	6							8	10		**81**

Maxi MOST—Tool Use data card for standard threaded fasteners. (Fig. 5.13, p. 210)

Maxi MOST®System	ADJUST STANDARD THREADED FASTENER(S)									T - TOOL USE
INDEX X 100	SCREWDRIVER	WRENCH			RATCHET		POWER TOOL			HAND	INDEX X 100
THREAD DIAMETER (UP TO)	ALL	3/4" (20 mm)	1-1/2" (40 mm)	>1-1/2" (>40 mm)	3/4" (20 mm)	1-1/2" (40 mm)	1/4" (6 mm)	1" (25 mm)	>1" (>25 mm)	1/4" (6 mm)	THREAD DIAMETER (UP TO)
1							1	1			1
3	1						5	3	2	2	3
6	3	1			1	1	10	7	3	4	6
10	6	2	1		2		17	12	6	7	10
16	9	3		1	4	2			10	10	16
24	13	4	3		5	3					24
32		6	4	2	7	5					32
42		8	5		10	6					42
54		10	6	3		8					54
67			8	4		10					67
81			9								81

Maxi MOST—Tool Use data card for Adjust Standard Threaded Fasteners. (Fig. 5.14, p. 215)

Maxi MOST® System		ASSEMBLE OR DISASSEMBLE LONG STANDARD THREADED FASTENER(S) COMPLETE										T - TOOL USE	
Index X 100	SCREWDRIVER		WRENCH			RATCHET			POWER TOOL				Index X 100
LENGTH	2"	4"	2"	4"		2"	4"		2"		4"		LENGTH
THREAD DIAMETER	ALL	ALL	3/4" (20 mm)	3/4" (20 mm)	>3/4" (>20 mm)	3/4" (20 mm)	3/4" (20 mm)	>3/4" (>20 mm)	1/4" (6 mm)	3/4" (20 mm)	1/4" (6 mm)	3/4" (20 mm)	THREAD DIAMETER
6									1	1	1	1	6
10	1								2	3		2	10
16									4	5	3	3	16
24	2	1		1		1			6	7	4	5	24
32	3		1					1	8	10	6	7	32
42	4	2			2				11		7	9	42
54	5					2	1	2			10	12	54
67	7	3	2	1	3								67
81	8	4				3		3					81
96	10	5	3	4			2						96
113		6			5	4		4					113

Maxi MOST—Tool Use data card for Long Standard Threaded Fasteners. (Fig. 5.15, p. 214)

Maxi MOST® System	ADJUST LONG STANDARD THREADED FASTENER(S)														T-TOOL USE
Index X 100	SCREWDRIVER		WRENCH				RATCHET				POWER TOOL				Index X 100
LENGTH	2"	4"	2"		4"		2"		4"		2"		4"		LENGTH
THREAD DIAMETER (UP TO)	ALL	ALL	3/4" (20 mm)	>3/4" (>20 mm)	3/4" (20 mm)	>3/4" (>20 mm)	3/4" (20 mm)	1 1/2" (40 mm)	3/4" (20 mm)	1 1/2" (40 mm)	1/4" (6 mm)	>1/4" (>6 mm)	1/4" (6 mm)	>1/4" (>6 mm)	THREAD DIAMETER (UP TO)
3											1	2		1	3
6	1										3	4	1	2	6
10	2										5	7	3	4	10
16		1						1			8	12	4	7	16
24	3				1						12		7	10	24
32	5	2					1	2		1		9			32
42	6		1			1						12			42
54	8	3			2		2	3	1	2					54
67	10	4			3			4							67
81		5	2			1	3	5		3					81

Maxi MOST—Tool Use data card for Adjust Long Standard Threaded Fasteners. (Fig. 5.16, p. 216)

Maxi MOST® System										GENERAL TOOLS I	
	TURN BY HAND			SHOVE OR DRAW		PRY	STRIKE				
				NO. OF ACTIONS		NO. OF ACTIONS	NUMBER OF BLOWS				
INDEX X 100	NUMBER OF ACTIONS		REVS.	HAND			HAND		HAMMER		MALLET	SLEDGE
	FINGER-TURNS	WRIST-TURNS	ARM-TURNS	NORMAL	HEAVY	PRY-BAR	WRIST-STROKES	ARM-STROKES	WRIST-STROKES	ARM-STROKES	ARM-STROKES	ARM-STROKES
1	3	4	2	6	1	3	10	5	17	4	3	
3	26	15	16	19	7	16	31	15	59	16	11	4
6	58	31	36		16	34		30		32	22	10
10	102	53	63			60					37	18
16												29
24												43

Maxi MOST—Tool Use data card: General Tools I.   (Fig. 5.17, pp. 218–219)

T-TOOL USE

APPLY MATERIAL WITH TOOL								INDEX X 100
SEAL-GUN	GREASE-GUN	SQUEEZE-BOTTLE	TUBE	FINGER, HAND, BRUSH, OR STICK	SQUIRT-CAN	AEROSOL CAN	TAPE-ROLL	
PULLS	LEVER-ACTIONS	DROP	1" SPOT (25 mm)	1" SPOT (25 mm)	SQUIRT	SQ. FT. (0.1 m²)	FOOT OR STRIP	
		1						**1**
1	4	7		2	8		1	**3**
5	14	16	6	6	20	1	3	**6**
11	28		16	12		3	5	**10**
19	48					6	8	**16**
28	72					9	12	**24**

Maxi MOST® System									
INDEX X 100	CLEAN SURFACE			CUT OR SLICE					TWIST OR BEND WITH PLIERS
	SQ. FT. (0,1 m²)			CUTS OR STROKES					
	AIR CLEAN	BRUSH CLEAN	WIPE	PLIERS			SCISSORS	KNIFE	LOOPS
				SOFT	MEDIUM	HARD			
1				2	1		3	1	1
3	4	3	2	6	4	2	16	7	4
6	11	9	8	12	8	5	35	16	8
10	23	16	15		14	9		27	15
16	39	27	25			15			
24	57	40	37						
32		53	51						
42									
54									

Maxi MOST—Tool Use data card: General Tools II. (Fig. 5.18, pp. 224–225)

GENERAL TOOLS II **T - TOOL USE**

WRITE / MARKER / CHARACTER OR MARK / SIZE		MARK / HAMMER & DIE	THINK / INSPECT	THINK / READ	DEBURR WITH FILE	FREE TOOL WITH DRIFT PIN	TAP OR THREAD BY HAND / NO. OCCURRENCES / DIAMETER		WAIT OR PROCESS TIME		INDEX X 100
1" (25 mm)	3" (75 mm)	LETTER OR FIGURE	POINTS	WORD OR VALUE	FEET	NO. TOOLS	5/16" (8 mm)	3/4" (20 mm)	SEC.	MIN.	
			2	4					3.5		**1**
9	5	1	7	13	1	2			11		**3**
23	13	4	13		2	6			22		**6**
41	24	7			3	10			36		**10**
	40	12			5	16	1		58	1	**16**
		17			8			1			**24**
		23			11					2	**32**
							2				**42**
							3	2		3	**54**

Maxi MOST® System — **OPERATE MACHINE CONTROLS** — **M - MACHINE HANDLING**

INDEX X 100	BUTTON OR SWITCH	LEVER 1 OR 2 STAGES	LEVER DIFFICULT 3 OR 4 STAGES	CRANK	KNOB	HAND WHEEL NORMAL WHEEL	HAND WHEEL HEAVY WHEEL	CHANGE TOOL TYPE OF DEVICE	INDEX X 100
	NO. OF CONTROLS	NO. OF CONTROLS	NO. OF CONTROLS	NO. OF REVS.	NO. OF ACTIONS	NO. OF ACTIONS	NO. OF ACTIONS	TYPE OF DEVICE	
1	4	2	1	2	4	3	1	Quick Change Post	1
3	12	7	3	16	17	11	4		3
6		13	6	36	34	23	9	Jacobs Chuck	6
10			10	53			16	Carbide Insert	10
16									16

Maxi MOST—Machine Handling data card: Operate Machine Controls.   (Fig. 5.20, p. 236)

Maxi MOST® System — **SECURE OR RELEASE PARTS** — **M - MACHINE HANDLING**

INDEX X 100	OPEN OR CLOSE	INSTALL OR REMOVE LATHE DOG	OPEN OR CLOSE VISE	ENGAGE OR DISENGAGE TAIL STOCK CENTER	INSTALL OR REMOVE JACK SCREW	INSTALL OR REMOVE C-CLAMP	TIGHTEN OR LOOSEN PART IN FIXTURE — WITH WRENCH	BY HAND	WITH CAM OR ECCENTRIC CLAMP	CLAMP OR UNCLAMP PART ON BED — CLAMP AND NUT REMAIN ON STUD OR RELIEVE STRAIN	CLAMP AND NUT REMOVED FROM STUD	INDEX X 100
					NUMBER OF DEVICES					NUMBER OF CLAMPS		
1	Collet	Cam Type	Hand or Air Operated	Lever-Operated			1	1	2			1
3	3 - Jaw Chuck	Standard	Mallet	Crank-Operated	1	1	1	3	6	1		3
6	4 - Jaw Chuck				2	2	3	6	12	2	1	6
10	6 - Jaw Chuck				4	3	5	10		4	2	10
16					6	5	8			6	4	16
24					9	7	12			9	6	24
32					16	10				13	8	32
42											10	42

Maxi MOST—Machine Handling data card: Secure or Release Parts.   (Fig. 5.21, p. 237)

Maxi MOST® System   A T K T P T A   **POWERED CRANE TRANSPORT**

INDEX X 100	A — ACTION DISTANCE, FEET (M)	T — TRANSPORT, FEET (M)	K — HOOK UP AND UNHOOK, HOLDING DEVICE	P — PLACEMENT, DIFFICULTY	INDEX X 100
1	24 (7)				1
3	61 (19)			Without or With Single Change of Direction	3
6	127 (39)		Single Hook or Electromagnet		6
10	220 (67)	2 (.5)			10
16	360 (110)	25 (8)		With Double Change of Direction	16
24	505 (154)	50 (16)	1 Hook Plus Slings or Chains	With Several Changes of Direction	24
32	673 (205)	80 (25)	2 Hooks Plus Slings or Chains		32

Maxi MOST—Powered Crane Transport data card.   (Fig. 5.23, p. 246)

Maxi MOST® Systems			A S T L T L T A					WHEELED TRUCK TRANSPORT	
INDEX X 100	A	S	T					L	INDEX X 100
			TRANSPORT WITH OR WITHOUT LOAD-FEET (M)						
			RIDING		WALKING				
	ACTION DISTANCE FEET (m)	START AND PARK	FORK LIFT TRUCK	HIGH STACKER	STACKER	LOW LIFT PALLET TRUCK	HAND TRUCK	LOAD OR UNLOAD	
1	24 (7)		27 (8)	21 (6)	11 (3)	14 (4)	24 (7)		**1**
3	61 (19)	Walking Truck	67 (20)	50 (15)	27 (8)	34 (10)	50 (15)	Floor - Simple	**3**
6	127 (39)	Riding Truck	132 (40)	100 (30)	50 (15)	67 (20)	100 (30)	Floor	**6**
10	220 (67)		198 (60)	165 (50)	83 (25)	100 (30)	165 (50)	Pallet Rack	**10**
16	360 (110)		329 (100)	247 (75)	116 (35)	165 (50)	264 (80)		**16**
24	505 (154)		460 (140)	362 (110)	182 (55)				**24**

Maxi MOST—Wheeled Truck data card.   (Fig. 5.28, p. 255)

Index